Computer Methods in
Advanced Structural Analysis

The Intext Series in Civil Engineering

Series Editor
Russell C. Brinker
New Mexico State University

Bouchard and Moffitt— *SURVEYING*, 5th edition
Brinker— *ELEMENTARY SURVEYING*, 5th edition
Clark, Viessman, and Hammer— *WATER SUPPLY AND POLLUTION CONTROL*, 2nd edition
Ghali and Neville— *STRUCTURAL ANALYSIS: A UNIFIED CLASSICAL AND MATRIX APPROACH*
Jumikis— *FOUNDATION ENGINEERING*
McCormac— *STRUCTURAL ANALYSIS*, 2nd edition
McCormac— *STRUCTURAL STEEL DESIGN*, 2nd edition
Meyer— *ROUTE SURVEYING AND DESIGN*, 4th edition
Moffitt— *PHOTOGRAMMETRY*, 2nd edition
Salmon and Johnson— *STEEL STRUCTURES: DESIGN AND BEHAVIOR*
Spangler and Handy— *SOIL ENGINEERING*, 3rd edition
Ural— *FINITE ELEMENT METHOD: Basic Concepts and Applications*
Ural— *MATRIX OPERATIONS AND USE OF COMPUTERS IN STRUCTURAL ENGINEERING*
Viessman, Harbaugh, and Knapp— *INTRODUCTION TO HYDROLOGY*
Wang— *COMPUTER METHODS IN ADVANCED STRUCTURAL ANALYSIS*
Wang— *MATRIX METHODS OF STRUCTURAL ANALYSIS*, 2nd edition
Wang and Salmon— *REINFORCED CONCRETE DESIGN*, 2nd edition
Winfrey— *ECONOMIC ANALYSIS FOR HIGHWAYS*

Computer Methods in Advanced Structural Analysis

CHU-KIA WANG
University of Wisconsin—Madison

INTEXT EDUCATIONAL PUBLISHERS

New York and London

Library of Congress Cataloging in Publication Data

Wang, Chu-kia, 1917-
    Computer methods in advanced structural analysis.

      1. Electronic data processing—Structures, Theory
of. I. Title.
TA641.W27   624'.171'02854   73—1586
ISBN 0-7002-2429-7

INTEXT EDUCATIONAL PUBLISHERS
257 Park Avenue South
New York, New York 10010

Text design by Chris Simon

Contents

Preface   *xi*

Chapter 1   **Free Vibrations of Structural Frames with Lumped
             Masses**   1

1.1.   General Description   1
1.2.   Differential Equations of Free Vibration   2
1.3.   The Matrix of Stiffness- or Flexibility-Influence Coefficients   5
1.4.   The Eigenvalue Problem   8
1.5.   Orthogonality of Mode Vectors   13
1.6.   Fundamental Frequency and Mode Vector by Iteration   14
1.7.   Higher Frequency and Mode Vector from the Reduced $[\delta_m M]$
        Matrix   18
1.8.   The Computer Program   23
1.9.   Input and Output of Numerical Examples   23

Chapter 2   **Free Vibrations of Continuous Beams and Rigid Frames with Distributed Masses**   31

2.1.   General Introduction   31
2.2.   Differential Equation of Free Vibration of a Structural Member   32
2.3.   Solution of the Differential Equation of Free Vibration   33
2.4.   Member End Forces and Deformations   36
2.5.   The Member-Flexibility Matrix   37
2.6.   The Member-Stiffness Matrix   38
2.7.   The Dynamic External Stiffness Matrix of Continuous Beams and Rigid Frames without Sidesway   39
2.8.   Effects of Sidesway in Free Vibration   46
2.9.   The Sidesway Inertia-Force Matrix   49
2.10. Free Vibration of Rigid Frames with Sidesway   56
2.11. The Computer Program   62

Chapter 3   **Undamped Forced Motion of Structural Frames with Lumped Masses**   65

3.1.   General Introduction   65
3.2.   Differential Equations of Undamped Forced Motion   66
3.3.   Normalized Mode Vectors of Free Vibration   67
3.4.   The Transformation Matrix $[a]$ 68
3.5.   The Natural Frequency Matrix $[P]$ 69
3.6.   Uncoupling the Differential Equations of Undamped Forced Motion   70
3.7.   Solving the Differential Equations of Undamped Forced Motion   71
3.8.   Procedure for Obtaining the Displacement, Velocity, and Acceleration at Each Lumped Mass   72
3.9.   Computer Solution   77

Chapter 4   **Displacement Method of Stability Analysis**   81

4.1.   Stability of Rigid Frames   81
4.2.   Equilibrium Conditions at Buckling Mode   82
4.3.   Effect of Primary Axial Force on Member Flexure   83
4.4.   Formulation of the Stability Stiffness Matrix $[K]$ at Bifurcation   85
4.5.   Definitions for the Critical Standard Stability Angle (ϕ_{CRc}) and the Effective Length Ratio K_m of the mth Member   92
4.6.   Statics and Deformation Checks   98
4.7.   Elastic Curves at Bifurcation   103
4.8.   The Second-Order Stiffness Matrix $[K_2]$ 103
4.9.   The Computer Program   111

Chapter 5   Stability Analysis of Rigid Frames with Nonuniform
             Members   113

5.1.   General Description   113
5.2.   The Eigenvalue Problem   114
5.3.   The Sidesway Flexibility Matrix   118
5.4.   The Second-Order Stiffness Matrix   118
5.5.   Direct Solution of the Eigenvalue Equation   121
5.6.   Iteration Solution of the Eigenvalue Equation   127
5.7.   The Computer Program   130

Chapter 6   Second-Order Analysis of Rigid Frames   135

6.1.   General Introduction   135
6.2.   The Local $[A']$ Matrix   137
6.3.   Internal Deformations versus External Displacements   138
6.4.   Internal Force-Deformation Relationships   142
6.5.   Stiffness and Flexibility Coefficients in Flexure   143
6.6.   The Displacement Method of Second-Order Analysis   153
6.7.   Numerical Example   156

Chapter 7   Treatment of Prismatic Beam Element by the
             Energy Method   165

7.1.   General Introduction   165
7.2.   The Reciprocal Energy Theorem   166
7.3.   Four Basic Q-Y Modes of a Prismatic Beam Element   167
7.4.   Stiffness Matrix of an Ordinary Beam Element   169
7.5.   Fixed-Condition Forces for an Ordinary Beam Element   174
7.6.   Stiffness Matrix of a Prismatic Beam Element in Axial Compression 176
7.7.   Stiffness Matrix of a Prismatic Beam Element in Free Vibration 182
7.8.   Eigenvalue Solution of Stability and Free Vibration Problems   187

Chapter 8   Finite-Element Formulation of Plane Stress
             Analysis   189

8.1.   Plane Stress versus Plane Strain Analysis   189
8.2.   General Description of Finite-Element Method   193
8.3.   Stiffness Matrix of a Finite Element   194
8.4.   Triangular Finite Element   196
8.5.   Rectangular Finite Element   201
8.6.   Arbitrary Stress Functions   205

8.7.   Compatible Edge Displacement versus Compatible Edge Stress   210
8.8.   Principal Stress Modes   211
8.9.   Effects of Symmetrical Finite Element   213
8.10. Independent Elements in the Stiffness Matrix of Rectangular
       Finite Elements   215
8.11. Nodal Forces in the Fixed Condition   219
8.12. Numerical Example   224
8.13. The Computer Program   225

**Chapter 9   Stiffness Matrix of Rectangular Element in
Bending**   229

9.1.   Flat Plates in Bending   229
9.2.   Relationships between Internal Forces and Internal Deformations   231
9.3.   The Exact Differential Equation for Plate Bending   234
9.4.   The Approximate Displacement Equation   235
9.5.   The Deformation Matrix $[B]$ 236
9.6.   The Stiffness Matrix $[K]$ 240
9.7.   Principal Stress Modes   247
9.8.   Effect of Symmetrical Finite Element   250
9.9.   Independent Elements in the Stiffness Matrix   251
9.10. Fixed-Condition Nodal Forces of Uniform Load   255
9.11. The Computer Program   258

Chapter 10   Introduction to Linear Programming   263

10.1.   General Remarks   263
10.2.   A Minimization Problem in Two Dimensions   263
10.3.   Solution Trivial   265
10.4.   Solution Indeterminate   266
10.5.   Solution Infeasible   267
10.6.   General Formulation for More than Two Design Variables   268
10.7.   The Intermediate Matrix Form   269
10.8.   The Gauss-Jordan Substitution   270
10.9.   Simplex Method: Solution Successful   272
10.10. Simplex Method: Solution Trivial   275
10.11. Simplex Method: Solution Indeterminate   276
10.12. Simplex Method: Solution Infeasible   278
10.13. Flow Chart for Computer Program   279

Chapter 11   **Minimum-Weight Design of Trusses**   281

11.1.   General Description   281
11.2.   Initial Design   282
11.3.   Changes in Bar Forces per Changes in Bar Areas   285
11.4.   Building the Constraints   289
11.5.   Optimization by Linear Programming   293
11.6.   The Computer Program   298

Appendixes   **Fortran Programs**   299

Appendix A   **Free Vibrations of Rigid Frames with Lumped
              Masses**   301

Appendix B   **Free Vibrations of Rigid Frames with Distributed
              Masses**   309

Appendix C   **Undamped Forced Motion of Rigid Frames with
              Lumped Masses**   319

Appendix D   **Displacement Method of Stability Analysis**   329

Appendix E   **Stability Analysis of Rigid Frames with Nonuni-
              form Members**   339

Appendix F   **Second-Order Analysis of Rigid Frames**   347

Appendix G   **Plane Stress Analysis (Rectangular Element with
              Linear Edge Displacement)**   355

Appendix H   **Plate Bending Analysis**   365

Appendix I   **Minimizing a Linear Function by Simplex
              Method**   379

Appendix J   **Coefficients in Minimum Truss Weight
              Equations**   391

Index   *399*

Preface

The eleven chapters and ten computer programs offered here are the result of work I have done over the past several years. To a degree, this volume may be regarded as a sequel to my earlier textbook, *Matrix Methods of Structural Analysis*, Second Edition (Intext Educational Publishers, New York and London, 1970).

I have limited my discussion to structural dynamics, structural stability, finite-element analysis, and minimum-weight design by linear programming. Each chapter deals concisely with a specific problem of limited scope. My objective has been to show how short, basic computer programs can be developed so that the reader may acquire a capability to apply similar techniques to other more complex subjects.

Although the reader must look elsewhere for broad treatises and bibliographical references on the four general areas to which the ten computer programs may apply, every care has been exercised to substantiate the statements made by simple reasoning.

Numerical examples with answers are provided within each chapter so that the reader may use them as debugging tools to adjust or modify the computer programs listed in the appendixes to the machines available to him. Once a reader gets a computer program working, he can conveniently experiment with exercises made out of his own initiative and verify the correctness of the computer output by conventional means. Also, teachers may wish to advise the students to check the longhand solutions of assigned problems with the computer output, or to learn the effects of a parameter variation from a set of computer solutions. It is hoped that teachers, students, and practicing engineers in structural engineering may find the contents useful in their curriculum schedule as well as in design, research, or development.

The author wishes to acknowledge the assistance of several former and present graduate students through thesis work or independent study. Drs. Ottar P. Halldorsson, Quassim M. Al-Mawsawi, Franklin Y. Cheng, Karl M. Romstad, Madasamy Arockiasamy, and Tarun R. Naik, as well as Mr. Jaafar K. Al-Abdulla are among this group. The author also appreciates the cooperation received from the staff of the Engineering Computing Laboratory of the University of Wisconsin.

Mrs. Audrey M. Miller, Secretary of the Structural Engineering Faculty at the University of Wisconsin, has been excellent in typing the material into lecture-notes form, which has been used a number of times in regular graduate courses, in short courses for practicing engineers, and in summer institutes for college teachers supported by the National Science Foundation.

Computer Methods in
Advanced Structural Analysis

CHAPTER 1

■

Free Vibrations of Structural Frames with Lumped Masses

1.1. General Description

Consider the structural frame ABC shown in Fig. 1.1.1a. Assume that members AB and BC have finite values of flexural rigidity EI but infinite values of axial rigidity EA. Also assume that members AB and BC are massless, but lumped masses M_1 and M_2 are securely attached at points 1 and 2. Thus, in idealizing a practical problem, a member may be divided into a number of massless segments, and the distributed mass of each segment is considered to be concentrated at its midpoint.

A state of motion of the two masses M_1 and M_2 may be described by the displacements X_{m1} and X_{m2}, the velocities $\dot{X}_{m1}$ and $\dot{X}_{m2}$, and the accelerations $\ddot{X}_{m1}$ and $\ddot{X}_{m2}$, as shown in Fig. 1.1.1b, where the positive directions of the X_{m1} and X_{m2} axes are indicated. By D'Alembert's principle, this state of motion may be translated to a state of static equilibrium, in which the inertia forces $M_1\ddot{X}_{m1}$ and $M_2\ddot{X}_{m2}$, acting in the negative directions of the X_{m1} and X_{m2} axes, would maintain exactly the shape of the elastic curve, as shown in Fig. 1.1.1c.

1

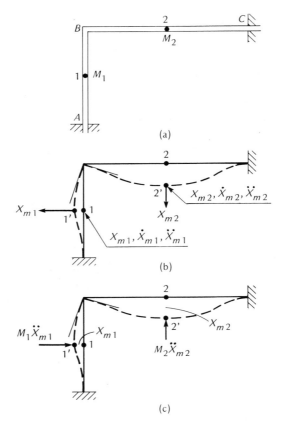

Figure 1.1.1. *Free vibration of a structural frame.*
(a) Structural frame with lumped masses; (b) a state of
motion; (c) a state of static equilibrium.

Not only is it indeed possible for the occurrence of the state of motion as described in the preceding paragraph, but this motion has also been found to be cyclic or vibratory in nature with respect to a definite time period. Since the structural frame itself is free of external disturbance of any kind, this kind of motion is called *free vibration*. The present chapter will deal with ways of determining the possible modes of free vibrations of structural frames with many lumped masses.

1.2. Differential Equations of Free Vibration

The elastic properties of the structural frame in Fig. 1.1.1a, with respect to points 1 and 2 at which lumped masses exist, can be totally described by either

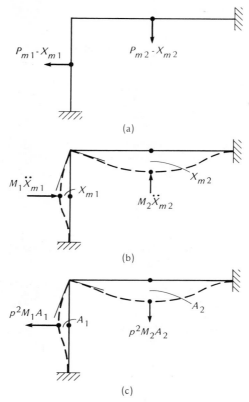

Figure 1.2.1. *Solution of differential equation.*
(a) A frame in the elastic range; (b) inertia forces;
(c) amplitude forces.

a matrix of stiffness-influence coefficients $[K_m]$, or a matrix of flexibility-influence coefficients $[\delta_m]$, where, referring to Fig. 1.2.1a,

$[K_m] =$	$\begin{array}{c}X_m\\ \hline P_m\end{array}$	1	2
	1	K_{m11}	K_{m12}
	2	K_{m21}	K_{m22}

$(1.2.1a)$

P_m X_m	1	2
1	δ_{m11}	δ_{m12}
2	δ_{m21}	δ_{m22}

$$[\delta_m] = \qquad\qquad\qquad\qquad\qquad\qquad\qquad (1.2.1b)$$

Thus, for instance, K_{m11} and K_{m21} are the nodal forces required to maintain a unit displacement at 1 but no displacement at 2; and δ_{m11} and δ_{m21} are the nodal displacements due to a unit force at 1 but no force at 2. Of course,

$$[K_m]\,[\delta_m] = [I] \qquad\qquad\qquad (1.2.1c)$$

Since in free vibration the inertia forces $M_1\ddot{X}_{m1}$ and $M_2\ddot{X}_{m2}$ acting in the negative X_{m1} and X_{m2} directions should just maintain the displacements X_{m1} and X_{m2}, as shown in Fig. 1.2.lb, then following Eq. 1.2.lb,

$$X_{m1} = \delta_{m11}\,(-M_1\ddot{X}_{m1}) + \delta_{m12}\,(-M_2\ddot{X}_{m2})$$

$$X_{m2} = \delta_{m21}\,(-M_1\ddot{X}_{m1}) + \delta_{m22}\,(-M_2\ddot{X}_{m2})$$

or, in matrix notation,

$$\begin{Bmatrix} X_{m1} \\ X_{m2} \end{Bmatrix} = -\begin{bmatrix} \delta_{m11} & \delta_{m12} \\ \delta_{m21} & \delta_{m22} \end{bmatrix} \begin{bmatrix} M_1 & 0 \\ 0 & M_2 \end{bmatrix} \begin{Bmatrix} \ddot{X}_{m1} \\ \ddot{X}_{m2} \end{Bmatrix}$$

In general,

$$\{X_m\} = -\,[\delta_m]\,[M]\,\{\ddot{X}_m\} \qquad\qquad (1.2.2a)$$

Multiplying both sides of Eq. 1.2.2a by $[K_m]$,

$$[K_m]\,\{X_m\} = -\,[M]\,\{\ddot{X}_m\} \qquad\qquad (1.2.2b)$$

Equations 1.2.2ab show the two ways of expressing the differential equations of free vibration of structural frames with lumped masses.

By letting

$$\{X_m\} = \cos(pt - \alpha)\,\{A\} \qquad\qquad (1.2.3a)$$

and

$$\{\ddot{X}_m\} = -p^2 \cos(pt - \alpha)\{A\} \tag{1.2.3b}$$

the differential equations 1.2.2a or 1.2.2b may be transformed to the linear equations

$$\{A\} \doteq p^2 [\delta_m][M]\{A\} \tag{1.2.4a}$$

or

$$[K_m]\{A\} = p^2 [M]\{A\} \tag{1.2.4b}$$

Equations 1.2.4ab can be represented physically by Fig. 1.2.1c, in which the amplitude forces $p^2 M_1 A_1$ and $p^2 M_2 A_2$ acting in the positive X_{m1} and X_{m2} directions just cause the displacements A_1 and A_2, also in the positive X_{m1} and X_{m2} directions.

The method of finding the circular frequency p in radians per second and the proportionate values of the nodal displacements $\{A\}$ will be shown later in this chapter.

1.3. The Matrix of Stiffness- or Flexibility-Influence Coefficients

The matrix of stiffness-influence coefficients $[K_m]$, or of flexibility-influence coefficients $[\delta_m]$, depends only on the dimensional and elastic properties of the structural frame and can be derived from the total external stiffness matrix $[ASA^T]$ of the entire structure,† provided the displacements in which the lumped masses may move are included in the degrees of freedom.

Consider the structural frame of Fig. 1.3.1a on which there are two lumped masses. If points 1 and 2 are considered as two joints, the total degree of freedom becomes 5, as shown in Fig. 1.3.1b. Note that the 4th and 5th degrees of freedom coincide with the positive directions of the displacements of the lumped masses.

Let

$$\{P_0\} = \begin{Bmatrix} P_1 \\ P_2 \\ P_3 \end{Bmatrix} \qquad\qquad\qquad \{X_0\} = \begin{Bmatrix} X_1 \\ X_2 \\ X_3 \end{Bmatrix}$$

$$\{P_m\} = \begin{Bmatrix} P_4 \\ P_5 \end{Bmatrix} = \begin{Bmatrix} P_{m1} \\ P_{m2} \end{Bmatrix} \qquad\qquad \{X_m\} = \begin{Bmatrix} X_4 \\ X_5 \end{Bmatrix} = \begin{Bmatrix} X_{m1} \\ X_{m2} \end{Bmatrix}$$

†For definition and treatment of $[ASA^T]$, see C. K. Wang, *Matrix Methods of Structural Analysis*, Second Edition (New York and London: Intext Educational Publishers, 1970), Chaps. 4–7.

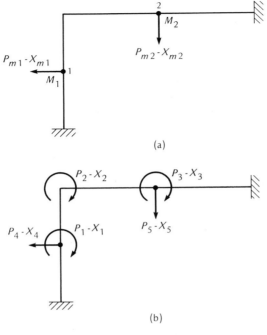

Figure 1.3.1. *Dynamic vs. static degree of freedom.*
(a) The lumped masses; (b) the P-X *diagram.*

Then,

$$[ASA^T] = [K] = \begin{array}{c|c|c} \diagdown \begin{matrix} X \\ P \end{matrix} & X_0 & X_m \\ \hline P_0 & K_1 & K_2 \\ \hline P_m & K_3 & K_4 \end{array}$$

(1.3.1)

and,

$$[ASA^T]^{-1} = [\delta] = \begin{array}{c|c|c} \diagdown \begin{matrix} P \\ X \end{matrix} & P_0 & P_m \\ \hline X_0 & \delta_1 & \delta_2 \\ \hline X_m & \delta_3 & \delta_4 \end{array}$$

(1.3.2)

Equations 1.3.1 and 1.3.2 may be expanded to

$$\{P_o\} = [K_1]\{X_o\} + [K_2]\{X_m\} \qquad (1.3.3a)$$

$$\{P_m\} = [K_3]\{X_o\} + [K_4]\{X_m\} \qquad (1.3.3b)$$

and,

$$\{X_o\} = [\delta_1]\{P_o\} + [\delta_2]\{P_m\} \qquad (1.3.4a)$$

$$\{X_m\} = [\delta_3]\{P_o\} + [\delta_4]\{P_m\} \qquad (1.3.4b)$$

respectively.

Setting $\{P_o\} = 0$, Eqs. 1.3.3 and 1.3.4 may be condensed to

$$\{P_m\} = [K_4 - K_3 K_1^{-1} K_2]\{X_m\} \qquad (1.3.5)$$

and

$$\{X_m\} = [\delta_4]\{P_m\} \qquad (1.3.6)$$

By definition,

$$\{P_m\} = [K_m]\{X_m\} \qquad (1.3.7)$$

and

$$\{X_m\} = [\delta_m]\{P_m\} \qquad (1.3.8)$$

Comparing Eq. 1.3.5 with Eq. 1.3.7 and Eq. 1.3.6 with Eq. 1.3.8,

$$[K_m] = [K_4 - K_3 K_1^{-1} K_2] \qquad (1.3.9)$$

and,

$$[\delta_m] = [\delta_4] \qquad (1.3.10)$$

Equations 1.3.9 and 1.3.10 suggest two methods of computing $[\delta_m]$: (1) by computing $[K_m]$ from $[K_m] = [K_4 - K_2^T K_1^{-1} K_2]$ and then inverting the $[K_m]$ matrix; or (2) by inverting the total $[ASA^T]$ matrix of the entire structure and then taking the submatrix $[\delta_4]$ at the lower right-hand corner. Unless computer memory space becomes a problem, the second method is more straightforward and will be used in the computer program in Appendix A.

1.4. The Eigenvalue Problem

Since Eq. 1.2.4a and Eq. 1.2.4b are substantially identical, either can be used to solve for the circular frequency p and mode shape vector $\{A\}$. It can be shown that there are as many sets of p and $\{A\}$ values which may satisfy Eqs. 1.2.4a or b as there are moving lumped masses. The lowest value of p is the fundamental frequency and the corresponding vector $\{A\}$ the fundamental mode. The frequencies p associated with free vibrations are sometimes called the *natural frequencies.*

For the special case of two lumped masses, Eq. 1.2.4a may be expanded to the form

$$(p^2 (\delta_m M)_{11} - 1) A_1 + (p^2 (\delta_m M)_{12}) A_2 = 0$$

$$(p^2 (\delta_m M)_{21}) A_1 + (p^2 (\delta_m M)_{22} - 1) A_2 = 0 \qquad (1.4.1a)$$

where $(\delta_m M)_{11}$, $(\delta_m M)_{12}$, $(\delta_m M)_{21}$, and $(\delta_m M)_{22}$ are elements of the $[\delta_m M]$ matrix. Likewise, Eq. 1.2.4b may take the form

$$(K_{m11} - p^2 M_1) A_1 + (K_{m12}) A_2 = 0$$

$$(K_{m21}) A_1 + (K_{m22} - p^2 M_2) A_2 = 0 \qquad (1.4.1b)$$

For a nontrivial solution of either Eq. 1.4.1a or Eq. 1.4.1b to exist, the determinant of the coefficients of A_1 and A_2 must be zero. Setting this determinant to zero will yield a quadratic equation in p^2, whose roots are called the *eigenvalues* and the associated vectors $\{A\}$ the *eigenvectors*. In this chapter all eigenvectors will be "unitized," which means that the largest absolute value in the vector is made equal to unity. The word "unitized" is specially chosen in distinction to the word "normalized" which is later used in Chapter 3.

From the above discussion it can be inferred that there should be as many sets of eigenvalues (which are values of p^2) and eigenvectors as there are lumped masses. The general eigenvalue equation in p^2 can be observed from Eq. 1.2.4a or Eq. 1.2.4b to be

$$\text{DET} \,[p^2 \,[\delta_m M] - [I]\,] = 0 \qquad (1.4.2a)$$

or

$$\text{DET} \,[\,[K_m] - p^2 [M]\,] = 0 \qquad (1.4.2b)$$

When the number of lumped masses becomes large, however, it would be impractical to solve for the roots of a high-degree polynomial. Thus an iterative procedure will be presented in the subsequent sections.

Example 1.4.1. Compute the two natural frequencies and the corresponding unitized nodal deflection vectors, in the free vibration of the structural frame with two lumped masses as shown in Fig. 1.4.1a.

Solution: (a) The $[K_m]$ and $[\delta_m]$ matrices. Equations 1.3.9 and 1.3.10 may be used to compute the $[K_m]$ and $[\delta_m]$ matrices. Using the *P-X* and *F-e* numbers in Fig. 1.4.1b,

$$[A] =$$

P \ F	1	2	3	4	5	6	7	8
1	0	+1	+1	0	0	0	0	0
2	0	0	0	+1	+1	0	0	0
3	0	0	0	0	0	+1	+1	0
4	$+\dfrac{1}{6}$	$+\dfrac{1}{6}$	$-\dfrac{1}{6}$	$-\dfrac{1}{6}$	0	0	0	0
5	0	0	0	0	$-\dfrac{1}{10}$	$-\dfrac{1}{10}$	$+\dfrac{1}{10}$	$+\dfrac{1}{10}$

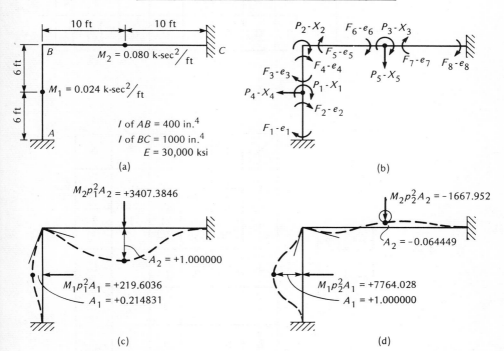

Figure 1.4.1. *Free vibration of a structural frame with two lumped masses. (a) Structural frame with two lumped masses; (b) the P-X and F-e numbers; (c) the first mode, $p_1 = 206.379$ rad/sec; (d) the second mode, $p_2 = 568.772$ rad/sec.*

$[S]$ in 10^6 ft-kips =

F \ e	1	2	3	4	5	6	7	8
1	$+\frac{1}{18}$	$+\frac{1}{36}$	0	0	0	0	0	0
2	$+\frac{1}{36}$	$+\frac{1}{18}$	0	0	0	0	0	0
3	0	0	$+\frac{1}{18}$	$+\frac{1}{36}$	0	0	0	0
4	0	0	$+\frac{1}{36}$	$+\frac{1}{18}$	0	0	0	0
5	0	0	0	0	$+\frac{1}{12}$	$+\frac{1}{24}$	0	0
6	0	0	0	0	$+\frac{1}{24}$	$+\frac{1}{12}$	0	0
7	0	0	0	0	0	0	$+\frac{1}{12}$	$+\frac{1}{24}$
8	0	0	0	0	0	0	$+\frac{1}{24}$	$+\frac{1}{12}$

Then,

$$[ASA^T] = \begin{array}{|c|c|} \hline K_1 & K_2 \\ \hline K_3 & K_4 \\ \hline \end{array} = 10^6$$

P \ X	1	2	3	4	5
1	$+\frac{1}{9}$	$+\frac{1}{36}$	0	0	0
2	$+\frac{1}{36}$	$+\frac{5}{36}$	$+\frac{1}{24}$	$-\frac{1}{72}$	$-\frac{1}{80}$
3	0	$+\frac{1}{24}$	$+\frac{1}{6}$	0	0
4	0	$-\frac{1}{72}$	0	$+\frac{1}{108}$	0
5	0	$-\frac{1}{80}$	0	0	$+\frac{1}{200}$

from which

$$[K_1] = 10^6 \text{ ft-kips} \begin{bmatrix} +\dfrac{1}{9} & +\dfrac{1}{36} & 0 \\ +\dfrac{1}{36} & +\dfrac{5}{36} & +\dfrac{1}{24} \\ 0 & +\dfrac{1}{24} & +\dfrac{1}{6} \end{bmatrix} \qquad [K_2] = 10^6 \text{ kips} \begin{bmatrix} 0 & 0 \\ -\dfrac{1}{72} & -\dfrac{1}{80} \\ 0 & 0 \end{bmatrix}$$

$$[K_3] = 10^6 \text{ kips} \begin{bmatrix} 0 & -\dfrac{1}{72} & 0 \\ 0 & -\dfrac{1}{80} & 0 \end{bmatrix} \qquad [K_4] = 10^6 \text{ kips/ft} \begin{bmatrix} +\dfrac{1}{108} & 0 \\ 0 & +\dfrac{1}{200} \end{bmatrix}$$

and

$$[K_m] = [K_4 - K_3 K_1^{-1} K_2] = \frac{10^6}{37,800} \text{ kips/ft} \begin{bmatrix} +290 & -54 \\ -54 & +140.4 \end{bmatrix}$$

$[\delta_m]$ may be obtained from inverting the $[K_m]$ matrix above or from taking the submatrix at the lower right corner of the $[ASA^T]^{-1}$ matrix; thus,

$$[\delta_m] = 10^{-6} \text{ ft/kip} \begin{bmatrix} +140.4 & +54.0 \\ +54.0 & +290.0 \end{bmatrix}$$

(b) The eigenvalue equation in p^2. Using Eq. 1.4.2a,

$$\text{DET} \, [p^2 \, [\delta_m M] - [I]] = 0$$

$$\text{DET} \left[p^2 \times 10^{-6} \begin{bmatrix} +140.4 & +54.0 \\ +54.0 & +290.0 \end{bmatrix} \begin{bmatrix} 0.024 & 0 \\ 0 & 0.080 \end{bmatrix} - \begin{bmatrix} 1 & 0 \\ 0 & 1 \end{bmatrix} \right] = 0$$

$$\text{DET} \begin{bmatrix} +3.3696 \times 10^{-6} p^2 - 1 & +4.32 \times 10^{-6} p^2 \\ +1.296 \times 10^{-6} p^2 & +23.2 \times 10^{-6} p^2 - 1 \end{bmatrix} = 0$$

$$1 - 26.5696 \times 10^{-6} p^2 + 72.576 \times 10^{-12} p^4 = 0$$

Using Eq. 1.4.2b,

$$\text{DET } [[K_m] - p^2 [M]] = 0$$

$$\text{DET } \left[\frac{10^6}{37,800} \begin{bmatrix} +290 & - & 54 \\ - & 54 & +140.4 \end{bmatrix} - p^2 \begin{bmatrix} 0.024 & 0 \\ 0 & 0.080 \end{bmatrix} \right] = 0$$

$$\text{DET } \begin{bmatrix} + \dfrac{290 \times 10^6}{37,800} - 0.024p^2 & - \dfrac{54 \times 10^6}{37,800} \\[3mm] - \dfrac{54 \times 10^6}{37,800} & + \dfrac{140.4 \times 10^6}{37,800} - 0.080p^2 \end{bmatrix} = 0$$

$$10^{12} - 26.5696 \times 10^6 p^2 + 72.576 \times 10^{12} p^4 = 0$$

Naturally Eq. 1.4.2a or Eq. 1.4.2b should give exactly the same eigenvalue equation.

(c) The natural frequencies and the unitized mode vectors. Since the eigenvalue equation for two lumped masses is a quadratic equation in p^2, the roots are found to be

$$p_1^2 = 42{,}592.308 \qquad p_1 = 206.37904 \text{ rad/sec}$$

$$p_2^2 = 323{,}501.16 \qquad p_2 = 568.77162 \text{ rad/sec}$$

The equation $[p^2 [\delta_m M] - [I]] \{A\} = 0$ becomes, in the first mode,

$$(3.3696 \times 10^{-6} \times 42{,}592.308 - 1) A_1 + (4.32 \times 10^{-6} \times 42{,}592.308) A_2 = 0$$

$$(1.296 \times 10^{-6} \times 42{,}592.308) A_1 + (23.2 \times 10^{-6} \times 42{,}592.308 - 1) A_2 = 0$$

Letting $A_2 = +1.000000$ and solving for A_1 from either of the above two equations,

$$A_1 = + 0.214831$$

Thus the first mode vector is

$$\{A_1\} = \begin{Bmatrix} A_{11} \\ A_{21} \end{Bmatrix} = \begin{Bmatrix} +0.214831 \\ +1.000000 \end{Bmatrix}$$

The second mode vector is found in a similar manner to be

$$\{A_2\} = \begin{Bmatrix} A_{12} \\ A_{22} \end{Bmatrix} = \begin{Bmatrix} +1.000000 \\ -0.064449 \end{Bmatrix}$$

(d) Deflections due to amplitude forces. As a final check, the deflections due to amplitude forces $M_1 p^2 A_1$ and $M_2 p^2 A_2$ should be the amplitudes themselves. Thus, for the first mode (Fig. 1.4.1c),

$$[\delta_m] \begin{Bmatrix} M_1 p_1^2 A_{11} \\ M_2 p_1^2 A_{21} \end{Bmatrix} = \begin{bmatrix} +140.4 & +54.0 \\ +54.0 & +290.0 \end{bmatrix} \times 10^{-6} \begin{Bmatrix} +219.6036 \\ +3407.3846 \end{Bmatrix} = \begin{Bmatrix} +0.214831 \\ +1.000000 \end{Bmatrix}$$

and, for the second mode (Fig. 1.4.1d),

$$[\delta_m] \begin{Bmatrix} M_1 p_2^2 A_{12} \\ M_2 p_2^2 A_{22} \end{Bmatrix} = \begin{bmatrix} +140.4 & +54.0 \\ +54.0 & +290.0 \end{bmatrix} \times 10^{-6} \begin{Bmatrix} +7764.028 \\ -1667.952 \end{Bmatrix} = \begin{Bmatrix} +1.000000 \\ -0.064449 \end{Bmatrix}$$

1.5. Orthogonality of Mode Vectors

It will be shown in this section that any two mode vectors in the free vibrations of structures with two or more lumped masses are orthogonal to each other with respect to the lumped masses; or, in equation form,

$$\{A_i\}^T [M] \{A_j\} = 0. \tag{1.5.1}$$

where $[M]$ is the diagonal mass matrix and $\{A_i\}$ and $\{A_j\}$ are the ith and jth mode vectors respectively. Thus for the example in the preceding section,

$$\{A_1^T\} [M] \{A_2\} = \begin{Bmatrix} +0.214831 \\ +1.000000 \end{Bmatrix}^T \begin{bmatrix} 0.024 & 0 \\ 0 & 0.080 \end{bmatrix} \begin{Bmatrix} +1.000000 \\ -0.064449 \end{Bmatrix}$$

$$= (+0.214831)(0.024)(+1.000000) + (+1.000000)(0.080)$$

$$\times (-0.064449)$$

$$= +0.0051561 - 0.0051559 \approx 0$$

A little reflection will show that Eq. 1.5.1 may be written as

$$\{A_i\}^T [M] \{A_j\} = \sum_{k=1}^{k=\text{NTLM}} A_{ki} M_k A_{kj} = 0 \qquad (1.5.2)$$

where NTLM is the total number of lumped masses.

The proof for orthogonality may be made as follows:

Given: (1) $[K_m] \{A_i\} = p_i^2 [M] \{A_i\}$

(2) $[K_m] \{A_j\} = p_j^2 [M] \{A_j\}$

(3) $[M] = [M^T]$

(4) $[K_m] = [K_m^T]$

To Prove: $\{A_i\}^T [M] \{A_j\} = 0$

Proof:

Statement	Reason
1. $A_i^T K_m = p_i^2 A_i^T M$	1. Take transpose of Given (1).
2. $A_i^T K_m A_j = p_i^2 A_i^T M A_j$	2. Postmultiply Statement 1 by A_j.
3. $A_i^T K_m A_j = p_j^2 A_i^T M A_j$	3. Premultiply Given (2) by A_i^T.
4. $0 = (p_i^2 - p_j^2)(A_i^T M A_j)$	4. Subtract Statement 3 from Statement (2).
5. $A_i^T M A_j = 0$	5. $(p_i^2 - p_j^2)$ in Statement 4 is not equal to zero.

1.6. Fundamental Frequency and Mode Vector by Iteration

It is common in structural dynamics to call the number of moving lumped masses the degree of freedom. When the degree of freedom is large, the eigenvalue equation (or the frequency equation) becomes a high-degree polynomial and difficult to solve. Furthermore, it is generally desirable to obtain the numerical value of the fundamental (or the lowest) frequency first. The key concept in the iteration procedure is contained in the statement made near the end of Sec. 1.2, i.e., the amplitude forces $p^2 M_1 A_1$, $p^2 M_2 A_2$, ..., $p^2 M_n A_n$ just cause the displacements $A_1, A_2, \ldots, A_n$; or, in equation form,

$$\{A\} = p^2 [\delta_m M] \{A\} \qquad (1.2.4a)$$

At the beginning of the iteration, all the amplitudes A_i are assumed to be equal to unity; then nodal displacements $(\delta_m MA)_i$ are computed and unitized. In the

next cycle, the just obtained unitized displacements are assumed to be the amplitudes A_i, and the nodal displacements $(\delta_m MA)_i$ again computed and unitized.
These cycles are then repeated until the difference between each element in the
newly obtained unitized nodal displacement vector and the corresponding element in the assumed amplitude vector is smaller than a preset tolerance, such as
0.000001. Then p^2 is taken as the ratio of the largest element (unity in every
case) in the assumed amplitudes and the corresponding element is the last obtained displacement vector. And, of course, the mode vector being sought is the
last obtained unitized displacement vector.

The above described iteration procedure can be easily written into a computer
program, which is presented in Appendix A. A proof for convergence would
seem desirable at this point and is shown as follows:

Given: (1) The general equation $\{A\} = p^2 [\delta_m M] \{A\}$

(2) The arbitrary vector at the beginning: $\{A_0\}^1$

(3) The definition: $\{A_0\}^{r+1} = [\delta_m M] \{A_0\}^r = [\delta_m M]^r \{A_0\}^1$

(4) The approximate eigenvalue:

$$p_1^2 = \frac{\{A_0\}^r}{\{A_0\}^{r+1}} = \frac{[\delta_m M]^{r-1} \{A_0\}^1}{[\delta_m M]^r \{A_0\}^1}$$

To Prove: p_1^2 is the smallest possible p^2 when $r \longrightarrow \infty$.

Proof: Statement	Reason
1. Let $\{A_i\}$ be the true ith eigenvector. Let $\{A_0\}^1 = \displaystyle\sum_{i=1}^{n} \alpha_i \{A_i\}$	1. n values of α_i exist. $i = 1, 2, \ldots, n$
2. $\{A_0\}^2 = [\delta_m M] \{A_0\}^1 = [\delta_m M] \displaystyle\sum_{i=1}^{n} \alpha_i \{A_i\}$ $= \displaystyle\sum_{i=1}^{n} \alpha_i [\delta_m M] \{A_i\} = \displaystyle\sum_{i=1}^{n} \frac{\alpha_i}{p_i^2} \{A_i\}$	2. $\{A_i\}$ is a true eigenvector.
3. $\{A_0\}^3 = [\delta_m M] \{A_0\}^2 = \displaystyle\sum_{i=1}^{n} \frac{\alpha_i}{p_i^2} [\delta_m M] \{A_i\}$ $= \displaystyle\sum_{i=1}^{n} \frac{\alpha_i}{p_i^4} \{A_i\}$	3. Substitute Statement 2 here.

4. $\{A_0\}^{r+1} = \sum_{i=1}^{n} \dfrac{\alpha_i}{p_i^{2r}} \{A_i\}$

4. Generalize Statement 3 to $\{A_0\}^{r+1}$.

---

5. $\{A_0\}^{r+1} = \dfrac{\alpha_1 \{A_1\}}{p_1^{2r}} + \sum_{i=2}^{n} \dfrac{\alpha_i \{A_i\}}{p_i^{2r}}$

$= \dfrac{1}{p_1^{2r}} \left[\alpha_1 \{A_1\} + \sum_{i=2}^{n} \left(\dfrac{p_1}{p_i}\right)^{2r} \alpha_i \{A_i\} \right]$

5. Take $\{A_1\}$ and p_1^{2r} out of the summation.

---

6. $\{A_0\}^{r+1} = [\delta_m M]^r \{A_0\}^1$

6. See Given (3).

---

7. $[\delta_m M]^r \{A_0\}^1$

$= \dfrac{1}{p_1^{2r}} \left[\alpha_1 \{A_1\} + \sum_{i=2}^{n} \left(\dfrac{p_1}{p_i}\right)^{2r} \alpha_i \{A_i\} \right]$

7. Substitute Statement 6 into Statement 5.

---

8. As $r \longrightarrow \infty$

$[\delta_m M]^r \{A_0\}^1 \longrightarrow \dfrac{\alpha_1}{p_1^{2r}} \{A_1\}$

8. $\sum_{i=2}^{n} \left(\dfrac{p_1}{p_i}\right)^{2r} \alpha_i \{A_i\}$

becomes smaller and smaller and α_1 becomes fuller and fuller.

Example 1.6.1. Given the $[\delta_m]$ and $[M]$ matrices in Example 1.4.1,

$$[\delta_m] = 10^{-6} \text{ ft/kip} \begin{bmatrix} +140.4 & +54.0 \\ +54.0 & +290.0 \end{bmatrix}$$

$$[M] = \dfrac{\text{kip-sec}^2}{\text{ft}} \begin{bmatrix} 0.024 & 0 \\ 0 & 0.080 \end{bmatrix}$$

compute the smallest possible value of p^2 and the unitized eigenvector $\{A\}$ such that

$$\{A\} = p^2 [\delta_m M] \{A\}.$$

Solution: The $[\delta_m M]$ matrix is first computed to be

$$[\delta_m M] = 10^{-6} \text{ sec}^2 \begin{bmatrix} +3.3696 & +4.32 \\ +1.296 & +23.2 \end{bmatrix}$$

Just for the purpose of illustrating the iteration procedure, only 4 decimal places will be used in the unitized eigenvector.

First cycle: Try

$$\{A\} = \begin{Bmatrix} +1.0000 \\ +1.0000 \end{Bmatrix}$$

$$[\delta_m M] \begin{Bmatrix} +1.0000 \\ +1.0000 \end{Bmatrix} = \begin{Bmatrix} +7.6896 \times 10^{-6} \\ +24.4960 \times 10^{-6} \end{Bmatrix} \longrightarrow \begin{Bmatrix} +0.3139 \\ +1.0000 \end{Bmatrix}$$

Second cycle: Try

$$\{A\} = \begin{Bmatrix} +0.3139 \\ +1.0000 \end{Bmatrix}$$

$$[\delta_m M] \begin{Bmatrix} +0.3139 \\ +1.0000 \end{Bmatrix} = \begin{Bmatrix} +5.3777 \times 10^{-6} \\ +23.6068 \times 10^{-6} \end{Bmatrix} \longrightarrow \begin{Bmatrix} +0.2278 \\ +1.0000 \end{Bmatrix}$$

Third cycle: Try

$$\{A\} = \begin{Bmatrix} +0.2278 \\ +1.0000 \end{Bmatrix}$$

$$[\delta_m M] \begin{Bmatrix} +0.2278 \\ +1.0000 \end{Bmatrix} = \begin{Bmatrix} +5.0876 \times 10^{-6} \\ +23.4952 \times 10^{-6} \end{Bmatrix} \longrightarrow \begin{Bmatrix} +0.2165 \\ +1.0000 \end{Bmatrix}$$

Fourth cycle: Try

$$\{A\} = \begin{Bmatrix} +0.2165 \\ +1.0000 \end{Bmatrix}$$

$$[\delta_m M] \begin{Bmatrix} +0.2165 \\ +1.0000 \end{Bmatrix} = \begin{Bmatrix} +5.0495 \times 10^{-6} \\ +23.4806 \times 10^{-6} \end{Bmatrix} \longrightarrow \begin{Bmatrix} +0.2150 \\ +1.0000 \end{Bmatrix}$$

Fifth cycle: Try

$$\{A\} = \begin{Bmatrix} +0.2150 \\ +1.0000 \end{Bmatrix}$$

$$[\delta_m M] \begin{Bmatrix} +0.2150 \\ +1.0000 \end{Bmatrix} = \begin{Bmatrix} +5.0445 \times 10^{-6} \\ +23.4786 \times 10^{-6} \end{Bmatrix} \longrightarrow \begin{Bmatrix} +0.2148 \\ +1.0000 \end{Bmatrix}$$

Sixth cycle: Try

$$\{A\} = \begin{Bmatrix} +0.2148 \\ +1.0000 \end{Bmatrix}$$

$$[\delta_m M] \begin{Bmatrix} +0.2148 \\ +1.0000 \end{Bmatrix} = \begin{Bmatrix} +5.0438 \times 10^{-6} \\ +23.4784 \times 10^{-6} \end{Bmatrix} \longrightarrow \begin{Bmatrix} +0.2148 \\ +1.0000 \end{Bmatrix}$$

Thus,

$$p_1^2 = \frac{1.0000}{23.4784 \times 10^{-6}} = 42,592 \ \text{rad}^2/\text{sec}^2, \quad \text{or} \quad p_1 = 206.38 \ \text{rad/sec}$$

When an accuracy of 6 decimal places is used in the unitized eigenvector, the computer program in Appendix A gives, in eight cycles,

$$p_1 = 206.379 \ \text{rad/sec}$$

and

$$\{A\} = \begin{Bmatrix} +0.214831 \\ +1.000000 \end{Bmatrix}$$

1.7. Higher Frequency and Mode Vector from the Reduced $[\delta_m M]$ Matrix

It has been shown in Sec. 1.4 that there should be as many eigenvalues of p^2 as the size of the $[\delta_m M]$ matrix. The lowest possible value of p^2 can be found by the iteration procedure described in the preceding section. Intuitively it seems possible to modify or reduce the original $[\delta_m M]$ matrix to a new or reduced $[\delta_m M]$ matrix, of which the smallest possible value of p^2 is the next higher value of p^2 for the original $[\delta_m M]$ matrix. Indeed, this can be shown to be true. When all the eigenvalues have been thus extracted, the further reduced $[\delta_m M]$ matrix should become a null matrix; since there is no more eigenvalue left.

The new or reduced $[\delta_m M]$ matrix can be obtained from the previous $[\delta_m M]$ matrix by the equation

$$[\delta_m M]_{i+1} = [\delta_m M]_i - \frac{1}{p_i^2 \{A_i\}^T [M] \{A_i\}} \{A_i\} [MA_i]^T \qquad (1.7.1)$$

in which p_i^2 and $\{A_i\}$ are the eigenvalue and eigenvector of the $[\delta_m M]_i$ matrix.

The proof for the second mode on the basis of the first mode follows:

Given: (1) The general equation:

$$\{A_i\} = p_i^2 [\delta_m M] \{A_i\}$$

or

$$\{A_i\} = p_i^2 [\delta_m M]_1 \{A_i\}$$

Note: $[\delta_m M]$ and $[\delta_m M]_1$ are synonymous.

(2) The first true mode:

$$\{A_1\} = p_1^2 [\delta_m M]_1 \{A_1\}$$

(3) Let

$$[\delta_m M]_2 = [\delta_m M]_1 - \frac{1}{p_1^2 \{A_1\}^T [M] \{A_1\}} \{A_1\} [MA_1]^T$$

(4) The diagonal mass matrix:

$$[M] = [M]^T$$

(5) The orthogonality:

$$\{A_1\}^T [M] \{A_i\} = 0$$

To Prove: (1) $[\delta_m M]_2 \{A_1\} = 0$

(2) $[\delta_m M]_2 \{A_1\} = \dfrac{1}{p_i^2} \{A_i\}$

Proof: Statement	Reason
1. $[\delta_m M]_2 \{A_1\} = [\delta_m M]_1 \{A_1\}$ $$\qquad - \frac{1}{p_1^2 \{A_1\}^T [M] \{A_1\}} \{A_1\} [MA_1]^T \{A_1\}$$ $$= \frac{\{A_1\}}{p_1^2} - \frac{\{A_1\}}{p_1^2} = 0$$	1. Postmultiply Given (3) by $\{A_1\}$.

2. $[\delta_m M]_2 \{A_i\} = [\delta_m M]_1 \{A_i\}$

$$-\frac{1}{p_1^2 \{A_1\}^T [M] \{A_1\}} \{A_1\} [MA_1]^T \{A_i\}$$

$$= [\delta_m M]_1 \{A_i\} - 0 = \frac{1}{p_i^2} \{A_i\}$$

2. Postmultiply Given (3) by $\{A_i\}$. Also $\{A_1\}^T [M] \{A_i\}$ = 0 by Given (5).

Certainly the proof for the second mode on the basis of the first mode can be generalized to become a proof for the $(i+1)$th mode on the basis of the ith mode; hence the proof of Eq. 1.7.1.

In a numerical procedure, it is most enlightening to check the accuracy of the eigenvalue and eigenvector of a higher mode, which have been computed from the reduced $[\delta_m M]$ matrix, by substituting them into the original $[\delta_m M]$ matrix equation. One way of doing this is to compute a new unitized displacement vector from the original $[\delta_m M]$ matrix on the basis of an amplitude vector equal to the eigenvector of the reduced $[\delta_m M]$ matrix.

Example 1.7.1. Using the values of $[\delta_m M] = [\delta_m M]_1$, $[M]$, p_1^2, and $\{A_1\}$ in Example 1.6.1,

$$[\delta_m M] = [\delta_m M]_1 = 10^{-6} \ \mathrm{sec}^2 \begin{bmatrix} +3.3696 & +4.32 \\ +1.296 & +23.2 \end{bmatrix}$$

$$M = \frac{\mathrm{kip\text{-}sec}^2}{\mathrm{ft}} \begin{bmatrix} 0.024 & 0 \\ 0 & 0.080 \end{bmatrix}$$

$$p_1^2 = 42{,}592 \ \mathrm{rad/sec}^2$$

$$\{A_1\} = \begin{Bmatrix} +0.2148 \\ +1.0000 \end{Bmatrix}$$

compute $[\delta_m M]_2$, p_2^2, $\{A_2\}$, and $[\delta_m M]_3$.

Solution:

$$[\delta_m M]_2 = [\delta_m M]_1 - \frac{1}{p_1^2 \{A_1\}^T [M] \{A_1\}} \{A_1\} [MA_1]^T$$

$$= 10^{-6} \times \begin{bmatrix} +3.3696 & +4.32 \\ +1.296 & +23.2 \end{bmatrix}$$

$$\frac{\begin{Bmatrix} +0.2148 \\ +1.0000 \end{Bmatrix} \begin{bmatrix} 0.024 & 0 \\ 0 & 0.080 \end{bmatrix} \begin{Bmatrix} +0.2148 \\ +1.0000 \end{Bmatrix}^T}{42,592 \; [+0.2148 \quad +1.0000] \begin{bmatrix} 0.024 & 0 \\ 0 & 0.080 \end{bmatrix} \begin{Bmatrix} +0.2148 \\ +1.0000 \end{Bmatrix}}$$

$$= 10^{-6} \times \begin{bmatrix} +3.3696 & +4.32 \\ +1.296 & +23.2 \end{bmatrix}$$

$$- \frac{\begin{bmatrix} (+0.2148)^2 \, (0.024) & (+0.2148)\,(+1.0000)\,(0.080) \\ (+0.2148)\,(+1.0000)\,(0.024) & (+1.0000)^2\,(0.080) \end{bmatrix}}{42,592 \; [(+0.2148)^2 \, (0.024) + (+1.0000)^2 \, (0.080)]}$$

$$= 10^{-6} \times \begin{bmatrix} +3.3696 & +4.32 \\ +1.296 & +23.2 \end{bmatrix} - 10^{-6} \times \begin{bmatrix} +0.3205 & +4.9743 \\ +1.4923 & +23.1580 \end{bmatrix}$$

$$= 10^{-6} \sec^2 \begin{bmatrix} +3.0491 & -0.6543 \\ -0.1963 & +0.0420 \end{bmatrix}$$

First cycle: Try

$$\{A_2\} = \begin{Bmatrix} +1.0000 \\ +1.0000 \end{Bmatrix}$$

$$[\delta_m M]_2 \begin{Bmatrix} +1.0000 \\ +1.0000 \end{Bmatrix} = \begin{Bmatrix} +2.3948 \times 10^{-6} \\ -0.1543 \times 10^{-6} \end{Bmatrix} \longrightarrow \begin{Bmatrix} +1.0000 \\ -0.0644 \end{Bmatrix}$$

Second cycle: Try

$$\{A_2\} = \begin{Bmatrix} +1.0000 \\ -0.0644 \end{Bmatrix}$$

$$[\delta_m M]_2 \begin{Bmatrix} +1.0000 \\ -0.0644 \end{Bmatrix} = \begin{Bmatrix} +3.0912 \times 10^{-6} \\ -0.1990 \times 10^{-6} \end{Bmatrix} \longrightarrow \begin{Bmatrix} +1.0000 \\ -0.0644 \end{Bmatrix}$$

$$p_2^2 = \frac{1.0000}{3.0912 \times 10^{-6}} = 323{,}500 \text{ rad}^2/\text{sec}^2 \quad \text{or} \quad p_2 = 568.8 \text{ rad/sec}$$

$$[\delta_m M]_3 = [\delta_m M]_2 - \frac{1}{p_2^2 \{A_2\}^T [M] \{A_2\}} \{A_2\}[MA_2]^T$$

$$= 10^{-6} \times \begin{bmatrix} +3.0491 & -0.6543 \\ -0.1963 & +0.0420 \end{bmatrix}$$

$$- \frac{\begin{bmatrix} (+1.0000)^2 \ (0.024) & (+1.0000)\ (-0.0644)\ (0.080) \\ (+1.0000)\ (-0.0644)\ (0.024) & (-0.0644)^2 \ (0.080) \end{bmatrix}}{323{,}500 \ [(+1.0000)^2 \ (0.024) + (-0.0644)^2 \ (0.080)]}$$

$$= 10^{-6} \times \begin{bmatrix} +3.0491 & -0.6543 \\ -0.1963 & +0.0420 \end{bmatrix} - 10^{-6} \times \begin{bmatrix} +3.0453 & -0.6537 \\ -0.1962 & +0.0421 \end{bmatrix} \approx 0$$

Check:

$$[\delta_m M]_1 \{A_2\} = 10^{-6} \begin{bmatrix} +3.3696 & +\ 4.32 \\ +1.296 & +23.2 \end{bmatrix} \begin{Bmatrix} +1.0000 \\ -0.0644 \end{Bmatrix}$$

$$= \begin{Bmatrix} +3.0914 \times 10^{-6} \\ -0.1981 \times 10^{-6} \end{Bmatrix} \longrightarrow \begin{Bmatrix} +1.0000 \\ -0.0644 \end{Bmatrix}$$

At an accuracy of 6 decimal places in the unitized eigenvector, the computer program in Appendix A gives

$$[\delta_m M]_2 = 10^{-6} \begin{bmatrix} +3.04896 & -0.65501 \\ -0.19650 & +0.04222 \end{bmatrix}$$

$$p_2 = 568.772 \text{ rad/sec}^2$$

$$\{A_2\} = \begin{Bmatrix} +1.000000 \\ -0.064449 \end{Bmatrix}$$

$$[\delta_m M]_1 \{A_2\} \longrightarrow \begin{Bmatrix} +1.000000 \\ -0.064450 \end{Bmatrix}$$

$$[\delta_m M]_3 = \begin{bmatrix} -5.0000 \times 10^{-13} & +2.2000 \times 10^{-13} \\ +8.0000 \times 10^{-14} & +7.2500 \times 10^{-13} \end{bmatrix} \approx 0$$

1.8. The Computer Program

The computer program for free vibrations of rigid frames, with or without sidesway, in which axial deformation is neglected in the analysis, is presented in Appendix A. The two major parts in this computer program are: (1) the establishment of the $[ASA^T]$ matrix of the entire structure, from which the external flexibility matrix expressing the nodal displacements in terms of the nodal forces is obtained, and (2) the determination of circular frequencies and the mode vectors by an iteration procedure. Certainly for structural frames other than rigid frames without axial deformation (such as trusses, rigid frames with axial deformation, and plane grids) the second part of the program can be used intact.

1.9. Input and Output of Numerical Examples

Example 1.9.1 Using eight equal lumped masses, compute the first four natural frequencies and mode vectors of the simple beam shown in Fig. 1.9.1.

Solution: The nonzero elements in the 18 × 18 statics matrix $[A]$ are:

i	j	A (i, j)	i	j	A (i, j)	i	j	A (i, j)	i	j	A (i, j)
1	1	+1.	8	14	+1.	13	5	−0.4	16	12	−0.4
2	2	+1.	8	15	+1.	13	6	−0.4	16	13	+0.4
2	3	+1.	9	16	+1.	13	7	+0.4	16	14	+0.4
3	4	+1.	9	17	+1.	13	8	+0.4	17	13	−0.4
3	5	+1.	10	18	+1.	14	7	−0.4	17	14	−0.4
4	6	+1.	11	1	−0.8	14	8	−0.4	17	15	+0.4
4	7	+1.	11	2	−0.8	14	9	+0.4	17	16	+0.4
5	8	+1.	11	3	+0.4	14	10	+0.4	18	15	−0.4
5	9	+1.	11	4	+0.4	15	9	−0.4	18	16	−0.4
6	10	+1.	12	3	−0.4	15	10	−0.4	18	17	+0.8
6	11	+1.	12	4	−0.4	15	11	+0.4	18	18	+0.8
7	12	+1.	12	5	+0.4	15	12	+0.4			
7	13	+1.	12	6	+0.4	16	11	−0.4			

The (EI/L) values in ft-kips are 160,000 for members 1-2 and 17-18, and 80,000 for the other 7 members. The value of each lumped mass is 0.005 kip-sec^2/ft.

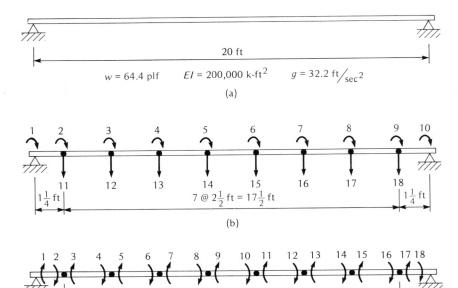

Figure 1.9.1. *Free vibration of a simple beam.* *(a) The given beam; (b) the* P-X *numbers; (c) the* F-e *numbers.*

The output for the first four modes is as follows:

Mode No.	1	2	3	4
p (rad/sec)	*246.73*	*986.66*	*2216.59*	*3919.18*
Δ at 11	+0.19891	−0.41421	+0.56645	+1.00000
Δ at 12	+0.56645	−1.00000	+1.00000	+1.00000
Δ at 13	+0.84776	−1.00000	+0.19891	−1.00000
Δ at 14	+1.00000	−0.41421	−0.84776	−1.00000
Δ at 15	+1.00000	+0.41421	−0.84776	+1.00000
Δ at 16	+0.84776	+1.00000	+0.19891	+1.00000
Δ at 17	+0.56645	+1.00000	+1.00000	−1.00000
Δ at 18	+0.19891	+0.41421	+0.56645	−1.00000

The exact solution† should give

$$p_i = i^2\pi^2 \sqrt{\frac{EI}{mL^4}} = i^2\pi^2 \sqrt{\frac{(200,000)\ (32.2)}{(0.0644)\ (20)^4}} = 25i^2\pi^2$$

or $p_1 = 246.74, p_2 = 986.96, p_3 = 2,220.7$, and $p_4 = 3,947.8$ rad/sec respectively.

†G. L. Rogers, *Dynamics of Framed Structures* (New York: John Wiley and Sons, Inc., 1959), p. 165.

Example 1.9.2. Using ten equal lumped masses, compute the first three natural frequencies and mode vectors of the continuous beam shown in Fig. 1.9.2.

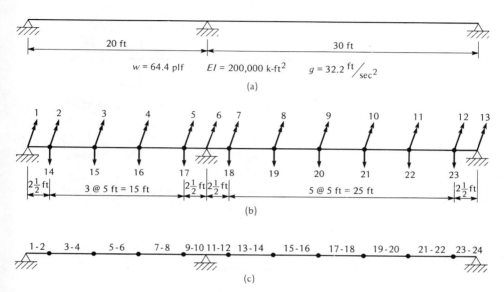

Figure 1.9.2. *Free vibration of a continuous beam. (a) The given beam; (b) the* P-X *numbers; (c) the* F-e *numbers.*

Solution: The nonzero elements in the 23 × 24 statics matrix [A] are:

i	j	A (i, j)	i	j	A (i, j)	i	j	A (i, j)	i	j	A (i, j)
1	1	+1.	9	17	+1.	16	5	−0.2	20	15	−0.2
2	2	+1.	10	18	+1.	16	6	−0.2	20	16	−0.2
2	3	+1.	10	19	+1.	16	7	+0.2	20	17	+0.2
3	4	+1.	11	20	+1.	16	8	+0.2	20	18	+0.2
3	5	+1.	11	21	+1.	17	7	−0.2	21	17	−0.2
4	6	+1.	12	22	+1.	17	8	−0.2	21	18	−0.2
4	7	+1.	12	23	+1.	17	9	+0.4	21	19	+0.2
5	8	+1.	13	24	+1.	17	10	+0.4	21	20	+0.2
5	9	+1.	14	1	−0.4	18	11	−0.4	22	19	−0.2
6	10	+1.	14	2	−0.4	18	12	−0.4	22	20	−0.2
6	11	+1.	14	3	+0.2	18	13	+0.2	22	21	+0.2
7	12	+1.	14	4	+0.2	18	14	+0.2	22	22	+0.2
7	13	+1.	15	3	−0.2	19	13	−0.2	23	21	−0.2
8	14	+1.	15	4	−0.2	19	14	−0.2	23	22	−0.2
8	15	+1.	15	5	+0.2	19	15	+0.2	23	23	+0.4
9	16	+1.	15	6	+0.2	19	16	+0.2	23	24	+0.4

The (EI/L) values in ft-kips are 80,000 for members 1-2, 9-10, 11-12, and 23-24, and 40,000 for the other 8 members. The value of each lumped mass is 0.01 kip-sec^2/ft.

The output for the first three modes is as follows:

Mode No.	1	2	3
p (rad/sec)	133.74	307.37	511.33
Δ at 14	−0.10243	+0.43222	+0.26590
Δ at 15	−0.26176	+1.00000	+0.50786
Δ at 16	−0.29507	+0.90382	+0.23589
Δ at 17	−0.14881	+0.30152	−0.08417
Δ at 18	−0.19586	−0.18515	+0.32864
Δ at 19	+0.62796	−0.20497	+1.00000
Δ at 20	+0.94314	+0.06996	+0.74576
Δ at 21	+1.00000	+0.35554	−0.29346
Δ at 22	+0.75776	+0.40998	−0.97216
Δ at 23	+0.28187	+0.17875	−0.52621

The trial-and-error solution considering distributed mass of Rogers† gives the fundamental natural frequency as

$$p_1 = 5.35 \sqrt{\frac{EI}{mL^4}} = 5.35 \sqrt{\frac{(200,000)\ (32.2)}{(0.0644)\ (20)^4}} = 5.35\ (25) = 133.75 \text{ rad/sec}$$

Example 1.9.3. Assuming that the rigid frame of Fig. 1.9.3 has rigid massive girders but flexible massless columns, determine its natural frequency and the mode vector.

Solution: Since there is only one lumped mass of 0.8 kip-sec^2/ft moving in the horizontal direction, the dynamic degree of freedom is 1, although the statical degree of freedom is 3, as shown in Fig. 1.9.3b.

The nonzero elements in the 3 × 6 statics matrix $[A]$ are

$$A(1,1) = +1. \qquad A(2,5) = +1.$$

$$A(3,1) = A(3,2) = -\frac{1}{24} \quad A(3,3) = A(3,4) = -\frac{1}{20}$$

$$A(3,5) = A(3,6) = -\frac{1}{16}$$

†Rogers, *ibid.*, p. 251.

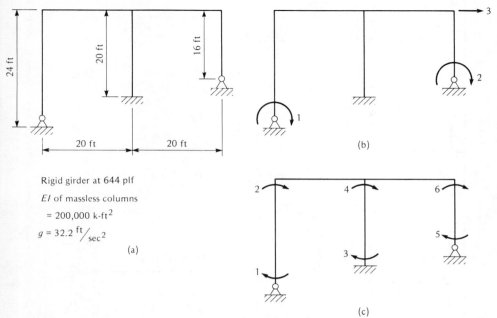

Figure 1.9.3. *Free vibration of a rigid frame with rigid massive girder and flexible massless columns. (a) The given rigid frame; (b) the P-X diagram; (c) the F-e diagram.*

The (EI/L) values in ft-kips of columns 1-2, 3-4, and 5-6 are 8,333.3333, 10,000, and 12,500, respectively.

The output shows, obviously in one iteration, $p_1 = 24.746$ rad/sec. The mode vector is, of course, a positive one by itself.

Rogers † gives, for a nondimensional solution,

$$T = 15.8 \sqrt{\frac{Ma^3}{EI}} = 15.8 \sqrt{\frac{0.80\,(4)^3}{200,000}} = 15.8\,(0.16) = 0.2528 \text{ sec}$$

$$p = \frac{2\pi}{T} = \frac{2\pi}{0.2528} = 24.85 \text{ rad/sec}$$

Example 1.9.4. Assuming that the rigid frame of Fig. 1.9.4 has rigid massive girders and flexible massy columns, and lumping the column masses at the mid-points of 4-ft segments, compute the first two natural frequencies and the associated mode vectors.

Solution: The nonzero elements in the 33×36 statics matrix $[A]$ are:

† *Ibid.*, p. 38.

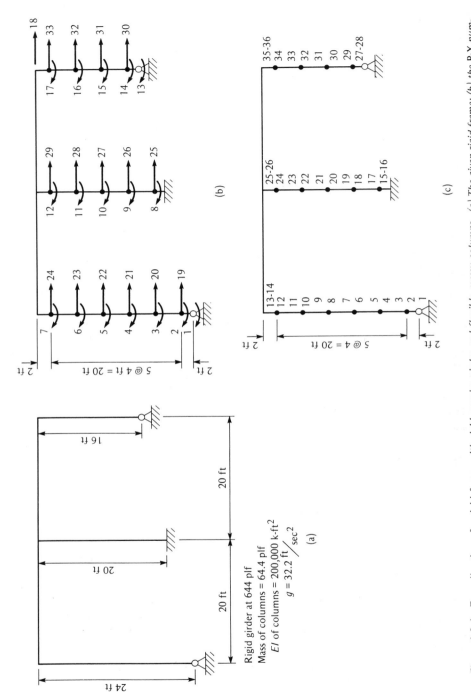

Figure 1.9.4. *Free vibration of a rigid frame with rigid massive girder and flexible massy columns. (a) The given rigid frame; (b) the P-X numbers; (c) the F-e numbers.*

Rigid girder at 644 plf
Mass of columns = 64.4 plf
EI of columns = 200,000 k-ft^2
$g = 32.2$ ft/sec^2

(a)

(b)

(c)

i	j	A (i, j)	i	j	A (i, j)	i	j	A (i, j)	i	j	A (i, j)
1	1	+1.	14	29	+1.	22	7	−0.25	28	22	−0.25
2	2	+1.	15	30	+1.	22	8	−0.25	28	23	+0.25
2	3	+1.	15	31	+1.	22	9	+0.25	28	24	+0.25
3	4	+1.	16	32	+1.	22	10	+0.25	29	23	−0.25
3	5	+1.	16	33	+1.	23	9	−0.25	29	24	−0.25
4	6	+1.	17	34	+1.	23	10	−0.25	29	25	+0.5
4	7	+1.	17	35	+1.	23	11	+0.25	29	26	+0.5
5	8	+1.	18	13	−0.5	23	12	+0.25	30	27	−0.5
5	9	+1.	18	14	−0.5	24	11	−0.25	30	28	−0.5
6	10	+1.	18	25	−0.5	24	12	−0.25	30	29	+0.25
6	11	+1.	18	26	−0.5	24	13	+0.5	30	30	+0.25
7	12	+1.	18	35	−0.5	24	14	+0.5	31	29	−0.25
7	13	+1.	18	36	−0.5	25	15	−0.5	31	30	−0.25
8	16	+1.	19	1	−0.5	25	16	−0.5	31	31	+0.25
8	17	+1.	19	2	−0.5	25	17	+0.25	31	32	+0.25
9	18	+1.	19	3	+0.25	25	18	+0.25	32	31	−0.25
9	19	+1.	19	4	+0.25	26	17	−0.25	32	32	−0.25
10	20	+1.	20	3	−0.25	26	18	−0.25	32	33	+0.25
10	21	+1.	20	4	−0.25	26	19	+0.25	32	34	+0.25
11	22	+1.	20	5	+0.25	26	20	+0.25	33	33	−0.25
11	23	+1.	20	6	+0.25	27	19	−0.25	33	34	−0.25
12	24	+1.	21	5	−0.25	27	20	−0.25	33	35	+0.5
12	25	+1.	21	6	−0.25	27	21	+0.25	33	36	+0.5
13	27	+1.	21	7	+0.25	27	22	+0.25			
14	28	+1.	21	8	+0.25	28	21	−0.25			

The (EI/L) values in ft-kips are 100,000 for members 1-2, 13-14, 15-16, 25-26, 27-28, and 35-36, and 50,000 for the other 12 members. The value of the lumped mass for the entire 40 ft of rigid girder is 0.80 kip-sec^2/ft and for the 4-ft segment of flexible column is 0.008 kip-sec^2/ft.

The output for the first two modes is as follows:

Mode No.	1	2
p (rad/sec)	23.953	269.63
Δ at 18	+1.00000	−0.01925
Δ at 19	+0.12649	+0.31144
Δ at 20	+0.37194	+0.81205
Δ at 21	+0.59495	+1.00000
Δ at 22	+0.78116	+0.82635
Δ at 23	+0.91709	+0.41705
Δ at 24	+0.99036	+0.04454
Δ at 25	+0.02812	−0.00094
Δ at 26	+0.21675	−0.00660
Δ at 27	+0.50120	−0.01344
Δ at 28	+0.78494	−0.01800

continued

Mode No.	1	2
p (rad/sec)	23.953	269.63
Δ at 29	+0.97219	−0.01928
Δ at 30	+0.18704	−0.00518
Δ at 31	+0.53730	−0.01391
Δ at 32	+0.81640	−0.01862
Δ at 33	+0.97774	−0.01940

The trial-and-error solution of Rogers† gives the fundamental natural frequency as

$$p_1 = 0.958 \sqrt{\frac{(200{,}000)\,(32.2)}{(0.0644)\,(20)^4}} = 0.958\,(25) = 23.95 \text{ rad/sec}$$

†*Ibid.*, p. 280.

CHAPTER 2

■

Free Vibrations of Continuous Beams and Rigid Frames with Distributed Masses

2.1. General Introduction

The treatment on free vibrations of structural frames by the lumped-mass method, as described in Chapter 1, is fairly general, as long as the external flexibility matrix expressing nodal displacements in terms of nodal forces is first solved by the displacement method of structural analysis. If axial deformation of the structural segments between lumped masses is to be considered, then another degree of freedom, in addition to that in the transverse direction, should be added in the axial direction at each lumped-mass location. Thus, aside from the disadvantage of the large dimensional requirement on the computer, the lumped-mass method may be used to investigate free vibrations of trusses, rigid frames with axial deformation, and structural frames with a mixture of hinged and rigid joints.

In this chapter free vibrations of continuous beams and rigid frames will be analyzed on the basis that each structural member has uniformly distributed mass along its length. The approach taken is first to solve the differential equation of free vibration of each member in terms of the natural frequency. Then

31

flexibility and stiffness matrices of this member relating end internal forces and deformations are obtained from the differential equation solution. Finally the natural frequency should be such as to make the determinant of the total dynamic external stiffness matrix $[ASA^T]$ of the structure equal to zero.

The discussion in this chapter, however, will be limited to rigid frames whose axial deformation may be neglected in the analysis.† When sideways are present, the movement of the total mass of each structural member, if any, in the direction of the member, should be considered. It will be shown that this latter effect can be taken care of by the subtraction of a sideway inertia-force matrix from the global $[ASA^T]$ matrix.

2.2. Differential Equation of Free Vibration of a Structural Member

Consider a structural member AB, which, in one of the modes of free vibration, may take the position and shape of $A'B'$, as shown in Fig. 2.2.1a. A free-

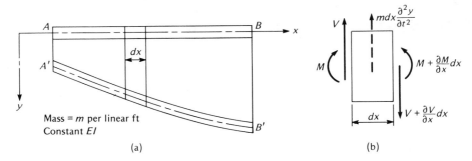

Figure 2.2.1. *Dynamics of a structural member.*

body diagram of an infinitesimal segment dx, subjected to shears and moments at the faces and an inertia force $(mdx)\ddot{y}$, is shown in Fig. 2.2.1b. Summing the transverse forces acting on this free body to zero,

$$V + mdx\,\frac{\partial^2 y}{\partial t^2} = V + \frac{\partial V}{\partial x}\,dx$$

or

†For treatment of rigid frames considering axial deformation, refer to Franklin Y. Cheng, "Free Vibrations of Trusses, Rigid Frames, Composite Structures and Mixed-Joint Structures," Ph.D. thesis, University of Wisconsin, 1966.

$$\frac{\partial V}{\partial x} = m \frac{\partial^2 y}{\partial t^2} \tag{2.2.1}$$

Summing the moments about any point on the right face,

$$M + V dx + m dx \frac{\partial^2 y}{\partial t^2} (dx/2) = M + \frac{\partial M}{\partial x} dx$$

or

$$\frac{\partial M}{\partial x} = V \tag{2.2.2}$$

The relationship between the elastic curve and the bending moment is

$$\frac{\partial^2 y}{\partial x^2} = -\frac{M}{EI} \tag{2.2.3}$$

Equations 2.2.1 to 2.2.3 are the basic equations of free vibration, since there are no other time-dependent forces acting on the member.

Differentiating Eq. 2.2.2 with respect to x and substituting Eq. 2.2.1 into it,

$$\frac{\partial^2 M}{\partial x^2} = \frac{\partial V}{\partial x} = m \frac{\partial^2 y}{\partial t^2} \tag{2.2.4}$$

Differentiating Eq. 2.2.3 twice with respect to x and substituting Eq. 2.2.4 into it,

$$\frac{\partial^4 y}{\partial x^4} = -\frac{m}{EI} \frac{\partial^2 y}{\partial t^2}$$

or

$$\frac{\partial^4 y}{\partial x^4} + \frac{m}{EI} \frac{\partial^2 y}{\partial t^2} = 0 \tag{2.2.5}$$

Equation 2.2.5 is the differential equation of free vibration of a structural member.

2.3. Solution of the Differential Equation of Free Vibration

The solution of the differential equation of free vibration, Eq. 2.2.5, may be obtained by assuming it to take the form

$$y = F(t)F(x) \qquad\qquad (2.3.1)$$

Substituting Eq. 2.3.1 in Eq. 2.2.5,

$$F(t)F^{IV}(x) + \frac{m}{EI}F''(t)F(x) = 0$$

Separating variables and equating each expression to $-p^2$,

$$\frac{F''(t)}{F(t)} = \frac{-F^{IV}(x)}{\dfrac{m}{EI}F(x)} = -p^2$$

for which

$$F''(t) + p^2 F(t) = 0 \qquad\qquad (2.3.2)$$

and,

$$F^{IV}(x) - \frac{mp^2}{EI}F(x) = 0 \qquad\qquad (2.3.3)$$

The solutions of Eqs. 2.3.2 and 2.3.3 are respectively

$$F(t) = C_1 \sin pt + C_2 \cos pt \qquad\qquad (2.3.4)$$

and

$$F(x) = A \sin\frac{\phi}{L}x + B \cos\frac{\phi}{L}x + C \sinh\frac{\phi}{L}x + D \cosh\frac{\phi}{L}x \qquad (2.3.5a)$$

where

$$\phi = L \sqrt[4]{\frac{mp^2}{EI}} \qquad\qquad (2.3.5b)$$

It may be noted that p is the natural frequency and $F(x)$ is the mode shape.
Substituting Eq. 2.3.1 and then Eq. 2.3.2 in Eq. 2.2.5,

$$\frac{\partial^4 y}{\partial x^4} + \frac{m}{EI}\frac{\partial^2 y}{\partial t^2} = \frac{\partial^4 y}{\partial x^4} + \frac{M}{EI}F''(t)F(x) = \frac{\partial^4 y}{\partial x^4} + \frac{m}{EI}[-p^2 F(t)]\,F(x)$$

$$= \frac{\partial^4 y}{\partial x^4} - \frac{mp^2}{EI} y = 0$$

or

$$\frac{\partial^4 y}{\partial x^4} = + \frac{mp^2 y}{EI} \qquad (2.3.6)$$

Comparing Eq. 2.3.6 with the usual differential equation of the elastic curve of a flexural member under static loading, the mode shape in free vibration may be considered to be the elastic curve of a member subjected to a distributed load of mp^2y per unit distance in the positive y-direction, as shown in Fig. 2.3.1. Furthermore, Eq. 2.3.6 is now an ordinary, instead of a partial differential

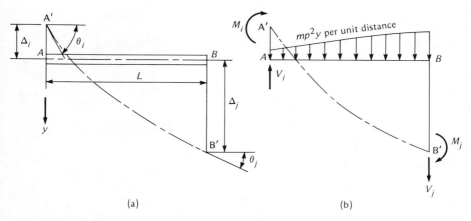

Figure 2.3.1. *Statical equivalent of a structural member in free vibration. (a) Member end deformations; (b) member end forces.*

equation, the solution of which is

$$y = A \sin \frac{\phi}{L} x + B \cos \frac{\phi}{L} x + C \sinh \frac{\phi}{L} x + D \cosh \frac{\phi}{L} x \qquad (2.3.7a)$$

where

$$\phi = L \sqrt[4]{\frac{mp^2}{EI}} \qquad (2.3.7b)$$

2.4. Member End Forces and Deformations

Having obtained the statical equivalent of a structural member in free vibration, which is in effect subjected to a distributed load of mp^2y in the positive y-direction and whose elastic curve can be expressed by Eq. 2.3.7, it is now desirable to express the end forces and deformations in terms of the four arbitrary constants A, B, C, and D. The four end deformations are θ_i, θ_j, Δ_i, and Δ_j, and the four corresponding end forces are M_i, M_j, V_i, and V_j, with their positive directions as indicated in Fig. 2.3.1.

The end deformations may be expressed in terms of the four arbitrary constants as

$$\theta_i = \left(+ \frac{dy}{dx} \quad \text{at} \quad x = 0 \right) = + \frac{\phi}{L}(A + C) \tag{2.4.1}$$

$$\theta_j = \left(+ \frac{dy}{dx} \quad \text{at} \quad x = L \right) = + \frac{\phi}{L}(A \cos\phi - B \sin\phi + C \cosh\phi + D \sinh\phi) \tag{2.4.2}$$

$$\Delta_i = (- y \quad \text{at} \quad x = 0) = -(B + D) \tag{2.4.3}$$

$$\Delta_j = (+ y \quad \text{at} \quad x = L) = +(A \sin\phi + B \cos\phi + C \sinh\phi + D \cosh\phi) \tag{2.4.4}$$

and the end forces as

$$M_i = \left(- EI \frac{d^2y}{dx^2} \quad \text{at} \quad x = 0 \right) = + \frac{\phi^2 EI}{L^2}(B - D) \tag{2.4.5}$$

$$M_j = \left(+ EI \frac{d^2y}{dx^2} \quad \text{at} \quad x = L \right) = + \frac{\phi^2 EI}{L^2}(- A \sin\phi - B \cos\phi + C \sinh\phi + D \cosh\phi) \tag{2.4.6}$$

$$V_i = \left(- EI \frac{d^3y}{dx^3} \quad \text{at} \quad x = 0 \right) = + \frac{EI\phi^3}{L^3}(A - C) \tag{2.4.7}$$

$$V_j = \left(- EI \frac{d^3y}{dx^3} \quad \text{at} \quad x = L \right) = + \frac{EI\phi^3}{L^3}(A \cos\phi - B \sin\phi - C \cosh\phi - D \sinh\phi) \tag{2.4.8}$$

2.5. The Member-Flexibility Matrix

The member-flexibility matrix, which expresses the end deformations in terms of the end forces, may be obtained by solving Eqs. 2.4.5 to 2.4.8 for A, B, C, and D and substituting the results in Eqs. 2.4.1 to 2.4.4; thus, calling $s = \sin\phi$, $c = \cos\phi$, $s' = \sinh\phi$, and $c' = \cosh\phi$,

$$A = \frac{L^2}{2\phi^2 EI(cc' - 1)}\left[(sc' + cs')M_i + (s' + s)M_j + \frac{L}{\phi}(ss' + cc' - 1)V_i + \frac{L}{\phi}(c' - c)V_j\right]$$

$$(2.5.1)$$

$$B = \frac{L^2}{2\phi^2 EI(cc' - 1)}\left[(cc' - ss' - 1)M_i - (c' - c)M_j + \frac{L}{\phi}(cs' - sc')V_i + \frac{L}{\phi}(s - s')V_j\right]$$

$$(2.5.2)$$

$$C = \frac{L^2}{2\phi^2 EI(cc' - 1)}\left[(sc' + cs')M_i + (s' + s)M_j + \frac{L}{\phi}(1 + ss' - cc')V_i + \frac{L}{\phi}(c' - c)V_j\right]$$

$$(2.5.3)$$

$$D = \frac{L^2}{2\phi^2 EI(cc' - 1)}\left[(1 - cc' - ss')M_i - (c' - c)M_j + \frac{L}{\phi}(cs' - sc')V_i + \frac{L}{\phi}(s - s')V_j\right]$$

$$(2.5.4)$$

and the member-flexibility matrix $[D]$ becomes

$$[D] =$$

	M_i	M_j	V_i	V_j
θ_i	$+\frac{L}{EI}(\text{TEMP1})$	$+\frac{L}{EI}(\text{TEMP2})$	$+\frac{L^2}{EI}(\text{TEMP3})$	$+\frac{L^2}{EI}(\text{TEMP4})$
θ_j	$+\frac{L}{EI}(\text{TEMP2})$	$+\frac{L}{EI}(\text{TEMP1})$	$+\frac{L^2}{EI}(\text{TEMP4})$	$+\frac{L^2}{EI}(\text{TEMP3})$
Δ_i	$+\frac{L^2}{EI}(\text{TEMP3})$	$+\frac{L^2}{EI}(\text{TEMP4})$	$+\frac{L^3}{EI}(\text{TEMP5})$	$+\frac{L^3}{EI}(\text{TEMP6})$
Δ_j	$+\frac{L^2}{EI}(\text{TEMP4})$	$+\frac{L^2}{EI}(\text{TEMP3})$	$+\frac{L^3}{EI}(\text{TEMP3})$	$+\frac{L^3}{EI}(\text{TEMP5})$

$$(2.5.5)$$

where

$$\text{TEMP1} = +\frac{sc' + cs'}{\phi(cc' - 1)} \qquad \text{TEMP2} = +\frac{s' + s}{\phi(cc' - 1)}$$

$$\text{TEMP3} = +\frac{ss'}{\phi^2(cc' - 1)} \qquad \text{TEMP4} = +\frac{c' - c}{\phi^2(cc' - 1)}$$

$$\text{TEMP5} = +\frac{sc' - cs'}{\phi^3(cc' - 1)} \qquad \text{TEMP6} = +\frac{s' - s}{\phi^3(cc' - 1)}$$

2.6. The Member-Stiffness Matrix

The member-stiffness matrix, which expresses the end forces in terms of the end deformations, may be obtained by solving Eqs. 2.4.1 to 2.4.4 for A, B, C, and D and substituting the results in Eqs. 2.4.5 to 2.4.8; thus, calling as before $s = \sin\phi$, $c = \cos\phi$, $s' = \sinh\phi$, and $c' = \cosh\phi$,

$$A = \frac{1}{2(1 - cc')}\left[\frac{L}{\phi}(1 - ss' - cc')\,\theta_i - \frac{L}{\phi}(c' - c)\,\theta_j + (sc' + cs)\,\Delta_i + (s' + s)\,\Delta_j\right] \tag{2.6.1}$$

$$B = \frac{1}{2(1 - cc')}\left[\frac{L}{\phi}(sc' - cs')\,\theta_i + \frac{L}{\phi}(s' - s)\,\theta_j + (cc' - ss' - 1)\,\Delta_i - (c' - c)\,\Delta_j\right] \tag{2.6.2}$$

$$C = \frac{1}{2(1 - cc')}\left[\frac{L}{\phi}(1 + ss' - cc')\,\theta_i + \frac{L}{\phi}(c' - c)\,\theta_j - (sc' + cs')\,\Delta_i - (s' + s)\,\Delta_j\right] \tag{2.6.3}$$

$$D = \frac{1}{2(1 - cc')}\left[\frac{L}{\phi}(cs' - sc')\,\theta_i - \frac{L}{\phi}(s' - s)\,\theta_j + (cc' + ss' - 1)\,\Delta_i + (c' - c)\,\Delta_j\right] \tag{2.6.4}$$

and the member-stiffness matrix $[S]$ becomes

$$[S] = $$

	θ_i	θ_j	Δ_i	Δ_j
M_i	$+\dfrac{EI}{L}(\text{TEMP1})$	$+\dfrac{EI}{L}(\text{TEMP2})$	$+\dfrac{EI}{L^2}(\text{TEMP3})$	$+\dfrac{EI}{L^2}(\text{TEMP4})$
M_j	$+\dfrac{EI}{L}(\text{TEMP2})$	$+\dfrac{EI}{L}(\text{TEMP1})$	$+\dfrac{EI}{L^2}(\text{TEMP4})$	$+\dfrac{EI}{L^2}(\text{TEMP3})$
V_i	$+\dfrac{EI}{L^2}(\text{TEMP3})$	$+\dfrac{EI}{L^2}(\text{TEMP4})$	$+\dfrac{EI}{L^3}(\text{TEMP5})$	$+\dfrac{EI}{L^3}(\text{TEMP6})$
V_j	$+\dfrac{EI}{L^2}(\text{TEMP4})$	$+\dfrac{EI}{L^2}(\text{TEMP3})$	$+\dfrac{EI}{L^3}(\text{TEMP6})$	$+\dfrac{EI}{L^3}(\text{TEMP5})$

$$\tag{2.6.5}$$

where

$$\text{TEMP1} = + \frac{\phi(sc' - cs')}{1 - cc'} \qquad \text{TEMP2} = + \frac{\phi(s' - s)}{1 - cc'}$$

$$\text{TEMP3} = - \frac{\phi^2 (ss')}{1 - cc'} \qquad \text{TEMP4} = - \frac{\phi^2 (c' - c)}{1 - cc'}$$

$$\text{TEMP5} = + \frac{\phi^3 (sc' + cs')}{1 - cc'} \qquad \text{TEMP6} = + \frac{\phi^3 (s' + s)}{1 - cc'}$$

When ϕ approaches zero, the values of TEMP1 to TEMP6 become +4, +2, −6, −6, +12, and +12, as they should when there is no load acting on the prismatic member. In Table 2.6.1 are shown the values of TEMP1 to TEMP6 for $\phi = 0$ to $\phi = 4.50$ at increments of 0.05. There is discontinuity in all TEMP-values near $\phi = 3\pi/2$.

2.7. The Dynamic External Stiffness Matrix of Continuous Beams and Rigid Frames without Sidesway

In continuous beams and rigid frames without sidesway, where axial deformation is neglected in the analysis, the uniformly distributed mass vibrates only in the transverse direction. Consequently in the statical equivalent of these systems, each member is subjected to a varying distributed load of mp^2y per unit length, in the y-direction. Since there is no external joint moment acting on any joint, the column matrix $\{P\}$ is zero; and in order that there be a nontrivial solution of the equation

$$\{P\} = [ASA^T] \{X\}$$

the determinant of the dynamic external stiffness matrix $[ASA^T]$ must be zero. Thus the equation of free vibration is

$$\text{DET} [ASA^T] = 0 \qquad\qquad (2.7.1)$$

The $[A]$ matrix in the dynamic external stiffness matrix $[ASA^T]$ depends only on the configuration of the continuous beams or rigid frames without sidesway. The member-stiffness matrix of the ith member is the 2 by 2 submatrix at the upper left corner of Eq. 2.6.5; thus,

TABLE 2.6.1

Stiffness Coefficients TEMP1 to TEMP6

ϕ	TEMP1	TEMP2	TEMP3	TEMP4	TEMP5	TEMP6
0	+4.0000	+2.0000	−6.0000	−6.0000	+12.000	+12.000
0.05	+4.0000	+2.0000	−6.0000	−6.0000	+12.000	+12.000
0.10	+4.0000	+2.0000	−6.0000	−6.0000	+12.000	+12.000
0.15	+4.0000	+2.0000	−6.0000	−6.0000	+12.000	+12.000
0.20	+4.0000	+2.0000	−5.9999	−6.0001	+11.999	+12.000
0.25	+4.0000	+2.0000	−5.9998	−6.0001	+11.999	+12.001
0.30	+3.9999	+2.0001	−5.9996	−6.0003	+11.997	+12.001
0.35	+3.9999	+2.0001	−5.9992	−6.0005	+11.994	+12.002
0.40	+3.9998	+2.0002	−5.9987	−6.0008	+11.990	+12.003
0.45	+3.9996	+2.0003	−5.9979	−6.0013	+11.985	+12.005
0.50	+3.9994	+2.0004	−5.9967	−6.0019	+11.977	+12.008
0.55	+3.9991	+2.0007	−5.9952	−6.0028	+11.966	+12.012
0.60	+3.9988	+2.0009	−5.9932	−6.0040	+11.952	+12.017
0.65	+3.9983	+2.0013	−5.9906	−6.0055	+11.934	+12.023
0.70	+3.9977	+2.0017	−5.9874	−6.0074	+11.911	+12.031
0.75	+3.9970	+2.0023	−5.9834	−6.0098	+11.882	+12.041
0.80	+3.9961	+2.0029	−5.9785	−6.0127	+11.848	+12.053
0.85	+3.9950	+2.0037	−5.9726	−6.0162	+11.806	+12.067
0.90	+3.9937	+2.0047	−5.9656	−6.0203	+11.756	+12.084
0.95	+3.9922	+2.0058	−5.9573	−6.0253	+11.697	+12.105
1.00	+3.9905	+2.0072	−5.9475	−6.0310	+11.628	+12.129
1.05	+3.9884	+2.0087	−5.9362	−6.0377	+11.548	+12.157
1.10	+3.9860	+2.0105	−5.9231	−6.0455	+11.455	+12.189
1.15	+3.9833	+2.0125	−5.9082	−6.0544	+11.349	+12.226
1.20	+3.9802	+2.0149	−5.8911	−6.0645	+11.228	+12.268
1.25	+3.9767	+2.0175	−5.8717	−6.0760	+11.091	+12.316
1.30	+3.9727	+2.0205	−5.8498	−6.0890	+10.936	+12.370
1.35	+3.9682	+2.0239	−5.8252	−6.1036	+10.762	+12.431
1.40	+3.9632	+2.0277	−5.7976	−6.1200	+10.568	+12.499
1.45	+3.9576	+2.0319	−5.7669	−6.1382	+10.351	+12.575
1.50	+3.9514	+2.0366	−5.7328	−6.1586	+10.110	+12.659
1.55	+3.9445	+2.0418	−5.6951	−6.1811	+9.8438	+12.753
1.60	+3.9369	+2.0475	−5.6534	−6.2060	+9.5499	+12.857
1.65	+3.9285	+2.0538	−5.6075	−6.2334	+9.2266	+12.971
1.70	+3.9193	+2.0608	−5.5571	−6.2636	+8.8719	+13.097
1.75	+3.9092	+2.0684	−5.5019	−6.2968	+8.4837	+13.235
1.80	+3.8982	+2.0768	−5.4415	−6.3331	+8.0599	+13.387
1.85	+3.8862	+2.0859	−5.3757	−6.3727	+7.5981	+13.552
1.90	+3.8731	+2.0958	−5.3040	−6.4160	+7.0960	+13.733
1.95	+3.8588	+2.1067	−5.2261	−6.4631	+6.5511	+13.930
2.00	+3.8433	+2.1184	−5.1417	−6.5143	+5.9608	+14.144
2.05	+3.8265	+2.1312	−5.0502	−6.5700	+5.3224	+14.377
2.10	+3.8084	+2.1451	−4.9512	−6.6304	+4.6331	+14.630
2.15	+3.7887	+2.1601	−4.8443	−6.6958	+3.8898	+14.905
2.20	+3.7675	+2.1764	−4.7289	−6.7667	+3.0895	+15.202

TABLE 2.6.1 (Continued)

ϕ	TEMP1	TEMP2	TEMP3	TEMP4	TEMP5	TEMP6
2.25	+3.7447	+2.1939	−4.6046	−6.8433	+2.2287	+15.524
2.30	+3.7200	+2.2129	−4.4707	−6.9261	+1.3041	+15.872
2.35	+3.6935	+2.2334	−4.3267	−7.0156	+0.31185	+16.248
2.40	+3.6649	+2.2555	−4.1720	−7.1122	−0.75186	+16.655
2.45	+3.6341	+2.2793	−4.0058	−7.2164	−1.8912	+17.095
2.50	+3.6011	+2.3050	−3.8273	−7.3288	−3.1105	+17.569
2.55	+3.5656	+2.3327	−3.6359	−7.4500	−4.4145	+18.082
2.60	+3.5275	+2.3625	−3.4307	−7.5807	−5.8081	+18.636
2.65	+3.4865	+2.3947	−3.2107	−7.7217	−7.2968	+19.233
2.70	+3.4426	+2.4293	−2.9749	−7.8736	−8.8861	+19.879
2.75	+3.3954	+2.4666	−2.7222	−8.0375	−10.582	+20.576
2.80	+3.3447	+2.5068	−2.4515	−8.2144	−12.392	+21.329
2.85	+3.2903	+2.5501	−2.1615	−8.4052	−14.322	+22.144
2.90	+3.2319	+2.5969	−1.8506	−8.6112	−16.381	+23.025
2.95	+3.1691	+2.6473	−1.5175	−8.8338	−18.577	+23.978
3.00	+3.1016	+2.7018	−1.1602	−9.0745	−20.919	+25.011
3.05	+3.0290	+2.7607	−0.77688	−9.3349	−23.417	+26.131
3.10	+2.9509	+2.8243	−0.36543	−9.6169	−26.083	+27.346
3.15	+2.8667	+2.8933	−0.07657	−9.9228	−28.929	+28.667
3.20	+2.7759	+2.9681	+0.55180	−10.255	−31.969	+30.105
3.25	+2.6779	+3.0493	+1.0633	−10.616	−35.218	+31.671
3.30	+2.5720	+3.1375	+1.6145	−11.009	−38.694	+33.381
3.35	+2.4573	+3.2337	+2.2092	−11.438	−42.415	+35.250
3.40	+2.3329	+3.3386	+2.8520	−11.907	−46.405	+37.299
3.45	+2.1977	+3.4534	+3.5480	−12.420	−50.688	+39.548
3.50	+2.0505	+3.5792	+4.3030	−12.984	−55.294	+42.024
3.55	+1.8897	+3.7174	+5.1241	−13.604	−60.257	+44.757
3.60	+1.7138	+3.8698	+6.0193	−14.290	−65.614	+47.783
3.65	+1.5206	+4.0384	+6.9980	−15.049	−71.413	+51.144
3.70	+1.3078	+4.2254	+8.0718	−15.892	−77.708	+54.890
3.75	+1.0724	+4.4338	+9.2542	−16.834	−84.564	+59.084
3.80	+0.81084	+4.6670	+10.562	−17.890	−92.059	+63.799
3.85	+0.51891	+4.9294	+12.015	−19.080	−100.29	+69.127
3.90	+0.19119	+5.2262	+13.638	−20.429	−109.37	+75.182
3.95	−0.17904	+5.5641	+15.464	−21.967	−119.46	+82.108
4.00	−0.60034	+5.9516	+17.531	−23.734	−130.73	+90.087
4.05	−1.0838	+6.3997	+19.891	−25.782	−143.44	+99.356
4.10	−1.6439	+6.9230	+22.613	−28.176	−157.89	+110.23
4.15	−2.3004	+7.5410	+25.787	−31.009	−174.52	+123.12
4.20	−3.0802	+8.2805	+29.539	−34.406	−193.91	+138.62
4.25	−4.0214	+9.1797	+34.047	−38.542	−216.88	+157.55
4.30	−5.1801	+10.294	+39.571	−43.678	−244.66	+181.11
4.35	−6.6415	+11.710	+46.507	−50.210	−279.08	+211.14
4.40	−8.5427	+13.563	+55.494	−58.774	−323.10	+250.59
4.45	−11.119	+16.089	+67.622	−70.462	−381.82	+304.55
4.50	−14.808	+19.727	+84.932	−87.313	−464.71	+382.49

$$[S]_{2\times2} \text{ of the } i\text{th member} = \begin{array}{|c|c|} \hline +\dfrac{EI_i}{L_i}(\text{TEMP1})_i & +\dfrac{EI_i}{L_i}(\text{TEMP2})_i \\ \hline +\dfrac{EI_i}{L_i}(\text{TEMP2})_i & +\dfrac{EI_i}{L_i}(\text{TEMP1})_i \\ \hline \end{array} \quad (2.7.2)$$

where

$$(\text{TEMP1})_i = +\frac{\phi_i(sc' - cs')}{1 - cc'} \qquad (\text{TEMP2})_i = +\frac{\phi_i(s' - s)}{1 - cc'}$$

and s, c, s', and c' are now $\sin\phi_i$, $\cos\phi_i$, $\sinh\phi_i$, and $\cosh\phi_i$ respectively.

Because the values of $(\text{TEMP1})_i$ and $(\text{TEMP2})_i$ of the ith member depend on the frequency angle ϕ_i, it will be desirable to choose a standard value ϕ_c and express ϕ_i as a multiple of ϕ_c. Let

$$L_i = \alpha_i L_c, \qquad m_i = \beta_i m_c, \qquad I_i = \gamma_i I_c, \qquad \phi_c = L_c \sqrt[4]{\frac{m_c p^2}{EI_c}} \qquad (2.7.3)$$

then

$$\phi_i = L_i \sqrt[4]{\frac{m_i p^2}{EI_i}} = \alpha_i \sqrt[4]{\frac{\beta_i}{\gamma_i}} \phi_c = \delta_i \phi_c \qquad (2.7.4a)$$

where

$$\delta_i = \alpha_i \sqrt[4]{\frac{\beta_i}{\gamma_i}} \qquad (2.7.4b)$$

The dynamic stiffness matrix $[ASA^T]$ is now dependent only on the standard frequency angle ϕ_c, which is to be determined by trial-and-error to satisfy the condition

$$\text{DET } [ASA^T] = 0$$

Example 2.7.1. Show that the determinant of the dynamic external stiffness matrix $[ASA^T]$ of the continuous beam shown in Fig. 2.7.1a changes sign between a standard frequency angle value of $\phi_c = 2.31$ and $\phi_c = 2.32$, on the basis of the properties of span AB. Using a linear interpolation show that the determinant of $[ASA^T]$ should be zero at $\phi_c = 2.313$, giving a natural frequency of 133.75 rad/sec.

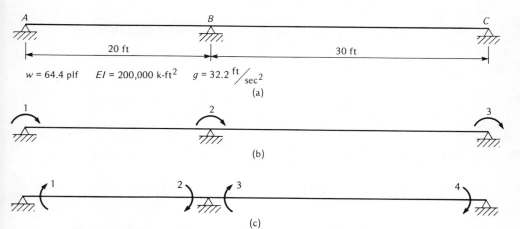

Figure 2.7.1. *Free vibration of a continuous beam.   (a) The given beam; (b) the P-X diagram; (c) the F-e diagram.*

Solution: On the basis of the properties of member 1-2, the α, β, γ, and δ values of members 1-2 and 3-4 are:

Member	i	$\alpha_i = \dfrac{L_i}{L_c}$	$\beta_i = \dfrac{m_i}{m_c}$	$\gamma_i = \dfrac{I_i}{I_c}$	$\delta_i = \alpha_i \sqrt[4]{\dfrac{\beta_i}{\gamma_i}}$
1-2	1	1.0	1.0	1.0	1.0
3-4	2	1.5	1.0	1.0	1.5

The $(\text{TEMP1})_i$ and $(\text{TEMP2})_i$ values in the member-stiffness matrices are obtained by linear interpolation from those listed in Table 2.6.1; thus

		$\phi_c = 2.31$			$\phi_c = 2.32$		
Member	i	$\phi_i = \delta_i \phi_c$	$(\text{TEMP1})_i$	$(\text{TEMP2})_i$	$\phi_i = \delta_i \phi_c$	$(\text{TEMP1})_i$	$(\text{TEMP2})_i$
1-2	1	2.31	+3.7147	+2.2170	2.32	+3.7094	+2.2211
3-4	2	3.465	+2.1535	+3.4911	3.48	+2.1093	+3.5289

For member 1-2 and $\phi_c = 2.31$,

$$S_{11} = S_{22} = (\text{TEMP1})_1 \frac{EI_1}{L_1} = +3.7147\left(\frac{200,000}{20}\right) = +37,147 \text{ ft-kips}$$

$$S_{12} = S_{21} = (\text{TEMP2})_1 \frac{EI_1}{L_1} = +2.2170\left(\frac{200,000}{20}\right) = +22,170 \text{ ft-kips}$$

For member 3-4 and $\phi_c = 2.31$,

$$S_{33} = S_{44} = (\text{TEMP1})_2 \frac{EI_2}{L_2} = +2.1535\left(\frac{200,000}{30}\right) = +14,357 \text{ ft-kips}$$

$$S_{34} = S_{43} = (\text{TEMP2})_2 \frac{EI_2}{L_2} = +3.4911\left(\frac{200,000}{30}\right) = +23,274 \text{ ft-kips}$$

For member 1-2 and $\phi_c = 2.32$,

$$S_{11} = S_{22} = (\text{TEMP1})_1 \frac{EI_1}{L_1} = +3.7094\left(\frac{200,000}{20}\right) = +37,094 \text{ ft-kips}$$

$$S_{12} = S_{21} = (\text{TEMP2})_1 \frac{EI_1}{L_1} = +2.2211\left(\frac{200,000}{20}\right) = +22,211 \text{ ft-kips}$$

For member 3-4 and $\phi_c = 2.32$,

$$S_{33} = S_{44} = (\text{TEMP1})_2 \frac{EI_2}{L_2} = +2.1093\left(\frac{200,000}{30}\right) = +14,062 \text{ ft-kips}$$

$$S_{34} = S_{43} = (\text{TEMP2})_2 \frac{EI_2}{L_2} = +3.5289\left(\frac{200,000}{30}\right) = +23,526 \text{ ft-kips}$$

Using the *P-X* and *F-e* numbers in Fig. 2.7.1, the statics matrix $[A]$ is

$$[A]_{3\times4} = \begin{array}{|c|c|c|c|} \hline +1 & 0 & 0 & 0 \\ \hline 0 & +1 & +1 & 0 \\ \hline 0 & 0 & 0 & +1 \\ \hline \end{array}$$

The $[S]$ matrix for $\phi_c = 2.31$ is

$$[S]_{4\times4} = \begin{array}{|c|c|c|c|} \hline +37,147 & +22,170 & 0 & 0 \\ \hline +22,170 & +37,147 & 0 & 0 \\ \hline 0 & 0 & +14,357 & +23,274 \\ \hline 0 & 0 & +23,274 & +14,357 \\ \hline \end{array}$$

The $[ASA^T]$ matrix for $\phi_c = 2.31$ is

$$[ASA^T]_{3\times3} = \begin{array}{|c|c|c|}
\hline
+37,147 & +22,170 & 0 \\
\hline
+22,170 & +51,504 & +23,274 \\
\hline
0 & +23,274 & +14,357 \\
\hline
\end{array}$$

The determinant of $[ASA^T]$ for $\phi_c = 2.31$ is

DET $[ASA^T] = 10^{12}$ [(3.7147) (5.1504) (1.4357) − (2.2170) (2.2170) (1.4357)

$\qquad$ − (3.7147) (2.3274) (2.3274)]

$\qquad = 10^{12}$ [27.4681 − 7.0567 − 20.1218] = +0.2896 × 10^{12}

The $[S]$ matrix for $\phi_c = 2.32$ is

$$[S]_{4\times4} = \begin{array}{|c|c|c|c|}
\hline
+37,094 & +22,211 & 0 & 0 \\
\hline
+22,211 & +37,094 & 0 & 0 \\
\hline
0 & 0 & +14,062 & +23,526 \\
\hline
0 & 0 & +23,526 & +14,062 \\
\hline
\end{array}$$

The $[ASA^T]$ matrix for $\phi_c = 2.32$ is

$$[ASA^T]_{3\times3} = \begin{array}{|c|c|c|}
\hline
+37,094 & +22,211 & 0 \\
\hline
+22,211 & +51,156 & +23,526 \\
\hline
0 & +23,526 & +14,062 \\
\hline
\end{array}$$

The determinant of $[ASA^T]$ for $\phi_c = 2.32$ is

DET $[ASA^T] = 10^{12}$ [(3.7094) (5.1156) (1.4062) − (2.2211) (2.2211) (1.4062)

$\qquad$ − (3.7094) (2.3526) (2.3526)]

$\qquad = 10^{12}$ [26.6838 − 6.9372 − 20.5305] = −0.7839 × 10^{12}

By linear interpolation, the value of ϕ_c which makes the determinant of $[ASA^T]$ equal to zero is

$$\phi_c = 2.31 + 0.010 \left(\frac{0.2896}{0.2896 + 0.7839} \right) = 2.313$$

Since

$$\phi_c = L_c \sqrt[4]{\frac{mp^2}{EI_c}}$$

$$p = \frac{\phi_c^2}{L_c^2} \sqrt{\frac{EI_c}{m_c}} = \frac{2.313)^2}{(20)^2} \sqrt{\frac{200,000\ (32.2)}{0.0644}} = (0.11565)^2\ (10,000)$$

$$= 133.75\ \text{rad/sec} \quad \text{(check with result of Example 1.9.2)}$$

2.8. Effects of Sidesway in Free Vibration

It has been noted in the preceding section that, in the establishment of the dynamic external stiffness matrix of continuous beams and rigid frames without sidesway, only the 2 × 2 submatrix in the upper left corner of the complete 4 × 4 member-stiffness matrix as expressed in Eq. 2.6.5 is needed. This is due to the fact that only member-end moments are involved in the statics matrix [A], and, since there are no linear joint displacements, member-end transverse displacements are all zero.

When axial deformation is neglected in rigid frame analysis, the statical degree of freedom in sidesway has been fully discussed in Chapters 6 and 7 of the present author's *Matrix Methods of Structural Analysis*. Once it is ascertained that sidesway displacements may occur, the full 4 × 4 member-stiffness matrix of Eq. 2.6.5 must be used in free-vibration analysis for those members whose transverse end displacements Δ_i and Δ_j are not zero but affected by sidesway displacements. Thus, 4 internal end forces and deformations, in the same order as $M_i - \theta_i$, $M_j - \theta_j$, $V_i - \Delta_i$, and $V_j - \Delta_j$ in Fig. 2.3.1, should be placed on each of these members.

There is a fundamental difference here between a stationary member and a free-vibrating member. In the former case, the member-stiffness matrix is always a 2 × 2 matrix, because the two end shears can always be expressed in terms of the two independent end moments and because the end rotations are measured from the member axis, which may have rotated by sidesway displacements, to the elastic curve. In the latter case the end moments and shears are independent quantities by themselves, and correspondingly, end rotations and transverse displacements are always measured from the *original* member axis.

As an illustration, for the *P-X* diagram of the rigid frame in Fig. 2.8.1a, the dynamic *F-e* diagram is shown in Fig. 2.8.1b. The statics matrix (the *equilibrium*

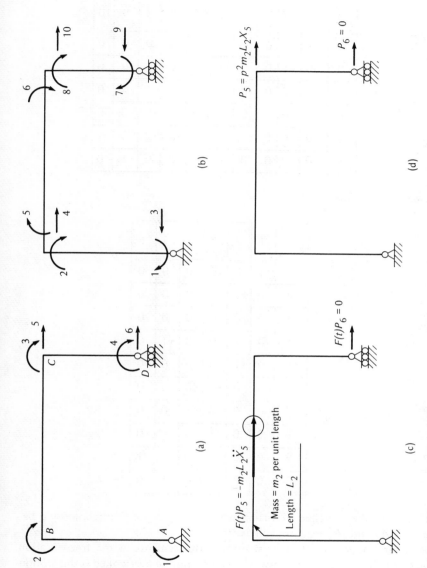

Figure 2.8.1. *A rigid frame in free vibration.* (a) *P-X diagram;* (b) *F-e diagram;* (c) *time-dependent sidesway inertia force;* (d) *statical equivalent of sidesway inertia force.*

47

matrix might be a better name) is:

$[A] =$

F P	1	2	3	4	5	6	7	8	9	10
1	+1	0	0	0	0	0	0	0	0	0
2	0	+1	0	0	+1	0	0	0	0	0
3	0	0	0	0	0	+1	0	+1	0	0
4	0	0	0	0	0	0	+1	0	0	0
5	0	0	0	+1	0	0	0	0	0	+1
6	0	0	0	0	0	0	0	0	-1	0

The deformation matrix $[B]$ is:

$[B] =$

X e	1	2	3	4	5	6
1	+1	0	0	0	0	0
2	0	+1	0	0	0	0
3	0	0	0	0	0	0
4	0	0	0	0	+1	0
5	0	+1	0	0	0	0
6	0	0	+1	0	0	0
7	0	0	0	+1	0	0
8	0	0	+1	0	0	0
9	0	0	0	0	0	-1
10	0	0	0	0	+1	0

Note that, by the principle of virtual work, the transposition relationship between the $[A]$ and $[B]$ matrices still exists.

One other important effect of sidesway displacements in the free-vibration analysis of rigid frames with sidesway which cannot be overlooked is the motion of the total mass of each member in its own axial direction. It can be shown that the statical equivalent of this effect is the action on the structure of external forces, each equal to p^2 times the product of the total mass of a member and its axial displacement, applied in the direction of the axial displacement. The entir-ety of these external forces may be described in a sidesway inertia-force matrix $[G]$, in the order of NPS X NPS, where NPS is the degree of freedom in side-sway; and the condition for free vibration becomes

$$[ASA^T] \{X\} = \begin{bmatrix} 0 & 0 \\ 0 & G \end{bmatrix} \begin{Bmatrix} X_R \\ X_S \end{Bmatrix} \tag{2.8.1}$$

where the X_R's are the joint displacements in rotation and the X_S's are the joint displacements in sidesway.

For instance, the time-dependent sidesway inertia forces for the rigid frame in Fig. 2.8.1a are shown in Fig. 2.8.1c as

$$F(t)P_5 = -m_2 L_2 \ddot{X}_5$$

$$F(t)P_6 = 0 \tag{2.8.2}$$

The statical equivalent force P_5 (Fig. 2.8.1d) is:

$$F(t)P_5 = -m_2 L_2 \ddot{X}_5 = -m_2 L_2 F''(t) X_5 = -m_2 L_2 (-p^2 F(t)) X_5 = +p^2 m_2 L_2 X_5 F(t)$$

from which

$$P_5 = +p^2 m_2 L_2 X_5 \tag{2.8.3}$$

and P_6 is still zero. The sidesway inertia-force matrix $[G]$ then becomes:

P \ X	5	6
5	$+m_2 L_2 p^2$	0
6	0	0

$$[G] =$$

Further treatment of the sidesway inertia-force matrix $[G]$ will be made in the next section.

2.9. The Sidesway Inertia-Force Matrix

While it is relatively simple to determine the sidesway inertia-force matrix $[G]$, as defined in the preceding section, by direct observation for vertically standing rigid frames with rectangular joints and horizontal sidesway displacements, it may be desirable to establish a general procedure for use in odd-shaped rigid frames with nonrectangular joints.

Define a statics matrix $[C^T]$ expressing the sidesway forces $\{P_s\}$ arisen from forces $\{F_s\}$ along the member axes, in the order of NPS $\times$ NMS, where NPS is the degree of freedom in sidesway and NMS is the number of members which shift in the axial directions during sidesway. Define a deformation matrix $[C]$ expressing the shifts in the axial directions $\{t_s\}$ of members due to sidesway displacements $\{X_s\}$, in the order of NMS $\times$ NPS. Define a sidesway mass matrix $[M_s]$ as the diagonal matrix expressing the total mass of each shifting member, in the order of NPM $\times$ NPM. Then the sidesway inertia-force matrix $[G]$ is

$$[G]_{\text{NPS}\times\text{NPS}} = p^2 \, [C^T] \, [M_s] \, [C] \qquad (2.9.1)$$

The reason for Eq. 2.9.1 should be obvious in that the $\{p^2 M_s C X_s\}$ vector represents the statical equivalent of the time-dependent inertia forces along the member directions, and the $\{C^T p^2 M_s C X_s\}$ vector should become the sidesway forces arisen from the statical forces in the member directions. Note that the $[C^T]$ and $[C]$ matrices may be independently established by their respective physical definitions and their transposition relationship verified.

Example 2.9.1. Establish the sidesway inertia-force matrix $[G]$ of the rigid frame shown in Fig. 2.8.1a by the equation $[G] = p^2 [C^T] [M_s] [C]$.

Solution: Member BC is the only member which may shift in the axial direction due to sidesway; thus

$$[C^T] = \begin{array}{c|c} & \begin{matrix} F_s \\ \hline P_s \end{matrix}\ BC \\ \hline 5 & +1 \\ \hline 6 & 0 \end{array}, \qquad [M_s] = \begin{array}{c|c} & BC \\ \hline BC & m_2 L_2 \end{array}, \qquad [C] = \begin{array}{c|cc} & \begin{matrix} X_s \\ \hline t_s \end{matrix}\ 5 & 6 \\ \hline BC & +1 & 0 \end{array}$$

and

$$[G] = p^2 [C^T] [M_s] [C] = p^2 \begin{array}{c|cc} & \begin{matrix} X_s \\ \hline P_s \end{matrix}\ 5 & 6 \\ \hline 5 & +m_2 L_2 & 0 \\ \hline 6 & 0 & 0 \end{array}$$

Example 2.9.2. For the rigid frame shown in Fig. 2.9.1a, establish the $[A]$, $[B] = [A^T]$, $[C^T]$, and $[C]$ matrices, each by its own physical definition, in the equation of free vibration:

$$[ASA^T]\,\{X\} = \begin{bmatrix} 0 & 0 \\ 0 & p^2 C^T M_s C \end{bmatrix} \begin{Bmatrix} X_R \\ X_s \end{Bmatrix}$$

Solution: (a) The $[A]$ matrix. On the basis of the P-X and F-e numbers, and the free-body diagrams of the 3 joints, as shown in Fig. 2.9.1 bcd, the $[A]$ matrix is:

$[A]_{5\times16} =$

F / P	1	2	3	4	5	6	7	8	9	10	11	12	13	14	15	16
1	0	+1	0	0	+1	0	0	0	0	0	0	0	0	0	0	0
2	0	0	0	0	0	+1	0	0	+1	0	0	0	0	0	0	0
3	0	0	0	0	0	0	0	0	0	+1	0	0	+1	0	0	0
4	0	0	0	+1	0	0	$-\dfrac{5}{13}$	$-\dfrac{99}{182}$	0	0	$+\dfrac{15}{14}$	0	0	0	0	0
5	0	0	0	0	0	0	0	$+\dfrac{13}{14}$	0	0	$-\dfrac{33}{70}$	$-\dfrac{3}{5}$	0	0	+1	0

The fourth and fifth rows are obtained by (1) solving for T_2 and T_3 from the two resolution equations of equilibrium of joint C, and (2) solving respectively for P_4 and P_5 from the horizontal resolution equations of equilibrium at joints B and D. Thus,

$$\Sigma F_x = 0 \text{ at joint } C, \qquad -\frac{12}{13}T_2 + \frac{4}{5}T_3 - \frac{5}{13}F_8 - \frac{3}{5}F_{11} = 0$$

$$\Sigma F_y = 0 \text{ at joint } C, \qquad -\frac{5}{13}T_2 - \frac{3}{5}T_3 + \frac{12}{13}F_8 - \frac{4}{5}F_{11} = 0$$

Solving the above two equations for T_2 and T_3,

$$T_2 = +\frac{33}{56}F_8 - \frac{65}{56}F_{11}$$

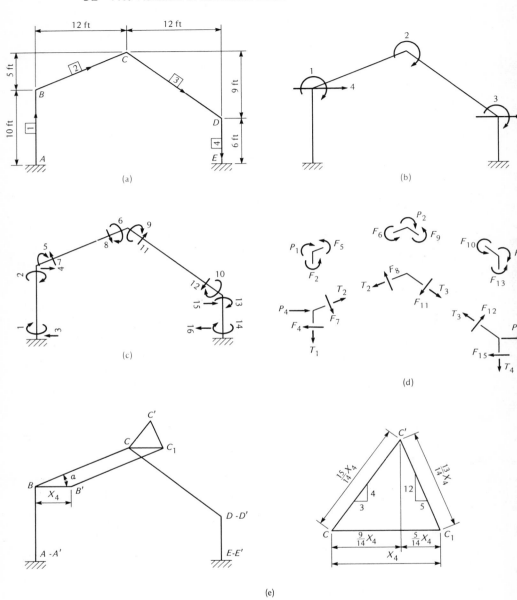

Figure 2.9.1. *A rigid frame in free vibration. (a) The given rigid frame; (b) the P-X diagram; (c) the F-e diagram; (d) free-body diagrams of joints, (e) joint displacement diagram due to X_4; (f) joint displacement diagram due to X_5; (g) sidesway forces due to forces along member axes.*

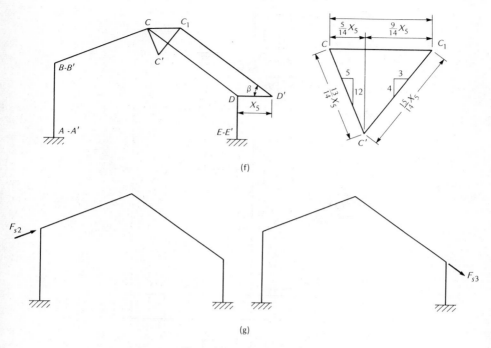

(f)

(g)

Figure 2.9.1. (*Continued*).

$$T_3 = +\frac{65}{56}F_8 - \frac{33}{56}F_{11}$$

$\Sigma F_x = 0$ at joint B, $P_4 = +F_4 - \dfrac{5}{13}F_7 - \dfrac{12}{13}T_2$

$$= +F_4 - \frac{5}{13}F_7 - \frac{99}{182}F_8 + \frac{15}{14}F_{11}$$

$\Sigma F_x = 0$ at joint D, $P_5 = +\dfrac{4}{5}T_3 - \dfrac{3}{5}F_{12} + F_{15}$

$$= +\frac{13}{14}F_8 - \frac{33}{70}F_{11} - \frac{3}{5}F_{12} + F_{15}$$

(b) The $[B] = [A^T]$ matrix. The $[B] = [A^T]$ matrix is:

$$[B]_{16\times5} =$$

e \ X	1	2	3	4	5
1	0	0	0	0	0
2	+1	0	0	0	0
3	0	0	0	0	0
4	0	0	0	+1	0
5	+1	0	0	0	0
6	0	+1	0	0	0
7	0	0	0	$-\dfrac{5}{13}$	0
8	0	0	0	$-\dfrac{99}{182}$	$+\dfrac{13}{14}$
9	0	+1	0	0	0
10	0	0	+1	0	0
11	0	0	0	$+\dfrac{15}{14}$	$-\dfrac{33}{70}$
12	0	0	0	0	$-\dfrac{3}{5}$
13	0	0	+1	0	0
14	0	0	0	0	0
15	0	0	0	0	+1
16	0	0	0	0	0

The fourth and fifth columns are obtained by (1) constructing the joint-displacement diagrams of Fig. 2.9.1ef, (2) computing the lengths of CC' and C_1C' in triangle CC_1C', and (3) observing the transverse end displacements in the directions of $e_3, e_4, e_7, e_8, e_{11}, e_{12}, e_{15}$, and e_{16}. For instance, in Fig. 2.9.1e,

$$e_8 = +(\text{hor. comp. of } CC')\left(\frac{5}{13}\right) - (\text{vert. comp. of } CC')\left(\frac{12}{13}\right)$$

$$= +\left(\frac{9}{14}\right)(X_4)\left(\frac{5}{13}\right) - \left(\frac{6}{7}X_4\right)\left(\frac{12}{13}\right) = -\frac{99}{182}X_4$$

In Fig. 2.9.1f,

$$e_{11} = +(\text{hor. comp. of } CC') \left(\frac{3}{5}\right) - (\text{vert. comp. of } CC') \left(\frac{4}{5}\right)$$

$$= + \left(\frac{5}{14}X_5\right)\left(\frac{3}{5}\right) - \left(\frac{6}{7}X_5\right)\left(\frac{4}{5}\right) = -\frac{33}{70}X_5$$

(c) The $[C^T]$ matrix. Since the sidesway displacements X_4 and X_5 can only cause shifts of members BC and CD in their respective axial directions, the $[C^T]$ matrix should express the sidesway forces arisen from two such forces F_{s2} and F_{s3}, as shown in Fig. 2.9.1g. The $[C^T]$ matrix is

$$[C^T] = \begin{array}{c|c|c}
\diagdown \begin{matrix} F_s \\ P_s \end{matrix} & 2 & 3 \\
\hline
4 & +\dfrac{12}{13} & 0 \\
\hline
5 & 0 & +\dfrac{4}{5}
\end{array}$$

(d) The $[C]$ matrix. In Fig. 2.9.1e, it can be seen that the shift in the direction of F_{s2} of member BC is $+(BB' \cos \alpha)$ and that of CD in the direction of F_{s3} is zero; in Fig. 2.9.1f, the shift in the direction of F_{s2} of member BC is zero and that of CD in the direction of F_{s3} is $+(DD' \cos \beta)$. Thus the $[C]$ matrix is

$$[C] = \begin{array}{c|c|c}
\diagdown \begin{matrix} X_s \\ t_s \end{matrix} & 4 & 5 \\
\hline
2 & +\dfrac{12}{13} & 0 \\
\hline
3 & 0 & +\dfrac{4}{5}
\end{array}$$

The $[G]$ matrix is:

$$[G] = p^2 [C^T] [M_s] [C] = p^2 \begin{bmatrix} +\dfrac{12}{13} & 0 \\ 0 & +\dfrac{4}{5} \end{bmatrix} \begin{bmatrix} m_2 L_2 & 0 \\ 0 & m_3 L_3 \end{bmatrix} \begin{bmatrix} +\dfrac{12}{13} & 0 \\ 0 & +\dfrac{4}{5} \end{bmatrix}$$

$$= p^2 \begin{bmatrix} +\dfrac{144}{169}m_2 L_2 & 0 \\ 0 & +\dfrac{16}{25}m_3 L_3 \end{bmatrix}$$

2.10. Free Vibration of Rigid Frames with Sidesway

The free-vibration equation of rigid frames with sidesway has been stated as

$$[ASA^T]\ \{X\} = \begin{bmatrix} 0 & 0 \\ 0 & G \end{bmatrix} \begin{Bmatrix} X_R \\ X_S \end{Bmatrix} \tag{2.8.1}$$

where $[G]$ may be either determined by inspection or computed from the equation

$$[G] = p^2\,[C^T]\,[M_s]\,[C] \tag{2.9.1}$$

The natural frequency p or the frequency angle ϕ_c should be such as to make the determinant of the coefficients of $\{X\}$ in Eq. 2.8.1 equal to zero; or,

$$\text{DET}\left[[ASA^T] - \begin{bmatrix} 0 & 0 \\ 0 & G \end{bmatrix}\right] = 0 \tag{2.10.1}$$

The conversion formulas between p and ϕ_c are

$$p = \frac{\phi_c^2}{L_c^2}\sqrt{\frac{EI_c}{m_c}} \quad \text{and} \quad \phi_c = L_c\sqrt[4]{\frac{m_c p^2}{EI_c}}$$

Again, L_c, m_c, and I_c are the length, mass per unit length, and moment of inertia of a standard member.

Example 2.10.1. Show that the determinant of the matrix

$$\left[[ASA^T] - \begin{bmatrix} 0 & 0 \\ 0 & G \end{bmatrix}\right]$$

of the rigid frame with sidesway shown in Fig. 2.10.1 changes sign between a standard frequency angle value of $\phi_c = 0.97$ and $\phi_c = 0.98$, on the basis of the properties of column BE. Using a linear interpolation show that this determinant should be zero at $\phi_c = 0.979$, giving a natural frequency of 23.961 rad per sec.

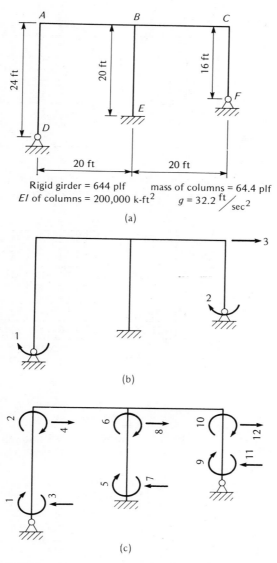

Rigid girder = 644 plf   mass of columns = 64.4 plf
EI of columns = 200,000 k-ft^2 $g = 32.2 \frac{ft}{sec^2}$

(a)

(b)

(c)

Figure 2.10.1. *A rigid frame in free vibration. (a) The given rigid frame; (b) the* P-X *diagram; (c) the* F-e *diagram.*

Solution: On the basis of the properties of member 5-6-7-8, the α, β, γ, and δ values of members 1-2-3-4, 5-6-7-8, and 9-10-11-12 are:

Member	i	$\alpha_i = \dfrac{L_i}{L_c}$	$\beta_i = \dfrac{m_i}{m_c}$	$\gamma_i = \dfrac{I_i}{I_c}$	$\delta_i = \alpha_i \sqrt[4]{\dfrac{\beta_i}{\gamma_i}}$
1-2-3-4	1	1.2	1.0	1.0	1.2
5-6-7-8	2	1.0	1.0	1.0	1.0
9-10-11-12	3	0.8	1.0	1.0	0.8

The $(TEMP1)_i$ to $(TEMP6)_i$ values in the member stiffness matrices are obtained by linear interpolation from those listed in Table 2.6.1; thus

Member	i	ϕ_c	$\phi_i = \delta_i\,\phi_c$	$(TEMP1)_i$	$(TEMP2)_i$	$(TEMP3)_i$	$(TEMP4)_i$	$(TEMP5)_i$	$(TEMP6)_i$
1-2-3-4	1	0.97	1.164	+3.9824	+2.0132	−5.9034	−6.0572	+11.315	+12.238
1-2-3-4	1	0.98	1.176	+3.9817	+2.0137	−5.8993	−6.0596	+11.286	+12.248
5-6-7-8	2	0.97	0.970	+3.9915	+2.0064	−5.9534	−6.0276	+11.669	+12.115
5-6-7-8	2	0.98	0.980	+3.9912	+2.0066	−5.9514	−6.0287	+11.656	+12.119
9-10-11-12	3	0.97	0.776	+3.9965	+2.0026	−5.9809	−6.0103	+11.864	+12.047
9-10-11-12	3	0.98	0.784	+3.9964	+2.0027	−5.9801	−6.0118	+11.859	+12.049

For member 1-2-3-4,

$$\frac{EI}{L} = 8333.333 \text{ ft-kips} \qquad \frac{EI}{L^2} = 347.2222 \text{ kips} \qquad \frac{EI}{L^3} = 14.46759 \text{ kips/ft}$$

$[S]$ for $(\phi_c = 0.97) =$

e\F	1	2	3	4
1	+33,187	+16,777	−2,049.8	−2,103.2
2	+16,777	+33,187	−2,103.2	−2,049.8
3	−2,049.8	−2,103.2	+163.70	+177.05
4	−2,103.2	−2,049.8	+177.05	+163.70

$[S]$ for ($\phi_c = 0.98$) =

e F	1	2	3	4
1	+33,181	+16,781	-2,048.4	-2,104.0
2	+16,781	+33,181	-2,104.0	-2,048.4
3	- 2,048.4	- 2,104.0	+ 163.28	+ 177.20
4	- 2,104.0	- 2,048.4	+ 177.20	+ 163.28

For member 5-6-7-8,

$$\frac{EI}{L} = 10,000 \text{ ft-kips} \qquad \frac{EI}{L^2} = 500 \text{ kips} \qquad \frac{EI}{L^3} = 25 \text{ kips/ft}$$

$[S]$ for ($\phi_c = 0.97$) =

e F	5	6	7	8
5	+39,915	+20,064	-2,967.7	-3,013.8
6	+20,064	+39,915	-3,013.8	-2,976.7
7	- 2,976.7	- 3,013.8	+ 291.72	+ 302.88
8	- 3,013.8	- 2,976.7	+ 302.88	+ 291.72

$[S]$ for ($\phi_c = 0.98$) =

e F	5	6	7	8
5	+39,912	+20,066	-2,975.7	-3,014.4
6	+20,066	+39,912	-3,014.4	-2,975.7
7	- 2,975.7	- 3,014.4	+ 291.40	+ 302.98
8	- 3,014.4	- 2,975.7	+ 302.98	+ 291.40

For member 9-10-11-12,

$$\frac{EI}{L} = 12,500 \text{ ft-kips} \qquad \frac{EI}{L^2} = 781.25 \text{ kips} \qquad \frac{EI}{L^3} = 48.82812 \text{ kips/ft}$$

$[S]$ for ($\phi_c = 0.97$) =

e F	9	10	11	12
9	+49,956	+25,032	−4,672.6	−4,695.5
10	+25,032	+49,956	−4,695.5	−4,672.6
11	− 4,672.6	− 4,695.5	+ 579.30	+ 588.23
12	− 4,695.5	− 4,672.6	+ 588.23	+ 579.30

$[S]$ for ($\phi_c = 0.98$) =

e F	9	10	11	12
9	+49,955	+25,034	−4,672.0	−4,696.7
10	+25,034	+49,955	−4,696.7	−4,672.0
11	− 4,672.0	− 4,696.7	+ 579.05	+ 588.33
12	− 4,696.7	− 4,672.0	+ 588.33	+ 579.05

Using the *P-X* and *F-e* numbers in Fig. 2.10.1, the statics matrix $[A]$ is

$[A]_{3 \times 12}$ =

F P	1	2	3	4	5	6	7	8	9	10	11	12
1	+1	0	0	0	0	0	0	0	0	0	0	0
2	0	0	0	0	0	0	0	0	+1	0	0	0
3	0	0	0	+1	0	0	0	+1	0	0	0	+1

Then, for $\phi_c = 0.97$,

$[ASA^T]_{3 \times 3}$ =

X P	1	2	3
1	+33,187	0	−2,103.2
2	0	+49,956	−4,695.5
3	− 2,103.2	− 4,695.5	+1,034.72

$[G]_{1 \times 1}$ =

	3
3	$p^2 \dfrac{644}{1000} \dfrac{1}{32.2} (40) = 500 \, \phi_c^4 = 442.64$

$$\text{DET}\left[[ASA^T] - \begin{bmatrix} 0 & 0 \\ 0 & G \end{bmatrix}\right] = \text{DET}$$

+33,187	0	−2,103.2
0	+49,956	−4,695.5
− 2,103.2	− 4,695.5	+ 592.08

$$= (+33,187)(+49,956)(+592.08)$$

$$\quad - (-2,103.2)(+49,956)(-2,103.2)$$

$$\quad - (+33,187)(-4,695.5)(-4,695.5)$$

$$= 10^{12}\,(+0.98160 - 0.22099 - 0.73170)$$

$$= +0.02891 \times 10^{12}$$

For $\phi_c = 0.98$,

$$[ASA^T]_{3\times3} =$$

X \ P	1	2	3
1	+33,181	0	−2,104.0
2	0	+49,955	−4,697.7
3	− 2,104.0	− 4,967.7	+1,033.73

$$[G]_{1\times1} =$$

	3
3	500 ϕ_c^4 = 461.18

$$\text{DET}\left[[ASA^T] - \begin{bmatrix} 0 & 0 \\ 0 & G \end{bmatrix}\right] = \text{DET}$$

+33,181	0	−2,104.0
0	+49,955	−4,696.7
− 2,104.0	− 4,696.7	+ 572.55

$$= (+33,181)(+49,955)(+572.55)$$

$$\quad - (-2,104.0)(+49,955)(-2,104.0)$$

$$\quad - (+33,181)(-4,696.7)(-4,696.7)$$

$$= 10^{12}\,(+0.94903 - 0.22114 - 0.73194)$$

$$= -0.00405 \times 10^{12}$$

By linear interpolation, the value of ϕ_c which makes the determinant of

$$\left[[ASA^T] - \begin{bmatrix} 0 & 0 \\ 0 & G \end{bmatrix} \right]$$

equal to zero is

$$\phi_c = 0.97 + 0.010 \left(\frac{0.02891}{0.02891 + 0.00405} \right) = 0.979$$

and

$$p = \frac{\phi_c^2}{L_c^2} \sqrt{\frac{EI_c}{m_c}} = 25 \, \phi_c^2 = 23.961 \text{ rad/sec} \qquad \text{(check with result of Example 1.9.3)}$$

2.11. The Computer Program

A computer program for obtaining the fundamental natural frequency of continuous beams and rigid frames with distributed masses is given in Appendix B. The purpose here is to show how typical programming may be done in solving problems of small dimensions. Sophistications such as the automatic formulation of the $[ASA^T]$ matrix without the use of the input $[A]$ matrix, and the computation of higher frequencies, modal displacements, and elastic curves, are not included.

In subroutine BUASAT the dynamic stiffness matrix

$$[ASA^T] - \begin{bmatrix} 0 & 0 \\ 0 & G \end{bmatrix}$$

as expressed by Eq. 2.10.1 is computed for any assigned value of ϕ_c. It is important to note that the member stiffness matrix of members without transverse end displacements is a 2 X 2 matrix as given by Eq. 2.7.2, but that of members with possible transverse end displacements is the full 4 X 4 matrix as given by Eq. 2.6.5. Thus it has been specified that, in assigning *F-e* numbers, two consecutive odd and even numbers *must* be first assigned to members with end rotations only, then four consecutive numbers are assigned to the two end rotations and two end displacements of members of the second type.

The first of the three DO-loops considers the contribution to the $[ASA^T]$ matrix from members of the first type, the second DO-loop does the same for members of the second type, and the third DO-loop makes the subtraction of the sidesway inertia-force matrix.

In subroutine COMDET the determinant of any square matrix with predominant diagonal elements is computed, with the assumption that all pivots in

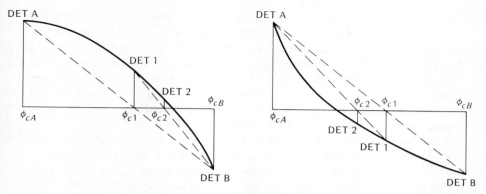

Figure 2.11.1. *Evaluation of ϕ_c causing zero determinant.*

TABLE 2.11.1

Input Data for Examples 2.7.1 and 2.10.1

Card No.	Elements	Format	Remarks
1	1	I5	1st data set
2	3 3 0 4 2 2 0	7I5	NP, NPR, NPS, NF, NM, NM1, NM2
3	1 1 +1.	2I5, F10.4	Nonzero elements in $[A]$
4	2 2 +1.	2I5, F10.4	Nonzero elements in $[A]$
5	2 3 +1.	2I5, F10.4	Nonzero elements in $[A]$
6	3 4 +1.	2I5, F10.4	Nonzero elements in $[A]$
7	−9	2I5, F10.4	No more nonzero elements in $[A]$
8	1. 20. 200000. .002	4F10.4	E, XLC, XIC, XMC
9	20. 30.	5F10.4	XL(1) . . . XL(NM)
10	200000. 200000.	5F10.4	XI(1) . . . XI(NM)
11	.002 .002	5F10.4	XM(1) . . . XM(NM)
12	2	I5	2nd data set
13	3 2 1 12 3 0 3	7I5	NP, NPR, NPS, NF, NM, NM1, NM2
14	1 1 +1	2I5, F10.4	Nonzero elements in $[A]$
15	2 9 +1.	2I5, F10.4	Nonzero elements in $[A]$
16	3 4 +1.	2I5, F10.4	Nonzero elements in $[A]$
17	3 8 +1.	2I5, F10.4	Nonzero elements in $[A]$
18	3 12 +1.	2I5, F10.4	Nonzero elements in $[A]$
19	−9	2I5, F10.4	No more nonzero elements in $[A]$
20	1 1 .8	2I5, F10.4	Nonzero elements in $[G]$
21	−9	2I5, F10.4	No more nonzero elements in $[G]$
22	1. 20. 200000. .002	4F10.4	E, XLC, XIC, XMC
23	24. 20. 16.	5F10.4	XL (1) . . . XL(NM)
24	200000. 200000. 200000.	5F10.4	XI (1) . . . XI(NM)
25	.002 .002 .002	5F10.4	XM (1) . . . XM(NM)
26	−9	I5	No more data set

the Gauss-Jordan elimination lie on the main diagonal. Thus the program is similar to the inversion routine in Appendices D or E of *Matrix Methods of Structural Analysis*. Examination of the TEMP1 and TEMP2 values in Table 2.6.1, for ϕ-values above 3.15, reveals that the far-end moments may become larger than the near-end moments in higher frequencies. Thus, when higher frequencies are desired, this subroutine should be changed to the routine of Appendix B of the earlier book, where a full panel search of the pivot is executed before each Gauss-Jordan elimination.

In the main program, the value of the fundamental frequency angle ϕ_c causing zero determinant is obtained by an iterative procedure within a tolerance of 0.0001. A search is first made for two successive values of ϕ_{cA} and ϕ_{cB} at which the determinant changes sign from positive to negative. It is written into the program that ϕ_{cB} and ϕ_{cA} are both multiples of 0.10 and $(\phi_{cB} - \phi_{cA})$ is equal to 0.10. Then the first approximate value ϕ_{c1}, as shown in Fig. 2.11.1a or b, is computed by a linear interpolation between ϕ_{cA} and ϕ_{cB}. If DET1 at ϕ_{c1} is positive, the second approximate value ϕ_{c2} is interpolated between ϕ_{c1} and ϕ_{cB}, as shown in Fig. 2.11.1a; but if DET1 is negative, the second approximate value ϕ_{c2} is interpolated between ϕ_{cA} and ϕ_{c1}, as shown in Fig. 2.11.1b. This process is repeated until the value of $[\phi_c(i) - \phi_c(i-1)]$ in Fig. 2.11.1a, or of $[\phi_c(i-1) - \phi_c(i)]$ in Fig. 2.11.1b, is less than 0.0001, where i is the number of linear interpolations.

The input data for Examples 2.7.1 and 2.10.1 to match the computer program in Appendix B is shown in Table 2.11.1.

CHAPTER 3

■

Undamped Forced Motion of Structural Frames with Lumped Masses

3.1. General Introduction

In the previous chapter the free vibration of a structural frame with lumped masses, such as shown in Fig. 3.1.1a, has been treated. The free vibration of two elastically connected lumped masses may be described as

$$X_{m1} = k_1 A_{11} \cos(p_1 t - \alpha_1) + k_2 A_{12} \cos(p_2 t - \alpha_2) \qquad (3.1.1a)$$

$$X_{m2} = k_1 A_{21} \cos(p_1 t - \alpha_1) + k_2 A_{22} \cos(p_2 t - \alpha_2) \qquad (3.1.1b)$$

where (p_1, A_{11}, A_{21}) and (p_2, A_{12}, A_{22}) are the natural frequencies and unitized mode vectors in the first and second modes, respectively; and k_1, k_2, α_1, and α_2 are unknown constants which may be determined from the initial conditions at $t = 0$ of lumped masses M_1 and M_2.

Suppose, with whatever given initial conditions at M_1 and M_2, two linear time-dependent forces $F_{t1} = C_1 - D_1 t$ and $F_{t2} = C_2 - D_2 t$ are applied to the lumped masses as shown in Fig. 3.1.1b, where C_1, C_2, D_1, and D_2 are usually positive quantities, but C_1/D_1 and C_2/D_2 need not be equal to each other. The problem

65

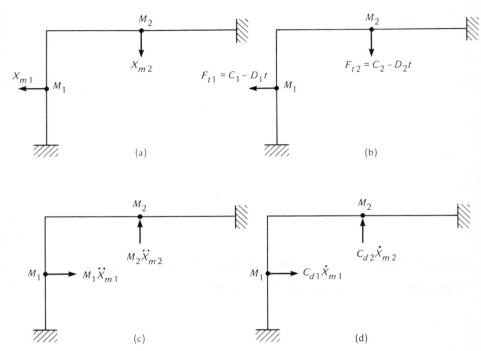

Figure 3.1.1. *Forced motion of structural frames with lumped masses. (a) Structural frame with lumped masses; (b) linear time-dependent forces; (c) inertia forces; (d) damping forces.*

is to trace the response of the structure; or in other words to find expressions for X_{m1} and X_{m2} as functions of time t.

Acting on the lumped masses, by D'Alembert's principle, are the inertia forces $M_1\ddot{X}_{m1}$ and $M_2\ddot{X}_{m2}$, in the negative directions of the X_{m1} and X_{m2} axes, as shown in Fig. 3.1.1c. Sometimes resistance may be encountered by the moving lumped masses; these damping forces, if assumed to be proportional to the velocities, are $C_{d1}\dot{X}_{m1}$ and $C_{d2}\dot{X}_{m2}$, as shown in Fig. 3.1.1d, where C_{d1} and C_{d2} are the damping coefficients. The inertia forces are, of course, always present whenever there are accelerations; but existence of damping depends on the nature of the physical systems. In this chapter, only undamped forced motion of structural frames with lumped masses will be considered.

3.2. Differential Equations of Undamped Forced Motion

The differential equations of undamped forced motion may be formulated by the use of either the matrix of flexibility-influence coefficients $[\delta_m]$ or the matrix of stiffness-influence coefficients $[K_m]$, as defined previously in Sec. 1.3.

In the case of two lumped masses and using the flexibility-influence coefficients,

$$X_{m1} = \delta_{m11} (F_{t1} - M_1 \ddot{X}_{m1}) + \delta_{m12} (F_{t2} - M_2 \ddot{X}_{m2})$$

$$X_{m2} = \delta_{m21} (F_{t1} - M_1 \ddot{X}_{m1}) + \delta_{m22} (F_{t2} - M_2 \ddot{X}_{m2})$$

or, in long matrix notation,

$$\begin{Bmatrix} X_{m1} \\ X_{m2} \end{Bmatrix} = \begin{bmatrix} \delta_{m11} & \delta_{m12} \\ \delta_{m21} & \delta_{m22} \end{bmatrix} \begin{Bmatrix} (F_{t1} - M_1 \ddot{X}_{m1}) \\ (F_{t2} - M_2 \ddot{X}_{m2}) \end{Bmatrix}$$

Again, in short matrix notation and for n lumped masses in general,

$$\{X_m\} = [\delta_m] \{\{F_t\} - [M] \{\ddot{X}_m\}\} \tag{3.2.1}$$

Using the stiffness-influence coefficients,

$$F_{t1} - M_1 \ddot{X}_{m1} = K_{m11} X_{m1} + K_{m12} X_{m2}$$

$$F_{t2} - M_2 \ddot{X}_{m2} = K_{m21} X_{m1} + K_{m22} X_{m2}$$

or, in long matrix notation,

$$\begin{Bmatrix} F_{t1} - M_1 \ddot{X}_{m1} \\ F_{t2} - M_2 \ddot{X}_{m2} \end{Bmatrix} = \begin{bmatrix} K_{m11} & K_{m12} \\ K_{m21} & K_{m22} \end{bmatrix} \begin{Bmatrix} X_{m1} \\ X_{m2} \end{Bmatrix}$$

and for n lumped masses,

$$[K_m] \{X_m\} = \{\{F_t\} - [M] \{\ddot{X}_m\}\} \tag{3.2.2}$$

Of course Eq. 3.2.2 may be obtained easily by premultiplying each side of Eq. 3.2.1 by $[K_m]$.

How the system of linear differential equations of Eqs. 3.2.1 or 3.2.2 may be uncoupled and solved will be gradually developed in the next several sections.

3.3. Normalized Mode Vectors of Free Vibration

When $\{F_t\}$ is equal to zero, Eqs. 3.2.1 and 3.2.2 become the differential equations of free vibration, for which there are n unitized mode vectors (n = number of lumped masses). A unitized mode vector has been defined in Sec. 1.4 as one in which the largest absolute value is made equal to unity. Let $A_{1j}, A_{2j},$

$\ldots$, A_{nj} be the elements in the unitized mode vector of the jth mode of free vibration. Define the length of the unitized vector as

$$L_j = \sqrt{\sum_{i=1}^{n} M_i A_{ij}^2}$$ (3.3.1)

A unitized mode vector is said to be normalized when each of its elements is divided by its length; thus if a_{1j}, a_{2j}, $\ldots$, a_{nj} are elements in the normalized mode vector,

$$a_{ij} = \frac{A_{ij}}{L_j}$$ (3.3.2)

It can be shown that

$$\sum_{i=1}^{n} M_i a_{ij}^2 = 1$$ (3.3.3)

The proof follows:

$$\sum_{i=1}^{n} M_i a_{ij}^2 = \sum_{i=1}^{n} M_i \left(\frac{A_{ij}}{L_j}\right)^2 = \frac{1}{L_j^2} \sum_{i=1}^{n} M_i A_{ij}^2 = 1$$

3.4. The Transformation Matrix $[a]$

The transformation matrix $[a]$, which will be found very useful in uncoupling the differential equations of undamped forced motion, is defined as a square matrix in which the normalized mode vectors of free vibration are arranged in columns; thus,

$[a]_{n \times n} =$

Mode No. / Lumped Mass	1	2	$\cdots$	n
1	a_{11}	a_{12}	$\cdots$	a_{1n}
2	a_{21}	a_{22}	$\cdots$	a_{2n}
$\vdots$	$\vdots$	$\vdots$	$\cdots$	$\vdots$
n	a_{n1}	a_{n2}	$\cdots$	a_{nn}

(3.4.1)

For the reasons that the length of a normalized mode vector is equal to one and that the normalized mode vectors should still be orthogonal to each other,

$$[a^T] \ [M] \ [a] = [I] \tag{3.4.2}$$

from which

$$[a^{-1}] = [a^T M] \tag{3.4.3}$$

That Eq. 3.4.2 is in fact so may be demonstrated by employing two lumped masses as follows:

$$[a^T] \ [M] \ [a] = \begin{bmatrix} a_{11} & a_{21} \\ a_{12} & a_{22} \end{bmatrix} \begin{bmatrix} M_1 & 0 \\ 0 & M_2 \end{bmatrix} \begin{bmatrix} a_{11} & a_{12} \\ a_{21} & a_{22} \end{bmatrix}$$

$$= \begin{bmatrix} a_{11} & a_{21} \\ a_{12} & a_{22} \end{bmatrix} \begin{bmatrix} M_1 a_{11} & M_1 a_{12} \\ M_2 a_{21} & M_2 a_{22} \end{bmatrix}$$

$$= \begin{bmatrix} a_{11} M_1 a_{11} + a_{21} M_2 a_{21} & a_{11} M_1 a_{12} + a_{21} M_2 a_{22} \\ a_{12} M_1 a_{11} + a_{22} M_2 a_{21} & a_{12} M_1 a_{12} + a_{22} M_2 a_{22} \end{bmatrix}$$

$$= \begin{bmatrix} 1 & 0 \\ 0 & 1 \end{bmatrix} = [I]$$

3.5. The Natural Frequency Matrix $[P]$

The eigenvalue equations of free vibration, Eqs. 1.2.4a and b, may be restated in terms of the normalized mode vectors as

$$\{a_j\} = p_j^2 \ [\delta_m] \ [M] \ \{a_j\} \quad \text{for } j = 1, 2, \ldots, n \tag{3.5.1a}$$

and

$$[K_m] \ \{a_j\} = p_j^2 \ [M] \ \{a_j\} \quad \text{for } j = 1, 2, \ldots, n \tag{3.5.1b}$$

If a natural frequency matrix $[P]$ is defined as a diagonal matrix whose elements are equal to p_j^2 such that

$$[P] = \begin{bmatrix} p_1^2 & 0 & \cdots & 0 \\ 0 & p_2^2 & \cdots & 0 \\ \vdots & & & \\ \vdots & \cdot & \cdots & 0 \\ 0 & 0 & \cdots & p_n^2 \end{bmatrix}$$ (3.5.2)

then the transformation matrix $[a]$, which is an expansion of the column vector $\{a_j\}$, can be used to compact Eq. 3.5.1a to the form

$$[a] = [\delta_m] \, [M] \, [a] \, [P] \tag{3.5.3a}$$

because postmultiplying by a diagonal matrix is equal to multiplying each column of the premultiplier by the respective element on the diagonal, in succession. Similarly Eq. 3.5.1b may be compacted to the form

$$[K_m] \, [a] = [M] \, [a] \, [P] \tag{3.5.3b}$$

3.6. Uncoupling the Differential Equations of Undamped Forced Motion

It can be shown that the transformation

$$\{X_m\} = [a] \, \{X_m'\} \tag{3.6.1a}$$

$$\{\dot{X}_m\} = [a] \, \{\dot{X}_m'\} \tag{3.6.1b}$$

$$\{\ddot{X}_m\} = [a] \, \{\ddot{X}_m'\} \tag{3.6.1c}$$

will uncouple the differential equations of undamped forced motion, Eqs. 3.2.1 or 3.2.2, to the form

$$\{\ddot{X}_m'\} + [P] \, \{X_m'\} = [a^T] \, \{F_t\} \tag{3.6.2}$$

which for two lumped masses and linear time-dependent forces become

$$\begin{Bmatrix} \ddot{X}_{m1}' \\ \ddot{X}_{m2}' \end{Bmatrix} + \begin{bmatrix} p_1^2 & 0 \\ 0 & p_2^2 \end{bmatrix} \begin{Bmatrix} X_{m1}' \\ X_{m2}' \end{Bmatrix} = \begin{bmatrix} a_{11} & a_{21} \\ a_{12} & a_{22} \end{bmatrix} \begin{Bmatrix} C_1 - D_1 t \\ C_2 - D_2 t \end{Bmatrix} \tag{3.6.3}$$

As shown in Tables 3.6.1 and 3.6.2, Eqs. 3.6.2 may be derived by substituting the transformation equations 3.6.1 in either Eq. 3.2.1 or Eq. 3.2.2.

TABLE 3.6.1

Derivation of Eq. 3.6.2

Statement	Reason
1. $X_m = \delta_m(F_t - M\ddot{X}_m)$	1. Eq. 3.2.1.
2. $aX'_m = \delta_m(F_t - Ma\ddot{X}'_m)$	2. Substitute Eq. 3.6.1 in Statement 1.
3. $\delta_m MaPX'_m = \delta_m(F_t - Ma\ddot{X}'_m)$	3. Substitute Eq. 3.5.3a in Statement 2.
4. $a^T MaPX'_m = a^T F_t - a^T Ma\ddot{X}'_m$	4. Multiply Item 3 by $a^T\delta_m^{-1}$.
5. $PX'_m = a^T F_t - \ddot{X}'_m$	5. Substitute Eq. 3.4.2 in Statement 4.

TABLE 3.6.2

Derivation of Eq. 3.6.2

Statement	Reason
1. $K_m X_m = F_t - M\ddot{X}_m$	1. Eq. 3.2.2.
2. $K_m aX'_m = F_t - Ma\ddot{X}'_m$	2. Substitute Eq. 3.6.1 in Statement 1.
3. $MaPX'_m = F_t - Ma\ddot{X}'_m$	3. Substitute Eq. 3.5.3b in Statement 2.
4. $a^T MaPX'_m = a^T F_t - a^T Ma\ddot{X}'_m$	4. Premultiply Item 3 by a^T.
5. $PX'_m = a^T F_t - \ddot{X}'_m$	5. Substitute Eq. 3.4.2 in Statement 4.

3.7. Solving the Differential Equations of Undamped Forced Motion

A representative type of force function which will be treated here is in the form of $C_i - D_i t$, where a high initial impact force C_i may diminish at the rate of D_i per unit of time. The uncoupled differential equation of Eq. 3.6.2 will then take the form

$$\{\ddot{X}'_m\} + [P]\{X'_m\} = [a^T]\{C - Dt\} \tag{3.7.1}$$

Letting

$$[a^T]\{C - Dt\} = \{C' - D't\} \tag{3.7.2}$$

Equation 3.7.1 becomes

$$\{\ddot{X}'_m\} + [P]\{X'_m\} = \{C' - D't\} \tag{3.7.3}$$

The solution of Eq. 3.7.3 may be shown to be

$$X'_{mi} = A'_i \sin p_i t + B'_i \cos p_i t + \frac{C'_i}{p_i^2} - \frac{D'_i t}{p_i^2} \quad \text{for } i = 1, 2, \ldots, n \tag{3.7.4}$$

where A'_i and B'_i are constants which may be evaluated from the initial conditions at the ith lumped mass.

If the initial displacement and velocity at each lumped mass are both zero, then

$$(1) \quad \text{when } t = 0, \quad \{X_m\} = 0 \qquad (3.7.5a)$$

$$(2) \quad \text{when } t = 0, \quad \{\dot{X}_m\} = 0 \qquad (3.7.5b)$$

The reverse transformation relationships to Eq. 3.6.1 are

$$\{X'_m\} = [a^{-1}] \{X_m\} = [a^T] [M] \{X_m\} \qquad (3.7.6a)$$

$$\{\dot{X}'_m\} = [a^{-1}] \{\dot{X}_m\} = [a^T] [M] \{\dot{X}_m\} \qquad (3.7.6b)$$

$$\{\ddot{X}'_m\} = [a^{-1}] \{\ddot{X}_m\} = [a^T] [M] \{\ddot{X}_m\} \qquad (3.7.6c)$$

Substituting Eq. 3.7.5 in Eq. 3.7.6,

$$(1) \quad \text{when } t = 0, \quad \{X'_m\} = 0 \qquad (3.7.7a)$$

$$(2) \quad \text{when } t = 0, \quad \{\dot{X}'_m\} = 0 \qquad (3.7.7b)$$

Upon evaluating the constants A'_i and B'_i in Eq. 3.7.4 from the initial conditions of Eq. 3.7.7, Eq. 3.7.4 becomes

$$X'_{mi} = + \frac{D'_i}{p_i^3} \sin p_i t - \frac{C'_i}{p_i^2} \cos p_i t + \frac{C'_i}{p_i^2} - \frac{D'_i t}{p_i^2} \qquad (3.7.8)$$

3.8. Procedure for Obtaining the Displacement, Velocity, and Acceleration at Each Lumped Mass

The general procedure for obtaining the displacement, velocity, and acceleration at each lumped mass, which is subjected to a force function $(C_i - D_i t)$ at zero initial conditions, from $t = 0$ to $t =$ the smallest value of C_i/D_i, may be summarized as follows:

1. Obtain the natural frequencies and unitized mode vectors of free vibration.
2. Normalize the mode vectors and establish the transformation matrix $[a]$.
3. Compute the $\{C'\}$ and $\{D'\}$ vectors from $\{C'\} = [a^T] \{C\}$ and $\{D'\} = [a^T] \{D\}$;
4. Obtain the displacement X'_{mi} in the principal (or uncoupled) coordinate

from

$$X'_{mi} = +\frac{D'_i}{p_i^3} \sin p_i t - \frac{C'_i}{p_i^2} \cos p_i t + \frac{C'_i}{p_i^2} - \frac{D'_i t}{p_i^2}$$

5. Obtain the displacement X_{mi} in the original coordinate from

$$\{X_m\} = [a]\,\{X'_m\}$$

6. Obtain the expressions for the velocity $\dot{X}_{mi}$ and acceleration $\ddot{X}_{mi}$ by differentiation.

7. Check the correctness of the solution by substituting the known expressions of $\{X_m\}$ and $\{\ddot{X}_m\}$ in the coupled differential equation

$$\{X_m\} = [\delta_m]\{\{C - Dt\} - [M]\,\{\ddot{X}_m\}\}$$

or

$$[K_m]\,\{X_m\} + [M]\,\{\ddot{X}_m\} = \{C - Dt\}$$

Example 3.8.1. Obtain the expressions for the displacement, velocity, and acceleration at each of the two lumped masses on the structural frame of Fig. 3.8.1a, due to the action of linear time-dependent forces shown in Fig. 3.8.1b. Note that the duration time of the force function, C_i/D_i, is the same at both lumped masses.

Solution: (a) Natural frequencies and unitized mode vectors of free vibration. Since the elastic properties of this structural frame are identical to those of Examples 1.6.1 and 1.7.1 and because the lumped masses are 100 times those in Example 1.6.1, the natural frequencies in this example should be 10 times smaller than those of Examples 1.6.1 and 1.7.1 but the unitized mode vectors remain unchanged. Thus, for this example,

$$p_1^2 = 425.92 \text{ (rad/sec)}^2 \qquad p_1 = 20.638 \text{ rad/sec}$$

$$p_2^2 = 3{,}235.0 \text{ (rad/sec)}^2 \qquad p_2 = 56.88 \text{ rad/sec}$$

$$\{A_1\} = \begin{Bmatrix} +0.2148 \\ +1.0000 \end{Bmatrix} \qquad \{A_2\} = \begin{Bmatrix} +1.0000 \\ -0.0644 \end{Bmatrix}$$

(b) The transformation matrix $[a]$. The lengths of the two unitized mode

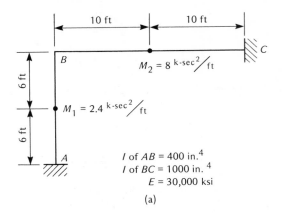

10 ft | 10 ft

B

$M_2 = 8$ k-sec^2/ft

$M_1 = 2.4$ k-sec^2/ft

6 ft

6 ft

A

I of $AB = 400$ in.^{4}
I of $BC = 1000$ in.^{4}
$E = 30,000$ ksi

(a)

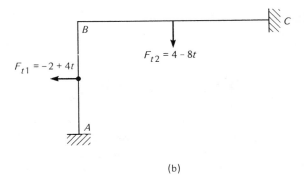

B

C

$F_{t2} = 4 - 8t$

$F_{t1} = -2 + 4t$

A

(b)

Figure 3.8.1. *Forced motion of structural frame of Example 3.8.1. (a) Structural frame with two lumped masses; (b) linear time-dependent forces.*

vectors are:

$$L_1 = \sqrt{2.4(+0.2148)^2 + 8(+1.0000)^2} = 2.848$$

$$L_2 = \sqrt{2.4(+1.0000)^2 + 8(-0.0644)^2} = 1.560$$

Thus,

$$\{a_1\} = \frac{1}{2.848} \begin{Bmatrix} +0.2148 \\ +1.0000 \end{Bmatrix} = \begin{Bmatrix} +0.0754 \\ +0.3511 \end{Bmatrix}$$

and,

$$\{a_2\} = \frac{1}{1.560} \begin{Bmatrix} +1.0000 \\ -0.0644 \end{Bmatrix} = \begin{Bmatrix} +0.6411 \\ -0.0413 \end{Bmatrix}$$

The transformation matrices are:

$$[a] = \begin{bmatrix} +0.0754 & +0.6411 \\ +0.3511 & -0.0413 \end{bmatrix} \qquad [a^T] = \begin{bmatrix} +0.0754 & +0.3511 \\ +0.6411 & -0.0413 \end{bmatrix}$$

Check by longhand to see if

$$[a^T] \, [M] \, [a] = [I]$$

(c) Computations for $\{C'\}$ and $\{D'\}$.

$$\{C'\} = [a^T] \, \{C\} = \begin{bmatrix} +0.0754 & +0.3511 \\ +0.6411 & -0.0413 \end{bmatrix} \begin{Bmatrix} -2 \\ +4 \end{Bmatrix} = \begin{Bmatrix} +1.2537 \\ -1.4475 \end{Bmatrix}$$

$$\{D'\} = [a^T] \, \{D\} = \begin{bmatrix} +0.0754 & +0.3511 \\ +0.6411 & -0.0413 \end{bmatrix} \begin{Bmatrix} -4 \\ +8 \end{Bmatrix} = \begin{Bmatrix} +2.5074 \\ -2.8950 \end{Bmatrix}$$

The uncoupled differential equations are

$$\ddot{X}_{m1}' + 425.92 \, X_{m1}' = +1.2537 - 2.5074t$$

$$\ddot{X}_{m2}' + 3235.0 \, X_{m2}' = -1.4475 + 2.8950t$$

(d) The displacements $\{X_m'\}$. In the first principal coordinate,

$$\frac{D_1'}{p_1^3} = \frac{(+2.5074)}{(20.638)^3} = +0.2852 \times 10^{-3} \text{ ft}$$

$$\frac{C_1'}{p_1^2} = \frac{(+1.2537)}{425.92} = +2.9435 \times 10^{-3} \text{ ft}$$

$$\frac{D_1'}{p_1^2} = \frac{(+2.5074)}{425.92} = +5.887 \times 10^{-3} \text{ ft/sec}$$

$$X_{m1}' = +0.2852 \times 10^{-3} \sin 20.638t - 2.9435 \times 10^{-3} \cos 20.638t$$
$$+ 2.9435 \times 10^{-3} - 5.887 \times 10^{-3}t$$

In the second principal coordinate,

$$\frac{D_2'}{p_2^3} = \frac{(-2.8950)}{(56.88)^3} = -0.01573 \times 10^{-3} \text{ ft}$$

$$\frac{C_2'}{p_2^2} = \frac{(-1.4475)}{3235.0} = -0.4474 \times 10^{-3} \text{ ft}$$

$$\frac{D_2'}{p_2^2} = \frac{(-2.8950)}{3235.0} = -0.8949 \times 10^{-3} \text{ ft/sec}$$

$$X_{m2}' = -0.01573 \times 10^{-3} \sin 56.88t + 0.4474 \times 10^{-3} \cos 56.88t$$
$$- 0.4474 \times 10^{-3} + 0.8949 \times 10^{-3}t$$

(e) The displacements $\{X_m\}$.

$$\begin{Bmatrix} X_{m1} \\ X_{m2} \end{Bmatrix} = [a] \begin{Bmatrix} X_{m1}' \\ X_{m2}' \end{Bmatrix}$$

$$= \begin{bmatrix} +0.0754 & +0.6411 \\ +0.3511 & -0.0413 \end{bmatrix} \begin{Bmatrix} X_{m1}' \\ X_{m2}' \end{Bmatrix}$$

$$X_{m1} \times 10^3 = +0.02152 \sin 20.638t - 0.2220 \cos 20.638t$$
$$- 0.01009 \sin 56.88t + 0.2869 \cos 56.88t$$
$$- 0.0648 + 0.1297t$$

$$X_{m2} \times 10^3 = +0.1002 \sin 20.638t - 1.0336 \cos 20.638t$$
$$+ 0.00065 \sin 56.88t - 0.01849 \cos 56.88t$$
$$+ 1.0521 - 2.1042t$$

(f) The velocities and accelerations by differentiation.

$$\dot{X}_{m1} \times 10^3 = +0.4440 \cos 20.638t + 4.582 \sin 20.638t$$
$$- 0.5737 \cos 56.88t - 16.316 \sin 56.88t + 0.1297$$

$$\dot{X}_{m2} \times 10^3 = +2.0671 \cos 20.638t + 21.331 \sin 20.638t$$
$$+ 0.03697 \cos 56.88t + 1.0516 \sin 56.88t - 2.1042$$

$$\ddot{X}_{m1} \times 10^3 = -9.164 \sin 20.638t + 94.567 \cos 20.638t$$
$$+32.63 \sin 56.88t - 928.0 \cos 56.88t$$

$$\ddot{X}_{m2} \times 10^3 = -42.66 \sin 20.638t + 440.2 \cos 20.638t$$
$$-2.1027 \sin 56.88t + 59.812 \cos 56.88t$$

(g) Check by back substitution in original coupled differential equation. From Example 1.4.1,

$$[K_m] = \frac{10^6}{37,800} \text{kips/ft} \begin{bmatrix} +290 & -54 \\ -54 & +140.4 \end{bmatrix}$$

Numerical values of $\{X_m\}$ and $\{\ddot{X}_m\}$ were substituted into the equation

$$[K_m]\{X_m\} + [M]\{\ddot{X}_m\} = \{C - Dt\}$$

and the identity

$$\begin{Bmatrix} -2.000 + 4.001t \\ +4.000 - 8.001t \end{Bmatrix} = \begin{Bmatrix} -2 + 4t \\ +4 - 8t \end{Bmatrix}$$

was obtained.

3.9. Computer Solution

Following the procedure of the preceding section, a general computer program has been written and shown in Appendix C, for the determination of displacement, velocity, and acceleration at each lumped mass in a structural frame, from $t = 0$ to $t =$ the smallest value of C_i/D_i, when each mass is subjected to a force function $(C_i - D_i t)$ at zero initial conditions. The first part of this computer program is almost identical to that of Appendix A, which is for the computation of natural frequencies and unitized mode vectors, except that all eigenvalues and eigenvectors are used here. The balance of the program is explained in Appendix C.

Example 3.9.1. Show the input and output for Example 3.8.1, using the computer program of Appendix C. Tabulate the acceleration, velocity, and displacement at lumped masses 1 and 2 between $t = 0$ and $t = 0.5$ sec at intervals of 0.05 sec.

Solution: (a) The input. The degree of freedom NP is 5; the number of members NM is 4; and the number of lumped masses NPS is 2. The matrix $[A]$ is

$[A]_{5\times8} =$

F\P	1	2	3	4	5	6	7	8
1	0	+1	+1	0	0	0	0	0
2	0	0	0	+1	+1	0	0	0
3	0	0	0	0	0	+1	+1	0
4	$+\frac{1}{6}$	$+\frac{1}{6}$	$-\frac{1}{6}$	$-\frac{1}{6}$	0	0	0	0
5	0	0	0	0	$-\frac{1}{10}$	$-\frac{1}{10}$	$+\frac{1}{10}$	$+\frac{1}{10}$

The (EI/L) values of the four members are 13888.8889, 13888.8889, 20833.3333 and 20833.3333 ft-kips. The lumped masses are 2.4 and 8.0 kip-sec^2/ft. The values of C are -2 and $+4$; and the values of D are -4 and $+8$. The number of intervals by which the time limit C_i/D_i is to be divided is 10.

(b) The output. The natural frequencies are:

$$p_1 = 20.638 \text{ rad/sec} \qquad p_2 = 56.877 \text{ rad/sec}$$

The displacements are:

$$X_{m1}(10^{-3} \text{ ft}) = +0.021517 \sin p_1 t - 0.22203 \cos p_1 t$$
$$-0.010086 \sin p_2 t + 0.28683 \cos p_2 t$$
$$-0.064800 + 0.12960 t$$

$$X_{m2}(10^{-3} \text{ ft}) = +0.10016 \sin p_1 t - 1.0335 \cos p_1 t$$
$$+0.0006500 \sin p_2 t - 0.018486 \cos p_2 t$$
$$+1.0520 - 2.1040 t$$

The velocities are:

$$\dot{X}_{m1}(10^{-3} \text{ ft/sec}) = +0.44406 \cos p_1 t + 4.5822 \sin p_1 t$$
$$-0.57366 \cos p_2 t - 16.314 \sin p_2 t + 0.12960$$

$$\dot{X}_{m2}(10^{-3} \text{ ft/sec}) = +2.0670 \cos p_1 t + 21.330 \sin p_1 t$$
$$+0.03697 \cos p_2 t + 1.0514 \sin p_2 t - 2.1040$$

The accelerations are:

$$\ddot{X}_{m1}(10^{-3}\text{ ft/sec}^2) = -9.1645 \sin p_1 t + 94.568 \cos p_1 t$$
$$+32.628 \sin p_2 t - 927.90 \cos p_2 t$$

$$\ddot{X}_{m2}(10^{-3}\text{ ft/sec}^2) = -42.659 \sin p_1 t + 440.20 \cos p_1 t$$
$$-2.1029 \sin p_2 t + 59.803 \cos p_2 t$$

The acceleration, velocity, and displacement from $t = 0$ to $t = 0.5$ sec at intervals of 0.05 sec are shown for lumped masses 1 and 2 in Tables 3.9.1 and 3.9.2, respectively.

TABLE 3.9.1

Acceleration, Velocity, and Displacement at Lumped Mass 1

t (sec)	Acceleration $(10^{-3}\text{ ft/sec}^2)$	Velocity (10^{-3} ft/sec)	Displacement (10^{-3} ft)
0	−833.33	0	0
0.05	+937.31	+ 0.053	−0.43097
0.10	−839.33	+12.632	+0.31531
0.15	+512.25	−12.454	−0.01025
0.20	−418.92	+11.002	+0.18147
0.25	+157.78	−20.022	−0.18138
0.30	+261.66	+16.211	−0.30050
0.35	−378.90	−10.401	−0.00092
0.40	+604.92	+15.826	−0.10746
0.45	−911.02	− 7.466	+0.46867
0.50	+858.01	− 0.488	−0.15907

TABLE 3.9.2

Acceleration, Velocity and Displacement at Lumped Mass 2

t (sec)	Acceleration $(10^{-3}\text{ ft/sec}^2)$	Velocity (10^{-3} ft/sec)	Displacement (10^{-3} ft)
0	+500.00	0	0
0.05	+131.50	+17.536	+0.52023
0.10	−195.22	+15.148	+1.40329
0.15	−480.82	− 2.394	+1.78552
0.20	−183.31	−21.993	+1.11077
0.25	+221.78	−19.398	−0.00898
0.30	+431.51	− 3.036	−0.61422
0.35	+252.68	+17.275	−0.22151
0.40	−253.08	+15.974	+0.71915
0.45	−389.29	− 0.721	+1.12642
0.50	−301.03	−20.237	+0.58719

CHAPTER 4

■

Displacement Method of Stability Analysis

4.1. Stability of Rigid Frames

Analysis of rigid frames has been treated in Chapters 5, 6, 7, 9, 10, 14, and 18 of the author's previous book. In particular, since consideration of axial deformation produces little effect in external joint displacements or internal forces and moments, such is not assumed in Chapters 5, 6, 7, and 9 of that book; but the more exact method is taken up in Chapters 10, 14, and 18. In this chapter, however, it will be shown that axial deformation should not be considered in the bifurcation theory of stability analysis.

Consider the rigid frame in Fig. 4.1.1a. Each of the three members is subjected to an axial force. If axial deformation is not assumed, obviously the structure is not deformed at all. This undeformed condition is called the *primary condition.*

Assuming that Hooke's Law applies without limit, the primary condition remains as long as the load factor N is below a critical value N_{CR}. At the value of N_{CR}, the rigid frame may stay either in the primary condition or in any ratio of the buckled condition of Fig. 4.1.1b; thus the term *bifurcation.* The critical value N_{CR} is to be called *buckling load factor;* and the shape of the buckled condition the *buckling mode.* The object of this chapter is the determination of the buckling load factor and its associated mode when a rigid frame without axial deformation is subjected to a set of axial forces in the primary condition.

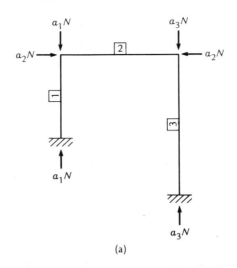

(a)

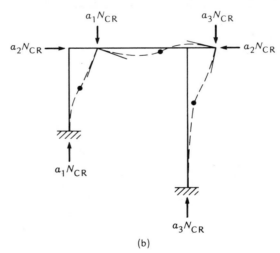

(b)

Figure 4.1.1. *Stability of rigid frames. (a) Primary condition; (b) buckling mode.*

4.2. Equilibrium Conditions at Buckling Mode

While the equilibrium conditions are obviously satisfied at the primary condition, those at the buckling mode need be investigated. The critical axial forces are usually of large magnitudes so that the moment couple due to the separation, if any, of the lines of action of the two axial forces in the pair must be considered. Traditionally, the name *second-order effects* is given to those of deflections in equilibrium equations; thus the moment couples described here may be called *second-order moments*. Since the magnitudes of the axial forces remain stationary at the critical values, the values of the secondary moment couples are modal functions.

Acting on the ends of each member in the buckled condition, there may be axial force, shear force, and bending moment—all functions of the buckling mode. However, the modal axial forces, being additional to the primary axial forces, should have no further second-order effect;.

What has just been discussed will be illustrated later in the statics checks of a numerical example.

4.3. Effect of Primary Axial Force on Member Flexure

The relationships between end moments and end rotations of a prismatic member in flexure without considering the deformation effects of the secondary moments ($N \times y$ in Fig. 4.3.1) can be expressed either by the flexibility matrix or by the stiffness matrix; thus

$$[D] = \begin{array}{c|c|c} & M_i & M_j \\ \hline \phi_i & +\dfrac{L}{3EI} & -\dfrac{L}{6EI} \\ \hline \phi_j & -\dfrac{L}{6EI} & +\dfrac{L}{3EI} \end{array} \tag{4.3.1}$$

$$[S] = \begin{array}{c|c|c} & \phi_i & \phi_j \\ \hline M_i & +\dfrac{4EI}{L} & +\dfrac{2EI}{L} \\ \hline M_j & +\dfrac{2EI}{L} & +\dfrac{4EI}{L} \end{array} \tag{4.3.2}$$

When the secondary moment, $N \times y$, is included in the differential equation of the elastic curve, the flexibilities are increased and stiffnesses decreased. The exact expressions will now be derived. Note, however, only compressive axial forces are considered in this chapter; the effects of tensile axial forces will be treated in Chapter 6.

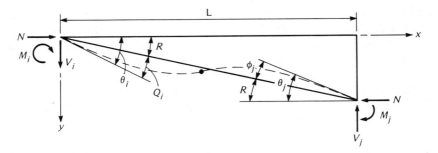

Figure 4.3.1. *Interaction of axial force with flexure.*

The differential equation of the elastic curve is, from Fig. 4.3.1,

$$EI \frac{d^2y}{dx^2} = -(M_i - V_ix + Ny) = -M_i + \frac{M_i + M_j + NRL}{L}x - Ny \qquad (4.3.3)$$

Solving Eq. 4.3.3,

$$y = A \sin \frac{\phi}{L}x + B \cos \frac{\phi}{L}x - \frac{M_i}{N} + \frac{(M_i + M_j + NRL)x}{NL} \qquad (4.3.4a)$$

in which

$$\phi = L \sqrt{\frac{N}{EI}} \qquad (4.3.4b)$$

The boundary conditions are: (1) when $x = 0$, $y = 0$; and (2) when $x = L$, $y = RL$. The arbitrary constants are then found to be

$$A = -\frac{M_i \cos\phi}{N \sin\phi} - \frac{M_j}{N \sin\phi}$$

$$B = +\frac{M_i}{N}$$

The slopes θ_i and θ_j at the member ends are:

$$\theta_i = \left(\frac{dy}{dx} \quad \text{at} \quad x = 0\right) = A\frac{\phi}{L} + \frac{M_i + M_j}{NL} + R$$

$$= \frac{M_iL}{EI}\left[\frac{\sin\phi - \cos\phi}{\phi^2 \sin\phi}\right] + \frac{M_jL}{EI}\left[-\frac{\phi - \sin\phi}{\phi^2 \sin\phi}\right] + R \qquad (4.3.5a)$$

$$\theta_j = \left(\frac{dy}{dx}\right) \quad \text{at} \quad x = L\right) = A\frac{\phi}{L}\cos\phi - B\frac{\phi}{L}\sin\phi + \frac{M_i + M_j}{NL} + R$$

$$= \frac{M_iL}{EI}\left[-\frac{\phi - \sin\phi}{\phi^2\sin\phi}\right] + \frac{M_jL}{EI}\left[\frac{\sin\phi - \cos\phi}{\phi^2\sin\phi}\right] + R \qquad (4.3.5b)$$

Using the relations $\phi_i = \theta_i - R$ and $\phi_j = \theta_j - R$, the end rotations ϕ_i and ϕ_j are expressed as functions of the end moments M_i and M_j by the flexibility matrix $[D]$; thus

		M_i	M_j
$[D] =$	ϕ_i	$+\left[\dfrac{\sin\phi - \cos\phi}{\phi^2\sin\phi}\right]\dfrac{L}{EI}$	$-\left[\dfrac{\phi - \sin\phi}{\phi^2\sin\phi}\right]\dfrac{L}{EI}$
	ϕ_j	$-\left[\dfrac{\phi - \sin\phi}{\phi^2\sin\phi}\right]\dfrac{L}{EI}$	$+\left[\dfrac{\sin\phi - \phi\cos\phi}{\phi^2\sin\phi}\right]\dfrac{L}{EI}$

$$(4.3.6)$$

Equation 4.3.6 becomes Eq. 4.3.1 at $\phi = 0$.
Inverting Eq. 4.3.6 gives the stiffness matrix $[S]$ as

		ϕ_i	ϕ_j
$[S] =$	M_i	$+\left[\dfrac{\phi\sin\phi - \phi^2\cos\phi}{2 - 2\cos\phi - \phi\sin\phi}\right]\dfrac{EI}{L}$	$+\left[\dfrac{\phi^2 - \phi\sin\phi}{2 - 2\cos\phi - \phi\sin\phi}\right]\dfrac{EI}{L}$
	M_j	$+\left[\dfrac{\phi^2 - \phi\sin\phi}{2 - 2\cos\phi - \phi\sin\phi}\right]\dfrac{EI}{L}$	$+\left[\dfrac{\phi\sin\phi - \phi^2\cos\phi}{2 - 2\cos\phi - \phi\sin\phi}\right]\dfrac{EI}{L}$

$$(4.3.7)$$

which gives the end moments M_i and M_j as functions of the end rotations ϕ_i and ϕ_j. Equation 4.3.7 becomes Eq. 4.3.2 at $\phi = 0$.
Tabulated values of flexibility and stiffness coefficients are shown in Table 6.5.1.

4.4. Formulation of the Stability Stiffness Matrix $[K]$ at Bifurcation

At bifurcation, the critical primary axial forces alone are capable of maintaining equilibrium and compatible deformation without externally applied forces. In matrix form,

$$\{P\} = [K]\{X\} = 0 \qquad (4.4.1)$$

The trivial solution of Eq. 4.4.1 is represented by the primary condition. The nontrivial solution requires that the determinant of the $[K]$ matrix be zero; thus the stability criterion is commonly stated as

$$\text{DET } [K] = 0 \tag{4.4.2}$$

It will be shown that the external stiffness matrix $[K]$ can be expressed as the sum of a first-order $[K_1]$ matrix and a second-order $[K_2]$ matrix; thus

$$[K] = [K_1] + [K_2] \tag{4.4.3a}$$

in which

$$[K_1] = [A_1 S A_1{}^T] \tag{4.4.3b}$$

Consider the rigid frame of Fig. 4.4.1a. The equilibrium conditions in the buckling mode, as discussed in Sec. 4.2 are

$$P_1 = F_2 + F_3$$

$$P_2 = F_4 + F_5$$

$$P_3 = -\frac{F_1 + F_2 + \alpha_1 N_{CR} X_3}{L_1} - \frac{F_5 + F_6 + \alpha_3 N_{CR} X_3}{L_3}$$

In matrix form,

$$\{P\} = [A_1] \{F\} + [K_2] \{X\} \tag{4.4.4}$$

in which

$[A_1] =$

F \ P	1	2	3	4	5	6
1	0.	+1.	+1.	0.	0.	0.
2	0.	0.	0.	+1.	+1.	0.
3	$-\dfrac{1}{L_1}$	$-\dfrac{1}{L_1}$	0.	0.	$-\dfrac{1}{L_3}$	$\dfrac{1}{L_3}$

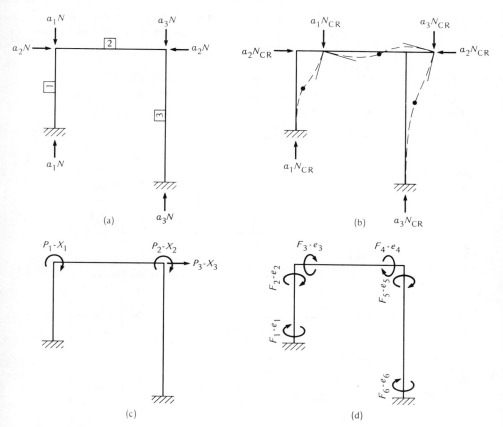

Figure 4.4.1. *Formulation of the matrix* $[K] = [K_1] + [K_2]$. *(a) Primary condition; (b) buckling mode; (c)* P-X *diagram; (d)* F-e *diagram.*

and,

$$[K_2] = N_{CR} \begin{array}{|c|c|c|c|} \hline \diagbox{P}{X} & 1 & 2 & 3 \\ \hline 1 & 0. & 0. & 0. \\ \hline 2 & 0. & 0. & 0. \\ \hline 3 & 0. & 0. & -\dfrac{\alpha_1}{L_1} - \dfrac{\alpha_3}{L_3} \\ \hline \end{array}$$

Thus the $[A_1]$ matrix is exactly the same as that in the usual first-order analysis, but the $[K_2]$ matrix expresses the external sidesway forces which can be balanced by the end shear forces arisen from the secondary moment couples due to each sidesway displacement.

The member-stiffness matrix $[S]$ expresses the end moments $\{F\}$ in terms of the end rotations $\{e\}$; in the present formulation, the effect of the critical primary forces must be considered. Thus

$$\{F\} = [S]\,\{e\} \tag{4.4.5}$$

in which

$$[S] = \begin{array}{c|cccccc}
\diagdown\!\!\!\!\begin{array}{c} e \\ F \end{array} & 1 & 2 & 3 & 4 & 5 & 6 \\
\hline
1 & S_{ii1}\dfrac{EI_1}{L_1} & S_{ij1}\dfrac{EI_1}{L_1} & & & & \\
\hline
2 & S_{ji1}\dfrac{EI_1}{L_1} & S_{jj1}\dfrac{EI_1}{L_1} & & & & \\
\hline
3 & & & S_{ii2}\dfrac{EI_2}{L_2} & S_{ij2}\dfrac{EI_2}{L_2} & & \\
\hline
4 & & & S_{ji2}\dfrac{EI_2}{L_2} & S_{jj2}\dfrac{EI_2}{L_2} & & \\
\hline
5 & & & & & S_{ii3}\dfrac{EI_3}{L_3} & S_{ij3}\dfrac{EI_3}{L_3} \\
\hline
6 & & & & & S_{ji3}\dfrac{EI_3}{L_3} & S_{jj3}\dfrac{EI_3}{L_3} \\
\end{array}$$

where

$$S_{ii} = S_{jj} \text{ for member } m = \frac{\phi_m \sin\phi_m - \phi_m^2 \cos\phi_m}{2 - 2\cos\phi_m - \phi_m \sin\phi_m}$$

$$S_{ij} = S_{ji} \text{ for member } m = \frac{\phi_m^2 - \phi_m \sin\phi_m}{2 - 2\cos\phi_m - \phi_m \sin\phi_m}$$

Finally, the deformation matrix $[A_1^T]$ should be the same as that in first-order analysis. Thus

$$\{e\} = [A_1^T]\{X\} \tag{4.4.6}$$

Combining Eqs. 4.4.4, 4.4.5, and 4.4.6,

$$\{P\} = [A_1 S A_1^T]\{X\} + [K_2]\{X\}$$

which is Eq. 4.4.3.

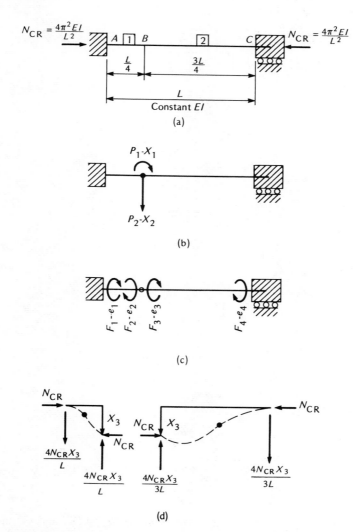

Figure 4.4.2. *Buckling of a fixed-ended beam. (a) Given beam; (b) P-X diagram; (c) F-e diagram; (d) second-order shear forces.*

For sake of convenience, the external stiffness matrix $[K] = [K_1] + [K_2]$ as defined here will be called the *stability stiffness matrix*.

Example 4.4.1. Show that the determinant of the stability stiffness matrix of the rigid frame ABC (actually a fixed-ended beam) shown in Fig. 4.4.2 is zero.

Solution: Since the critical primary axial force is given, the member stiffness coefficients can be computed. For member 1,

$$\phi_1 = \frac{L}{4} \sqrt{\frac{4\pi^2 EI/L^2}{EI}} = \frac{\pi}{2}$$

$$S_{ii1} = \frac{\frac{\pi}{2}\sin\frac{\pi}{2} - \frac{\pi^2}{4}\cos\frac{\pi}{2}}{2 - 2\cos\frac{\pi}{2} - \frac{\pi}{2}\sin\frac{\pi}{2}} = \frac{\pi}{4 - \pi}$$

$$S_{ij1} = \frac{\frac{\pi^2}{4} - \frac{\pi}{2}\sin\frac{\pi}{2}}{2 - 2\cos\frac{\pi}{2} - \frac{\pi}{2}\sin\frac{\pi}{2}} = \frac{\pi^2 - 2\pi}{8 - 2\pi}$$

For member 2,

$$\phi_2 = \frac{3L}{4}\sqrt{\frac{4\pi^2 EI/L^2}{EI}} = \frac{3}{2}\pi$$

$$S_{ii2} = \frac{\frac{3\pi}{2}\sin\frac{3\pi}{2} - \frac{9\pi^2}{4}\cos\frac{3\pi}{2}}{2 - 2\cos\frac{3\pi}{2} - \frac{3\pi}{2}\sin\frac{3\pi}{2}} = -\frac{3\pi}{4 + \pi}$$

$$S_{ij2} = \frac{\frac{9\pi^2}{4} - \frac{3\pi}{2}\sin\frac{3\pi}{2}}{2 - 2\cos\frac{3\pi}{2} - \frac{3\pi}{2}\sin\frac{3\pi}{2}} = \frac{9\pi^2 + 6\pi}{8 + 6\pi}$$

The first-order statics matrix $[A_1]$ is, according to the P-X and F-e members in Fig. 4.4.2,

$$[A_1] =$$

F \ P	1	2	3	4
1	0.	+1.	+1.	0.
2	$-\dfrac{4}{L}$	$-\dfrac{4}{L}$	$+\dfrac{4}{3L}$	$+\dfrac{4}{3L}$

The second-order $[K_2]$ matrix is, referring to Fig. 4.4.2d,

$$[K_2] =$$

X \ P	1	2
1	0.	0.
2	0.	$-\dfrac{16 N_{CR}}{3L}$

$=$

X \ P	1	2
1	0.	0.
2	0.	$-\dfrac{64\pi^2 EI}{3L^3}$

The member-stiffness matrix $[S]$ is

$$[S] =$$

e \ F	1	2	3	4
1	$S_{ii1}\dfrac{4EI}{L}$	$S_{ij1}\dfrac{4EI}{L}$		
2	$S_{ji1}\dfrac{4EI}{5}$	$S_{jj1}\dfrac{4EI}{L}$		
3			$S_{ii2}\dfrac{4EI}{3L}$	$S_{ij2}\dfrac{4EI}{3L}$
4			$S_{ji2}\dfrac{4EI}{3L}$	$S_{jj2}\dfrac{4EI}{3L}$

The stability stiffness matrix $[K]$ is computed to be

$$[K] = [K_1] + [K_2]$$
$$= [A_1 S A_1^T] + [K_2]$$

$$
= \begin{vmatrix} \left(\dfrac{4\pi}{4-\pi} - \dfrac{4\pi}{4+3\pi}\right)\dfrac{EI}{L} & \left(-\dfrac{8\pi^2}{4-\pi} + \dfrac{8\pi^2}{4+3\pi}\right)\dfrac{EI}{L^2} \\[4mm] \left(-\dfrac{8\pi^2}{4-\pi} + \dfrac{8\pi^2}{4+3\pi}\right)\dfrac{EI}{L^2} & \left(\dfrac{64\pi^2}{4-\pi} + \dfrac{64\pi^2}{3\,(4+3\pi)} - \dfrac{64\pi^2}{3}\right)\dfrac{EI}{L^3} \end{vmatrix}
$$

The determinant $[K]$ is found equal to zero.

$$
\text{DET } [K] = \frac{1024\pi^6}{[(4-\pi)(4+3\pi)]^2}\frac{(EI)^2}{L^4} - \frac{1024\pi^6}{[(4-\pi)(4+3\pi)]^2}\left(\frac{EI}{L^2}\right)^2 = 0
$$

4.5. Definitions for the Critical Standard Stability Angle $(\phi_{CR})_c$ and the Effective Length Ratio K_m of the mth Member.

There should be a sequence of critical values of the buckling load factor N_{CR} at which the determinant of the stability stiffness matrix $[K]$ of Eq. 4.4.3 is zero. The lowest value is usually the one needed in practice, and its shape in the buckled condition is called the fundamental mode. Hereafter, the name buckling load factor N_{CR} will only mean its lowest value.

Since the stiffness coefficients (S_{ii}, S_{ij}) and the flexibility coefficients (D_{ii}, D_{ij}) of a mth flexural member under axial compression are functions of an angle ϕ_m defined as

$$
\phi_m = L_m \sqrt{\frac{\alpha_m N}{EI_m}} \tag{4.5.1}
$$

the angle ϕ_m may be called the stability angle of the mth member. If some values of length and moment of inertia (which do not necessarily coincide with the actual length or moment of inertia of any member) are chosen as the standard values L_c and I_c, the standard stability angle ϕ_c is then

$$
\phi_c = L_c \sqrt{\frac{N}{EI_c}} \tag{4.5.2}
$$

The ratio β_m of ϕ_m to ϕ_c is

$$
\beta_m = \frac{\phi_m}{\phi_c} = \frac{L_m}{L_c}\sqrt{\frac{\alpha_m}{(I_m/I_c)}} \tag{4.5.3}
$$

Thus for each assigned value of the standard stability angle ϕ_c, there is a value of the determinant of the stability stiffness matrix of the entire structure. The lowest value of ϕ_c at which this determinant is zero is the critical standard stability angle $(\phi_{CR})_c$; or

$$(\phi_{CR})_c = L_c \sqrt{\frac{N_{CR}}{EI_c}} \tag{4.5.4}$$

The effective length $K_m L_m$ of the mth member in a rigid frame has been defined in metal design specifications as the equivalent member length whose Euler load is equal to $\alpha_m N_{CR}$; thus

$$\frac{\pi^2 EI_m}{(K_m L_m)^2} = \alpha_m N_{CR}$$

from which

$$K_m = \sqrt{\frac{\pi^2 EI_m}{\alpha_m N_{CR} L_m^2}} = \sqrt{\frac{\pi^2}{(\phi_{CR})_m^2}} = \frac{\pi}{(\phi_{CR})_m} = \frac{\pi}{\beta_m (\phi_{CR})_c} \tag{4.5.5}$$

K_m in Eq. 4.5.5 is the effective length ratio of the mth member in a rigid frame.

Example 4.5.1. Using the length and moment of inertia of member AB as the standard values, show that the critical standard stability angle of the rigid frame $ABCD$ in Fig. 4.5.1a lies between 1.60 and 1.70. If a straight line interpolation is used to obtain an approximate value of $(\phi_{CR})_c$, compute the determinant of the stability stiffness matrix at buckling and the effective length ratios of the members.

Solution: For convenience in computer programming, the *F-e* numbers are first assigned to the members with primary axial forces. Although unimportant in the present longhand solution, it may be desirable to form a habit. According to the *P-X* and *F-e* numbers of Fig. 4.5.1 bc, the three equilibrium equations are:

$$P_1 = F_2 + F_5$$

$$P_2 = F_4 + F_6$$

$$P_3 = -V_1 - V_2 = -\left(\frac{F_1 + F_2}{120} + \frac{2N_{CR}X_3}{120}\right) - \left(\frac{F_3 + F_4}{240} + \frac{N_{CR}X_3}{240}\right)$$

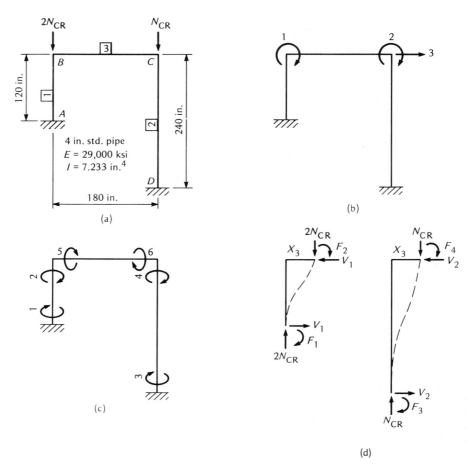

Figure 4.5.1. *Stability of a Rigid Frame. (a) Given rigid frame; (b) P-X numbers; (c) F-e numbers; (d) free-body diagrams.*

Thus the first-order statics matrix $[A_1]$ is

$[A_1] =$	F\P	1	2	3	4	5	6
	1		+1.			+1.	
	2				+1.		+1.
	3	$-\dfrac{1}{120}$	$-\dfrac{1}{120}$	$-\dfrac{1}{240}$	$-\dfrac{1}{240}$		

and the second-order stiffness matrix $[K_2]$ is

$$[K_2] = \begin{array}{|c|c|} \hline \diagdown X \atop P \quad 3 & 3 \\ \hline 3 & -\left(\dfrac{2N_{CR}}{120} + \dfrac{N_{CR}}{240}\right) \\ \hline \end{array} = \begin{array}{|c|c|} \hline \diagdown X \atop P \quad 3 & 3 \\ \hline 3 & -\dfrac{N_{CR}}{48} \\ \hline \end{array}$$

Taking $EI_c = (29,000)(7.233) = 209,757$ kip-in.^{2} and $L_c = 120$ in.,

$$(\phi_{CR})_c = L_c \sqrt{\frac{N_{CR}}{EI_c}} = 120 \sqrt{\frac{N_{CR}}{209,757}}$$

$$N_{CR} = \frac{209,757}{14,400} (\phi_{CR})_c^2 = 14.566 \, (\phi_{CR})_c^2$$

and

$$[K_2] = \begin{array}{|c|c|} \hline \diagdown X \atop P & 3 \\ \hline 3 & -\dfrac{N_{CR}}{48} = -\dfrac{14.566 \, (\phi_{CR})_c^2}{48} = -0.30347 \, (\phi_{CR})_c^2 \\ \hline \end{array}$$

The β-values for members with primary axial forces are:

$$\beta_1 = \frac{L_1}{L_c} \sqrt{\frac{\alpha_1}{I_1/I_c}} = 1.0 \sqrt{\frac{2.0}{1.0}} = 1.4142$$

$$\beta_2 = \frac{L_2}{L_c} \sqrt{\frac{\alpha_2}{I_2/I_c}} = 2.0 \sqrt{\frac{1.0}{1.0}} = 2.0$$

The stiffness coefficients are obtained by interpolating the values listed in Table 6.5.1.

For member 1:

$$\phi_c = 1.60 \qquad \phi_1 = \beta_1 \phi_c = 1.4142 \,(1.60) = 2.2627$$

$$S_{ii1} = 3.2654 \qquad S_{ii1} \, EI_1/L_1 = 5707.85 \text{ in.-kips}$$

$$S_{ij1} = 2.2024 \qquad S_{ij1} \, EI_1/L_1 = 3849.75 \text{ in.-kips}$$

$$\phi_c = 1.70 \qquad \phi_1 = \beta_1 \phi_c = 1.4142\ (1.70) = 2.4041$$

$$S_{ii1} = 3.1627 \qquad S_{ii1} EI_1/L_1 = 5528.34 \text{ in.-kips}$$

$$S_{ij1} = 2.2338 \qquad S_{ij1}\, EI_1/L_1 = 3904.64 \text{ in.-kips}$$

For member 2:

$$\phi_c = 1.60 \qquad \phi_2 = \beta_2 \phi_c = 2.0\ (1.60) = 3.20$$

$$S_{ii2} = 2.3990 \qquad S_{ii2}\, EI_2/L_2 = 2096.70 \text{ in.-kips}$$

$$S_{ij2} = 2.4924 \qquad S_{ij2}\, EI_2/L_2 = 2178.33 \text{ in.-kips}$$

$$\phi_c = 1.70 \qquad \phi_2 = \beta_2 \phi_c = 2.0\ (1.70) = 3.40$$

$$S_{ii2} = 2.1463 \qquad S_{ii2}\, EI_2/L_2 = 1875.84 \text{ in.-kips}$$

$$S_{ij2} = 2.5880 \qquad S_{ij2}\, EI_2/L_2 = 2261.89 \text{ in.-kips}$$

For member 3:

$$S_{ii3} = 4.0 \qquad S_{ii3}\, EI_3/L_3 = 4661.28 \text{ in.-kips}$$

$$S_{ij3} = 2.0 \qquad S_{ij3}\, EI_3/L_3 = 2330.64 \text{ in.-kips}$$

The determinant of the stability stiffness matrix $[K]$ at $\phi_c = 1.60$ is computed to be:

$$\text{DET}\ [K] = \text{DET}\ [A_1\, SA_1^T + K_2]$$

$= \text{DET}$

+10369.13	+2330.64	−79.6466	0	0	0
+2330.64	+6757.98	−17.8126	0	0	0
−79.6466	−17.8126	+1.47588	0	0	−0.77688

(with $+$ between the two matrix blocks)

$$= (48.982 + 3.306 + 3.306 - 42.870 - 3.797 - 3.290) \times 10^6$$

$$= +5.637 \times 10^6$$

and, at $\phi_c = 1.70$, it is

$$\text{DET}\ [K] = \text{DET}\ [A_1 SA_1^T + K_2]$$

$$= \text{DET}\begin{bmatrix} +10189.62 & +2330.64 & -78.6082 \\ +2330.64 & +6537.12 & -17.2405 \\ -78.6082 & -17.2405 & +1.45381 \end{bmatrix} + \begin{bmatrix} 0 & 0 & 0 \\ 0 & 0 & 0 \\ 0 & 0 & -0.87702 \end{bmatrix}$$

$$= (38.420 + 3.158 + 3.158 - 40.394 - 3.133 - 3.029) \times 10^6$$

$$= -1.820 \times 10^6$$

Using a straight-line interpolation,

$$(\phi_{CR})_c = 1.60 + 0.10 \left(\frac{5.637}{5.637 + 1.820}\right) = 1.675$$

$$N_{CR} = 14.566\,(1.675)^2 = 40.868 \text{ kips}$$

$$K_1 = \frac{\pi}{\beta_1\,(\phi_{CR})_c} = \frac{\pi}{1.4142\,(1.675)} = \frac{\pi}{2.3688} = 1.3262$$

$$K_2 = \frac{\pi}{\beta_2\,(\phi_{CR})_c} = \frac{\pi}{2.0\,(1.675)} = \frac{\pi}{3.35} = 0.9378$$

The stiffnesses of the members at $(\phi_{CR})_c = 1.675$ are:
For Member 1:

$$\phi_1 = 2.3688$$

$$S_{ii1} = 3.1889 \qquad S_{ii1}\,EI_1/L_1 = 5574.13 \text{ in.-kips}$$

$$S_{ij1} = 2.2257 \qquad S_{ij1}\,EI_1/L_1 = 3890.48 \text{ in.-kips}$$

For member 2:

$$\phi_2 = 3.35$$

$$S_{ii2} = 2.2113 \qquad S_{ii2}\,EI_2/L_2 = 1932.65 \text{ in.-kips}$$

$$S_{ij2} = 2.5631 \qquad S_{ij2}\,EI_2/L_2 = 2240.12 \text{ in.-kips}$$

The determinant of the stability stiffness $[K]$ at $(\phi_{CR})_c = 1.675$ is computed to be:

$$\text{DET}\,[K] = \text{DET}\,[A_1\,SA_1^T + K_2]$$

$$= \text{DET} \left[\begin{array}{ccc|ccc} +10235.41 & +2330.64 & -78.8718 & 0 & 0 & 0 \\ +2330.64 & +6593.93 & -17.3865 & 0 & 0 & 0 \\ -78.8718 & -17.3865 & +1.45942 & 0 & 0 & -0.85141 \end{array} \right]$$

$$= (41.036 + 3.196 + 3.196 - 41.019 - 3.303 - 3.094) \times 10^6$$

$$= +0.012 \times 10^6 \approx 0.0$$

4.6. Statics and Deformation Checks

In design applications only, the effective length ratios for a given set of primary axial forces are of direct interest and a computer program correctly verified to this point would suffice. However, statics and deformation checks as will be presented in this section serve to stimulate further understanding of the phenomenon of stability or instability at bifurcation.

The number of statics checks is equal to the degree of freedom. In other words, the $\{P\}$ matrix should be equal to zero, since no external joint forces are acting other than the primary axial forces. Because the determinant of the stability stiffness matrix $[K]$ is zero at bifurcation, it is possible to obtain a set of $\{X\}$ values from it in which the largest element is equal to positive 1. By nature of the symmetry and the predominance of the diagonal elements in the $[K]$ matrix, this $\{X\}$ vector may be computed by first locating the smallest diagonal element in the $[K]$ matrix, deleting the row containing it, shifting the column containing it to the other side of the equals sign, and solving the resulting system of $(NP - 1)$ linear simultaneous equations. The solution gives all the $\{X\}$ values except that associated with the deleted row or column, which is equal to positive 1. The complete $\{X\}$ vector describes the buckling mode.

With the buckling mode thus obtained, the end moments may be computed from

$$\{F\} = [SA_1^T] \, \{X\} \tag{4.6.1}$$

and the external forces from

$$\{P\} = [A_1] \, \{F\} + [K_2] \, \{X\} \approx \{0\} \tag{4.6.2}$$

In a small problem, it is instructive to check numerically the equilibrium of each member and of the structure as a whole, as will be illustrated by the numerical example in this section.

The number of deformation checks is equal to twice the number of members.

The end rotations of members as dictated by the $\{X\}$ vector are

$$\{\phi\} = [A_1^T] \ \{X\} \qquad\qquad (4.6.3)$$

But they are meanwhile functions of the end moments; thus

$$\{\phi\} = [D] \ \{F\} \qquad\qquad (4.6.4)$$

in which the member-flexibility matrix $[D]$ is that of Eq. 4.3.6. The fact that Eqs. 4.6.3 and 4.6.4 should give the same $\{\phi\}$ values constitutes the deformation checks.

In a numerical solution, it is only possible to find a value of $(\phi_{CR})_c$ to satisfy an acceptable tolerance in the value of the determinant of the stability stiffness matrix. Consequently, Eq. 4.6.2 can only be approximately satisfied to match that tolerance. However, the fact that Eqs. 4.6.3 and 4.6.4 should yield identical values of $\{\phi\}$ must be true for any set of $\{X\}$ values under any value of the buckling load factor.

In summary, it may be said that the residual $\{P\}$ values obtained in the statics check indicate how close the determinant $[K]$ is to zero, but the deformation checks are superficial except verification of the consistency between the flexibility and stiffness coefficients taken from the tabulated lists in the long-hand solution.

Example 4.6.1. Assuming that $(\phi_{CR})_c = 1.675$ for the rigid frame of Example 4.5.1, make the three statics checks and the six deformation checks. Sketch the free-body diagrams of members and the elastic curve at bifurcation.

Solution: From Example 4.5.1,

P \ X	1	2	3
1	+10235.41	+2330.64	−78.8718
2	+2330.64	+6593.93	−17.3865
3	−78.8718	−17.3865	+0.60801

$[K]$ at $((\phi_{CR})_c = 1.675) =$

Since K_{33} is smallest, choose $X_3 = +1.0$ in. and solve the two simultaneous equations

$$+10235.41 \, X_1 + 2330.64 \, X_2 = +78.8718$$
$$+ \ 2330.64 \, X_1 + 6593.93 \, X_2 = +17.3865$$

The buckling mode is represented by

$$\{X\} = \begin{Bmatrix} X_1 \\ X_2 \\ X_3 \end{Bmatrix} = \begin{Bmatrix} +0.0077273 \text{ rad} \\ -0.0000945 \text{ rad} \\ +1.000 \quad\text{ in.} \end{Bmatrix}$$

The end moments are computed from $\{F\} = [SA^T]\ \{X\}$.

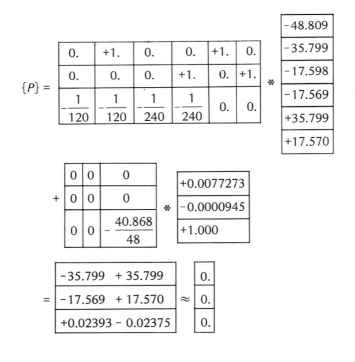

$$\{F\} = \begin{bmatrix} +3890.48 & 0. & -78.8718 \\ +5574.13 & 0. & -78.8718 \\ 0. & +2240.12 & -17.3865 \\ 0. & +1932.65 & -17.3865 \\ +4661.28 & +2330.64 & 0. \\ +2330.64 & +4661.28 & 0. \end{bmatrix} * \begin{Bmatrix} +0.0077273 \\ -0.0000945 \\ +1.000 \end{Bmatrix} = \begin{Bmatrix} -48.809 \\ -35.799 \\ -17.598 \\ -17.569 \\ +35.799 \\ +17.570 \end{Bmatrix}$$

The residual $\{P\}$ values are computed from $\{P\} = [A_1]\ \{F\} + [K_2]\ \{X\}$.

$$\{P\} = \begin{bmatrix} 0. & +1. & 0. & 0. & +1. & 0. \\ 0. & 0. & 0. & +1. & 0. & +1. \\ -\dfrac{1}{120} & -\dfrac{1}{120} & -\dfrac{1}{240} & -\dfrac{1}{240} & 0. & 0. \end{bmatrix} * \begin{Bmatrix} -48.809 \\ -35.799 \\ -17.598 \\ -17.569 \\ +35.799 \\ +17.570 \end{Bmatrix}$$

$$+ \begin{bmatrix} 0 & 0 & 0 \\ 0 & 0 & 0 \\ 0 & 0 & -\dfrac{40.868}{48} \end{bmatrix} * \begin{Bmatrix} +0.0077273 \\ -0.0000945 \\ +1.000 \end{Bmatrix}$$

$$= \begin{Bmatrix} -35.799 + 35.799 \\ -17.569 + 17.570 \\ +0.02393 - 0.02375 \end{Bmatrix} \approx \begin{Bmatrix} 0. \\ 0. \\ 0. \end{Bmatrix}$$

The free-body diagrams and the elastic curves are shown in Fig. 4.6.1. Note that, other than the critical primary axial forces, all end shears, end moments, joint rotations, and joint deflections are multiples of the quantity X_3. For the moment equilibrium of the two columns, the "second-order" moments due to the separation of the critical primary axial forces must be included.

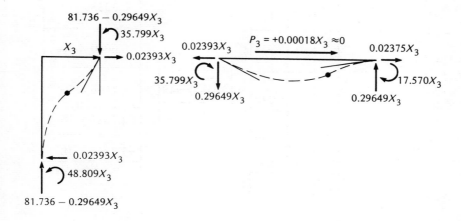

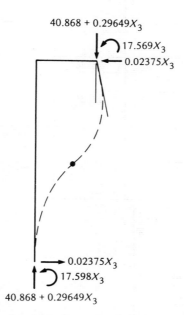

Figure 4.6.1. *Free-body diagrams and elastic curve at buckling.*

In making the deformation checks, the flexibility coefficients for $\phi_1 = 2.3688$ and $\phi_2 = 3.35$ are obtained by straight-line interpolation of the listed values in Table 6.5.1. Because of this approximation, the two sets of $\{\phi\}$ values are not exactly identical as they must be.

$$\{\phi\} = [A^T]\{X\} =$$

0.	0.	$-\dfrac{1}{120}$
+1.	0.	$-\dfrac{1}{120}$
0.	0.	$-\dfrac{1}{240}$
0.	+1.	$-\dfrac{1}{240}$
+1.	0.	0.
0.	+1.	0.

$*$

+0.0077273
-0.0000945
+1.000

$=$

-8.3333×10^{-3}
-0.6060×10^{-3}
-4.1666×10^{-3}
-4.2611×10^{-3}
$+7.7273 \times 10^{-3}$
-0.0945×10^{-3}

$$\{\phi\} = [D]\{F\} =$$

$+\dfrac{0.61258EI_1}{L_1}$	$-\dfrac{0.42789EI_1}{L_1}$				
$-\dfrac{0.42789EI_1}{L_1}$	$+\dfrac{0.61258EI_1}{L_1}$				
		$-\dfrac{1.41568EI_2}{L_2}$	$+\dfrac{1.62514EI_2}{L_2}$		
		$+\dfrac{1.62514EI_2}{L_2}$	$-\dfrac{1.41568EI_2}{L_2}$		
				$+\dfrac{0.33333EI_3}{L_3}$	$-\dfrac{0.16666EI_3}{L_3}$
				$-\dfrac{0.16666EI_3}{L_3}$	$+\dfrac{0.33333EI_3}{L_3}$

$*$

-48.809
-35.799
-17.598
-17.569
+35.799
+17.570

$=$

-8.3416×10^{-3}
-0.5978×10^{-3}
-4.1637×10^{-3}
-4.2644×10^{-3}
$+7.7276 \times 10^{-3}$
-0.0935×10^{-3}

4.7. Elastic Curves at Bifurcation

Oftentimes in research problems it may be desirable to plot accurately the elastic curve at buckling along the length of each member. Assuming that the $\{F\}$ and $\{\phi\}$ values have already been computed, the arbitrary constants A, B, C, and D in the equation of the elastic curve

$$y = A \sin \frac{\phi}{L} x + B \cos \frac{\phi}{L} x + Cx + D \tag{4.7.1}$$

may be computed either from the $\{F\}$ values by Eqs. 6.5.23abcd, or from the $\{\phi\}$ values by Eqs. 6.5.26abcd. It must be noted that the y-values as computed from Eq. 4.7.1 should be measured in the direction normal to the member axis in the undeformed position, but *from* the member axis in the deformed position of the buckling mode.

When there is no primary axial force on the member, the elastic curve is the cubic equation

$$y = Ax^3 + Bx^2 + Cx + D \tag{4.7.2}$$

in which

$$A = + \frac{(M_i + M_j)}{6LEI} \qquad B = -\frac{M_i}{2EI} \qquad C = + \frac{(2M_i - M_j)L}{6EI} \qquad D = 0 \tag{4.7.3}$$

or,

$$A = + \frac{(\phi_i + \phi_j)}{L^2} \qquad B = -\frac{(2\phi_i + \phi_j)}{L} \qquad C = + \phi_i \qquad D = 0 \tag{4.7.4}$$

Again, the y-values of Eq. 4.7.2 should be measured from the member axis in the deformed position.

4.8. The Second-Order Stiffness Matrix $[K_2]$

In large problems with multiple degree of freedom in sidesway and many members under primary axial forces, particularly in rigid frames having non-rectangular joints, it may be more convenient to let the computer generate the $[K_2]$ matrix by the formula

$$[K_2]_{\text{NPS} \times \text{NPS}} = -\frac{EI_c \phi_c^2}{L_c^2} [C]_{\text{NPS} \times \text{NMWN}} \{G\}_{\text{NMWN} \times \text{NMWN}} [C^T]_{\text{NMWN} \times \text{NPS}}$$

$$(4.8.1)$$

in which NPS is the degree of freedom in sidesway, NMWN is the number of members with primary axial forces, $[C]$ is a matrix expressing the sidesway forces which may be balanced by the end shear forces acting counterclockwise on member ends, and $[G]$ is a diagonal matrix with the element on the mth row or column equal to α_m/L_m.

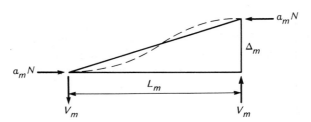

Figure 4.8.1. *End shears vs. relative end displacements.*

The derivation of Eq. 4.8.1 may be shown by considering Fig. 4.8.1, in which Δ_m is the relative displacement between member ends due to a counterclockwise rotation of the member axis. By the principle of virtual work, if

$$\{P_s\} = [C] \{V\} \qquad (4.8.2)$$

then

$$\{\Delta\} = [C^T] \{X_s\} \qquad (4.8.3)$$

Considering the moment equilibrium of the mth member in Fig. 4.8.1,

$$V_m = -\frac{(\alpha_m N)(\Delta_m)}{L_m}$$

or, in general,

$$\{V\} = -N[G] \{\Delta\} \qquad (4.8.4)$$

where

$$[G] = \begin{bmatrix} \dfrac{\alpha_1}{L_1} & 0 & \cdots & 0 \\[2mm] 0 & \dfrac{\alpha_2}{L_2} & \cdots & 0 \\[2mm] \cdot & \cdot & \cdots & \cdot \\[2mm] 0 & 0 & \cdots & \dfrac{\alpha_{NMWN}}{L_{NMWN}} \end{bmatrix}$$

Combining Eqs. 4.8.2, 4.8.3, and 4.8.4,

$$\{P_s\} = [C]\{V\} = -N[C][G]\{\Delta\} = -N[C][G][C^T]\{X_s\}$$
$$= -\frac{EI_c\phi_c^2}{L_c^2}[C][G][C^T]\{X_s\} = [K_2]\{X_s\}$$

which is Eq. 4.8.1.

In practice it is desirable to determine the $[C]$ and $[C^T]$ matrices independently of each other by their respective physical definitions and check the transposition relationship before the $[C]$ matrix is used as input in the computer program.

Example 4.8.1. Determine the matrices $[C]$ and $[C^T]$ independently of each other for the rigid frame of Fig. 4.5.1 and establish the $[K_2]$ matrix by $[K_2] = -N[CGC^T]$.

Solution: By assigning P_3 to joint C, joint B must satisfy horizontal equilibrium; thus at joint C of Fig. 4.8.2,

$$P_3 = -V_1 - V_2$$

and

$$[C] = \begin{array}{c|c|c} V & 1 & 2 \\ \hline P & & \\ \hline 3 & -1 & -1 \end{array}$$

Due to X_3 alone,

$$\Delta_1 = -X_3$$
$$\Delta_2 = -X_3$$

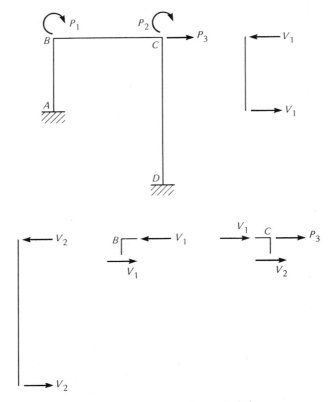

Figure 4.8.2. *The "P-V" matrix* [C].

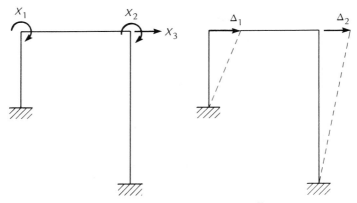

Figure 4.8.3. *The "Δ-X$_s$" matrix* [C^T].

because Δ_1 and Δ_2 here are due to clockwise rotation of the member axis (see Fig. 4.8.3); thus

$$[C^T] =$$

X_s \\ Δ	3
1	-1
2	-1

The matrix $[G]$ is

$$[G] =$$

Δ \\ V	1	2
1	$\dfrac{2}{120}$	
2		$\dfrac{1}{240}$

Thus

$$[K_2] = -N[C][G][C^T] = -N[-1\ -1]\begin{bmatrix} \dfrac{2}{120} & 0 \\ 0 & \dfrac{1}{240} \end{bmatrix}\begin{bmatrix} -1 \\ -1 \end{bmatrix} = -N\left[+\dfrac{1}{48}\right]$$

which is the same as determined directly from the equilibrium equation $\{P\} = [A_1]\{F\} + [K_2]\{X\}$ in Example 4.5.1.

Example 4.8.2. Determine the matrices $[C]$ and $[C^T]$ independently of each other for the rigid frame of Fig. 4.8.4a and establish the $[K_2]$ matrix by $[K_2] = -N[C][G][C^T]$.

Solution: The two resolution equations of equilibrium at joint C are:

$$0.6N_2 + 0.6N_3 = +0.8V_2 - 0.8V_3$$
$$0.8N_2 - 0.8N_3 = -0.6V_2 - 0.6V_3$$

from which

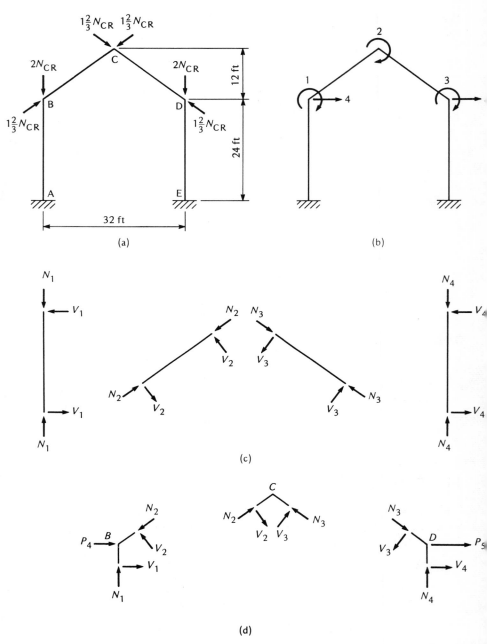

Figure 4.8.4. *The "P-V" matrix* [C]. *(a) The given rigid frame; (b) P-X numbers; (c) free-body diagrams of members; (d) free-body diagrams of joints.*

$$N_2 = + \frac{7}{24} V_2 - \frac{25}{24} V_3$$

$$N_3 = + \frac{25}{24} V_2 - \frac{7}{24} V_3$$

For the horizontal equilibrium at joints B and D,

$$P_4 = -V_1 + 0.6V_2 + 0.8N_2 = -V_1 + \frac{5}{6} V_2 - \frac{5}{6} V_3$$

$$P_5 = +0.6V_3 - V_4 - 0.8N_3 = -\frac{5}{6} V_2 + \frac{5}{6} V_3 - V_4$$

Thus,

P \ V	1	2	3	4
4	-1	$+\frac{5}{6}$	$-\frac{5}{6}$	0
5	0	$-\frac{5}{6}$	$+\frac{5}{6}$	-1

$$[C] =$$

From the joint displacement diagram of Fig. 4.8.5a, the Δ's due to X_4 alone

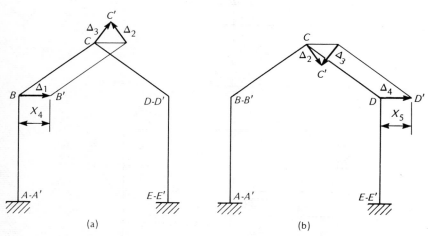

(a)   (b)

Figure 4.8.5. *The "Δ-X_s" matrix $[C^T]$.*

are:

$$\Delta_{14} = -X_4$$

$$\Delta_{24} = +\frac{5}{6}X_4$$

$$\Delta_{34} = -\frac{5}{6}X_4$$

$$\Delta_{44} = 0$$

Similarly, due to X_5 alone in Fig. 4.8.5b,

$$\Delta_{15} = 0$$

$$\Delta_{25} = -\frac{5}{6}X_5$$

$$\Delta_{35} = +\frac{5}{6}X_5$$

$$\Delta_{45} = -X_5$$

Thus,

$$[C^T] = $$

Δ \ X_s	4	5
1	-1	0
2	$+\dfrac{5}{6}$	$-\dfrac{5}{6}$
3	$-\dfrac{5}{6}$	$+\dfrac{5}{6}$
4	0	-1

The matrix $[G]$ is

$$[G] = $$

V \ Δ	1	2	3	4
1	2/288			
2		1.667/240		
3			1.667/240	
4				2/288

Thus,

$$[K_2] = -N[C][G][C^T] = -N \begin{bmatrix} +\dfrac{43}{2592} & -\dfrac{25}{2592} \\[3mm] -\dfrac{25}{2592} & +\dfrac{43}{2592} \end{bmatrix}$$

4.9. The Computer Program

A computer program for obtaining the critical standard stability angle $(\phi_{CR})_c$ for the fundamental buckling mode and the corresponding effective length ratios of all members with primary axial forces is shown in Appendix D. The purpose here is to show how typical programming may be done in solving problems of small dimensions. Sophistications such as the automatic formulation of the $[ASA^T]$ matrix without the use of the input $[A]$ matrix, and the computation of higher buckling modes, modal deflections, and elastic curves, are not included.

In subroutine BUASAT the stability stiffness matrix

$$[K] = [A_1 SA_1^T] + [K_2]$$

as expressed by Eq. 4.4.3 is computed for any assigned value of ϕ_c. It should be noted that the stiffness coefficients S_{ii} and S_{ij} are dependent on ϕ_c only in members with primary axial forces, but they take the constant values of 4 and 2 for members without primary axial forces. Thus it has been specified that the member numbers of those with primary axial forces *must precede* the member numbers of those without primary axial forces. The pairs of F-e numbers are then ordered in the same sequence as the member numbers; in other words, the F-e numbers for the mth member are $(2m - 1)$ and $2m$.

The first of the three DO-loops considers the contribution to the $[A_1 SA_1^T]$ matrix from members with primary axial forces where the S_{ii} and S_{ij} values are computed from Eq. 4.3.7, the second DO-loop does the same for members without primary axial forces where S_{ii} and S_{ij} are always equal to 4 and 2, and the third DO-loop makes the addition of the $[K_2]$ matrix which is expressed by Eq. 4.8.1 as

$$[K_2] = -\dfrac{EI_c \phi_c^2}{L^2} [C][G][C^T]$$

In subroutine COMDET the determinant of any square matrix with predominant diagonal elements is computed, with the assumption that all pivots in the Gauss-Jordan elimination lie on the main diagonal. Thus the program is similar to the inversion routine in Appendices D or E of *Matrix Methods of Structural Analysis.* Examination of the S_{ii} and S_{ij} values (with axial compression) in Table 6.5.1 shows that the S_{ij} values do not exceed the S_{ii} values until ϕ is above 3.20. Thus as far as the fundamental mode is concerned, even if the full panel search for each pivot is used, as shown in the routine of Appendix B of the previous book, at lower values of ϕ the chance is that the pivots will come from the main diagonal.

In the main program, the value of the critical standard stability angle $(\phi_{CR})_c$ causing zero determinant is obtained by an iterative procedure within a tolerance of 0.0001. Full explanation has been previously made in Sec. 2.11.

The input data for Example 4.5.1 to match the computer program in Appendix D is shown in Table 4.9.1.

TABLE 4.9.1

Input Data for Example 4.9.1

Card No.	Elements	Format	Remark
1	1	I5	1st data set
2	3 2 1 6 3 2 1	7I5	NP, NPR, NPS, NF, NM, NM1, NM2
3	1 2 +1.	2I5, F10.4	Nonzero elements in $[A]$
4	1 5 +1.	2I5, F10.4	Nonzero elements in $[A]$
5	2 4 +1.	2I5, F10.4	Nonzero elements in $[A]$
6	2 6 +1.	2I5, F10.4	Nonzero elements in $[A]$
7	3 1 −.0083333333	2I5, F10.4	Nonzero elements in $[A]$
8	3 2 −.0083333333	2I5, F10.4	Nonzero elements in $[A]$
9	3 3 −.0041666667	2I5, F10.4	Nonzero elements in $[A]$
10	3 4 −.0041666667	2I5, F10.4	Nonzero elements in $[A]$
11	−9	2I5, F10.4	No more nonzero elements in $[A]$
12	1 1 −1	2I5, F10.4	Nonzero elements in $[C]$
13	1 2 −1	2I5, F10.4	Nonzero elements in $[C]$
14	−9	2I5, F10.4	No more nonzero elements in $[C]$
15	29000. 120. 7.233	3F10.4	E, XLC, XIC
16	120. 240. 180.	5F10.4	XL (1) . . . XL (NM)
17	7.233 7.233 7.233	5F10.4	XI (1) . . . XI (NM)
18	2. 1.	5F10.4	ROFN (1) . . . ROFN (NM1)
19	−9	I5	No more data set

CHAPTER 5

■

Stability Analysis of Rigid Frames with Nonuniform Members

5.1. General Description

Stability analysis of rigid frames with prismatic members has been treated in Chapter 4, in which a trial-and-error method is used to make the determinant of the stability stiffness matrix equal to zero. If the cross sections of some or all of the members, or the primary axial forces in them, are not uniform, one approach is to divide the nonuniform member into several segments so that each segment may be considered to have a constant cross section as well as a constant axial force. When this is done, however, the stability angle $\phi = L\sqrt{N/(EI)}$ of the short segment may become well under 1.0, and thus the stiffness coefficients are only slightly different from the usual values of 4.0 and 2.0. Since an approximation has already been made in segmenting the nonuniform member, it seems logical to ignore the modification of the stiffness coefficients due to the presence of axial forces in the short segments.

It can be shown that, once the stiffness coefficients are assumed not to be affected by the axial forces, there is a direct eigenvalue solution of the buckling load factors and their associated mode shapes. Thus, even for rigid frames with

113

prismatic members only, an approximate direct solution is feasible, without trial and error, by using short member lengths for those portions of the rigid frame where there are primary axial forces.

5.2. The Eigenvalue Problem

Consider the simple beam ABCDE of Fig. 5.2.1a, with the left end hinged and the right end supported on rollers. Neglecting axial deformation (there is none in this case) and ignoring the modification of stiffness coefficients due to axial forces, it is required to find the buckling load factor N_{CR} and the mode shape.

The eight equations of statics, in which the secondary moments due to the separation of the lines of action of the pairs of primary axial forces are included, may be formulated by observing Fig. 5.2.1bcd; thus

$$P_1 = F_1$$

$$P_2 = F_2 + F_3$$

$$P_3 = F_4 + F_5$$

$$P_4 = F_6 + F_7$$

$$P_5 = F_8$$

$$P_6 = -V_1 + V_2 = -\left[\frac{F_1 + F_2 + \alpha_1 N_{CR} X_6}{L_1}\right] + \left[\frac{F_3 + F_4 + \alpha_2 N_{CR}(X_7 - X_6)}{L_2}\right]$$

$$P_7 = -V_2 + V_3 = -\left[\frac{F_3 + F_4 + \alpha_2 N_{CR}(X_7 - X_6)}{L_2}\right] + \left[\frac{F_5 + F_6 + \alpha_3 N_{CR}(X_8 - X_7)}{L_3}\right]$$

$$P_8 = -V_3 + V_4 = -\left[\frac{F_5 + F_6 + \alpha_3 N_{CR}(X_8 - X_7)}{L_3}\right] + \left[\frac{F_7 + F_8 - \alpha_4 N_{CR} X_8}{L_4}\right]$$

The equilibrium equations shown above may be expressed in general by

$$\begin{Bmatrix} P_R \\ P_S \end{Bmatrix}_{NPX1} = [A]_{NPXNF} \{F\}_{NFX1} - N_{CR} \begin{bmatrix} 0 & 0 \\ 0 & K_2 \end{bmatrix}_{NPXNP} \begin{Bmatrix} X_R \\ X_S \end{Bmatrix}_{NPX1} \qquad (5.2.1)$$

where the subscripts R and S refer to the degrees of freedom in rotation and in

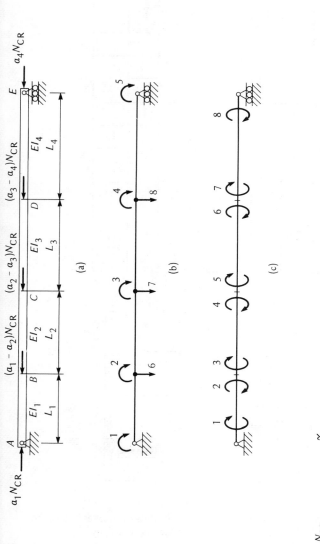

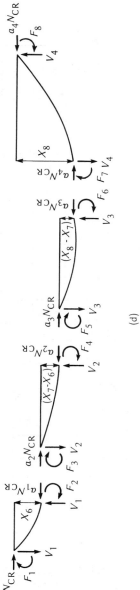

Figure 5.2.1. *Buckling of a segmented beam. (a) A simple beam; (b) the P-X numbers; (c) the F-e numbers; (d) free-body diagrams of members.*

115

sidesway respectively. In this particular case,

$$[A] = $$

F\P	1	2	3	4	5	6	7	8
1	+1.							
2		+1.	+1.					
3				+1.	+1.			
4						+1.	+1.	
5								+1.
6	$-\dfrac{1}{L_1}$	$-\dfrac{1}{L_1}$	$+\dfrac{1}{L_2}$	$+\dfrac{1}{L_2}$				
7			$-\dfrac{1}{L_2}$	$-\dfrac{1}{L_2}$	$+\dfrac{1}{L_3}$	$+\dfrac{1}{L_3}$		
8					$-\dfrac{1}{L_3}$	$-\dfrac{1}{L_3}$	$+\dfrac{1}{L_4}$	$+\dfrac{1}{L_4}$

$$[K_2] = $$

X\P	6	7	8
6	$+\left(\dfrac{\alpha_1}{L_1}+\dfrac{\alpha_2}{L_2}\right)$	$-\dfrac{\alpha_2}{L_2}$	
7	$-\dfrac{\alpha_2}{L_2}$	$+\left(\dfrac{\alpha_2}{L_2}+\dfrac{\alpha_3}{L_3}\right)$	$-\dfrac{\alpha_3}{L_3}$
8		$-\dfrac{\alpha_3}{L_3}$	$+\left(\dfrac{\alpha_3}{L_3}+\dfrac{\alpha_4}{L_4}\right)$

Note that the negative sign before $[K_2]$ in Eq. 5.2.1 is chosen in order that the second-order stiffness matrix $[K_2]$ may have positive elements on the main diagonal. Note also that the $[K_2]$ in this chapter is opposite in sign to the $[K_2]$ in Chapter 4.

Substituting the usual equation $\{F\} = [SA^T]\{X\}$ in Eq. 5.2.1,

$$\begin{Bmatrix} P_R \\ P_S \end{Bmatrix} = \left[[ASA^T] - N_{CR} \begin{bmatrix} 0 & 0 \\ 0 & K_2 \end{bmatrix} \right] \begin{Bmatrix} X_R \\ X_S \end{Bmatrix}$$

$$= \left[\begin{bmatrix} K_{RR} & K_{RS} \\ K_{SR} & K_{SS} \end{bmatrix} - N_{CR} \begin{bmatrix} 0 & 0 \\ 0 & K_2 \end{bmatrix} \right] \begin{Bmatrix} X_R \\ X_S \end{Bmatrix} \qquad (5.2.2)$$

in which K_{RR}, K_{RS}, K_{SR}, and K_{SS} are submatrices in the global external stiffness matrix.

At bifurcation, the external-force matrix is zero. Equation 5.2.1 becomes

$$K_{RR} X_R + K_{RS} X_S = 0 \qquad (5.2.3)$$

and

$$K_{SR} X_R + K_{SS} X_S - N_{CR} K_2 X_S = 0 \qquad (5.2.4)$$

Eliminating X_R between Eqs. 5.2.3 and 5.2.4,

$$(K_{SS} - K_{SR} K_{RR}^{-1} K_{RS}) X_S = N_{CR} K_2 X_S \qquad (5.2.5)$$

If the global external flexibility matrix is also partitioned, it becomes

$$[\delta] = [ASA^T]^{-1} = \begin{bmatrix} \delta_{RR} & \delta_{RS} \\ \delta_{SR} & \delta_{SS} \end{bmatrix} \qquad (5.2.6)$$

It has been shown previously in Sec. 1.3

$$[K_{SS} - K_{SR} K_{RR}^{-1} K_{RS}]^{-1} = \delta_{SS} \qquad (5.2.7)$$

Substituting Eq. 5.2.7 in Eq. 5.2.5,

$$\{X_S\} = N_{CR} [\delta_{SS} K_2] \{X_S\} \qquad (5.2.8)$$

Equation 5.2.8 shows that the buckling load factor N_{CR} is the eigenvalue of the matrix $[\delta_{SS} K_2]$, wherein δ_{SS} may be called the *sidesway flexibility matrix*, and $[K_2]$ the *second-order stiffness matrix*.

5.3. The Sidesway Flexibility Matrix

It may be helpful to reiterate the two ways by which the sidesway flexibility matrix $[\delta_{SS}]$ as defined in the previous section may be obtained. By its physical definition, the $[\delta_{SS}]$ matrix shows the deflections in the sidesway degree-of-freedom directions due to successive applications of the sidesway forces. Thus it is the square submatrix at the lower right corner of the global $[ASA^T]^{-1}$ matrix; or, symbolically,

$$[ASA^T]^{-1} = \begin{array}{|c|c|c|} \hline {}_X\!\diagdown^{P} & P_R & P_S \\ \hline X_R & \delta_{RR} & \delta_{RS} \\ \hline X_S & \delta_{SR} & \delta_{SS} \\ \hline \end{array} \qquad (5.3.1)$$

This method of obtaining $[\delta_{SS}]$ is used in the computer program of Appendix E. The alternate method of computing $[\delta_{SS}]$ is to use the formula

$$[\delta_{SS}] = [K_{SS} - K_{SR}K_{RR}^{-1}K_{RS}]^{-1} \qquad (5.3.2a)$$

where

$$[ASA^T] = \begin{array}{|c|c|c|} \hline {}_P\!\diagdown^{X} & X_R & X_S \\ \hline P_R & K_{RR} & K_{RS} \\ \hline P_S & K_{SR} & K_{SS} \\ \hline \end{array} \qquad (5.3.2b)$$

The use of Eq. 5.3.2a requires more operations in matrix multiplication and subtraction but two smaller inversions. When computer memory capacity is a problem, the use of this method may be the only choice.

5.4. The Second-Order Stiffness Matrix

The second-order stiffness matrix $[K_2]$ has been obtained, in Sec. 5.2, from the equilibrium equations in sidesway, whenever the sidesway forces are also

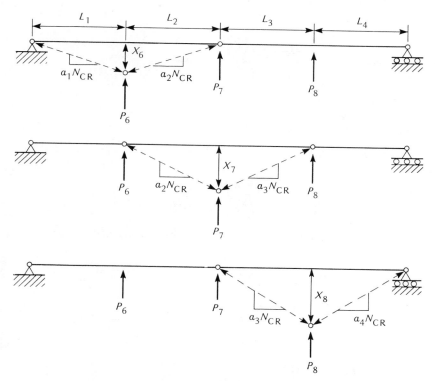

Figure 5.4.1. *Method for establishing the* $[K_2]$ *matrix.*

equilibrated by the secondary end shears due to the separation of the primary axial forces. In this section a systematic procedure by which the $[K_2]$ matrix may be established, alone by itself, will be shown.

The $[K_2]$ matrix can best be established by columns. Assuming that all joints are replaced by hinges, joint displacement diagrams as shown in Fig. 5.4.1 for the simple beam in Sec. 5.2 may be drawn for each joint displacement. Taking the force component in the unrotated direction of each rotated member as the primary axial force in it, a set of P_S forces opposite in direction to those in the P-X diagram are required to balance the joints; thus, due to X_6 only,

$$P_6 = +\alpha_1 N_{CR}(X_6/L_1) + \alpha_2 N_{CR}(X_6/L_2)$$

$$P_7 = -\alpha_2 N_{CR}(X_6/L_2)$$

$$P_8 = 0$$

due to X_7 only,

$$P_6 = -\alpha_2 N_{CR}(X_7/L_2)$$
$$P_7 = +\alpha_2 N_{CR}(X_7/L_2) + \alpha_3 N_{CR}(X_7/L_3)$$
$$P_8 = -\alpha_3 N_{CR}(X_7/L_3)$$

and due to X_8 only,

$$P_6 = 0$$
$$P_7 = -\alpha_3 N_{CR}(X_8/L_3)$$
$$P_8 = +\alpha_3 N_{CR}(X_8/L_3) + \alpha_4 N_{CR}(X_8/L_4)$$

Expressing these opposite sidesway forces as the product of N_{CR} and a $[K_2]$ matrix,

$$[K_2] = $$

$\!\!\diagdown\!\!\begin{smallmatrix}X\\[2pt]P\end{smallmatrix}$	6	7	8
6	$+\left(\dfrac{\alpha_1}{L_1}+\dfrac{\alpha_2}{L_2}\right)$	$-\dfrac{\alpha_2}{L_2}$	
7	$-\dfrac{\alpha_2}{L_2}$	$+\left(\dfrac{\alpha_2}{L_2}+\dfrac{\alpha_3}{L_3}\right)$	$-\dfrac{\alpha_3}{L_3}$
8		$-\dfrac{\alpha_3}{L_3}$	$+\left(\dfrac{\alpha_3}{L_3}+\dfrac{\alpha_4}{L_4}\right)$

which is the same as that obtained in Sec. 5.2.

Now the physical meaning of the eigenvalue equation

$$\{X_S\} = [\delta_{SS}]\, N_{CR}[K_2]\{X_S\}$$

should become clear. If a set of sidesway displacements $\{X_S\}$ is introduced, the sidesway forces resulting from the secondary end shears are given by $N_{CR}[K_2]\{X_S\}$. Bifurcation is achieved if this set of sidesway forces will just cause the sidesway displacements originally introduced at the beginning, thus the eigenvalue equation.

It should be noted that the eigenvalue equation itself is exact. The only approximation used in this chapter is that for members of short length the stiffness coefficients of +4.0 and +2.0 are good approximations, even though the members may be subjected to primary axial forces. Had the exact expressions of S_{ii} and S_{ij} as derived in Chapter 4 been used, the eigenvalue equation becomes implicit and the problem reverts back to the trial-and-error solution of

$$\text{DET } [K_{SS} - N_{CR}K_2] = 0$$

which is the condensed form of

$$\text{DET } [A_1 SA_1^T - N_{CR}\, C\, G\, C^T] = 0$$

as used in Chapter 4.

5.5. Direct Solution of the Eigenvalue Equation

The solution of the eigenvalue equation

$$\{X_S\} = N_{CR}[\delta_{SS}]\,[K_2]\,\{X_S\}$$

may be performed directly as long as $[\delta_{SS}K_2]$ is in the order of 1, 2, or even 3. Two examples of direct solution are shown in this section for the sole purpose of further clarifying the underlying principles. In the next section the iteration method suitable for solving problems of large dimension will be shown.

Example 5.5.1. Estimate the approximate buckling load N_{CR} of the simple beam shown in Fig. 5.5.1a by using the two segments of 8 ft and 12 ft in length. Compare the result with the exact Euler's load. Note that the approximate load is always too high or on the unconservative side.

Solution: In this problem it is convenient to find $[\delta_{SS}]$ by the conjugate-beam method as shown in Fig. 5.5.1b; thus,

$$\delta_{SS} = \frac{25.6}{EI}(8) - \frac{1}{2}\left(\frac{4.8}{EI}\right)(8)\left(\frac{8}{3}\right) = \frac{153.6}{EI}$$

From Fig. 5.5.1c,

$$[K_2] = \frac{1}{8} + \frac{1}{12} = \frac{5}{24}$$

The eigenvalue equation is

$$X_S = N_{CR}\left(\frac{153.6}{EI}\right)\left(\frac{5}{24}\right)X_S$$

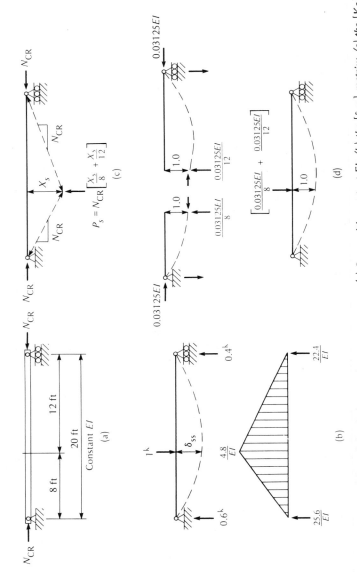

Figure 5.5.1. *Buckling of simple beam using two segments.* (a) Beam with constant EI; (b) the [δSS] matrix; (c) the [K2] matrix; (d) the superposition check.

122

from which

$$N_{CR} = 0.03125EI$$

The Euler's load should be

$$N_{CR} = \frac{\pi^2 EI}{L^2} = \frac{\pi^2 EI}{(20)^2} = 0.02467EI$$

It is interesting to note the superposition check of Fig. 5.5.1d. When the secondary end shears due to $X_S = +1.0$ are reversed to act on the beam, the flexural deflection is found to be equal to $X_S = +1.0$.

Example 5.5.2. Compute the approximate values of the fundamental and second buckling load of the simple beam shown in Fig. 5.5.2a by using three segments of 4 ft, 6 ft, and 10 ft. Note that the approximate fundamental load is much closer to the exact Euler's load than the result of the preceding example.

Solution: The four δ-values as defined in Fig. 5.5.2b are computed by the conjugate-beam method; thus,

$$[\delta_{SS}] = \begin{bmatrix} +68.267/EI & +94.667/EI \\ +94.667/EI & +166.667/EI \end{bmatrix}$$

The $[K_2]$ matrix can be established by observing Fig. 5.5.2c; thus,

$$[K_2] = \begin{bmatrix} +\left(\frac{1}{4}+\frac{1}{6}\right) & -\frac{1}{6} \\ -\frac{1}{6} & +\left(\frac{1}{6}+\frac{1}{10}\right) \end{bmatrix} = \begin{bmatrix} +0.41667 & -0.16667 \\ -0.16667 & +0.26667 \end{bmatrix}$$

The eigenvalue equation is

$$\begin{Bmatrix} X_{S1} \\ X_{S2} \end{Bmatrix} = N_{CR} \begin{bmatrix} +68.267/EI & +94.667/EI \\ +94.667/EI & +166.667/EI \end{bmatrix} \begin{bmatrix} +0.41667 & -0.16667 \\ -0.16667 & +0.26667 \end{bmatrix} \begin{Bmatrix} X_{S1} \\ X_{S2} \end{Bmatrix}$$

$$= N_{CR} \begin{bmatrix} +12.667/EI & +13.867/EI \\ +11.667/EI & +28.667/EI \end{bmatrix} \begin{Bmatrix} X_{S1} \\ X_{S2} \end{Bmatrix}$$

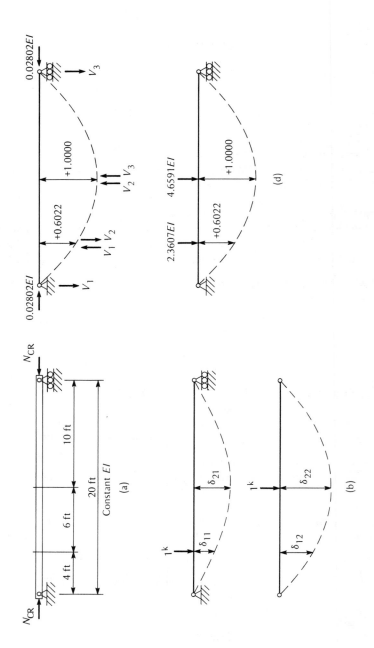

(a)

Constant EI

(b)

(d)

124

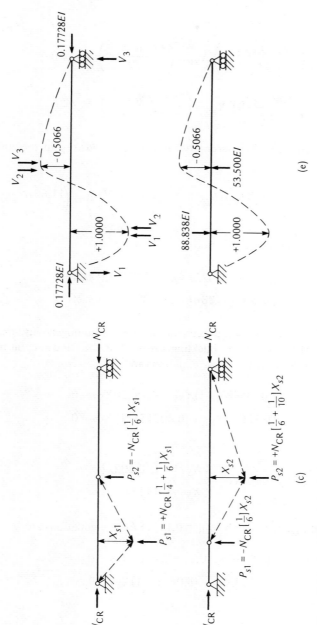

Figure 5.5.2. Buckling of simple beam using three segments. (a) Beam with constant EI; (b) the $[\delta_{SS}]$ matrix; (c) the $[K_2]$ matrix; (d) superposition check, first mode; (e) superposition check, second mode.

from which

$$\left(\frac{12.667N_{CR}}{EI} - 1\right) X_{S1} + \left(\frac{13.867N_{CR}}{EI}\right) X_{S2} = 0$$

$$\left(\frac{11.667N_{CR}}{EI}\right) X_{S1} + \left(\frac{28.667N_{CR}}{EI} - 1\right) X_{S2} = 0$$

Setting the determinant of the coefficients of X_{S1} and X_{S2} in the above two equations to zero.

$$\left(\frac{12.667N_{CR}}{EI} - 1\right) \left(\frac{28.667N_{CR}}{EI} - 1\right) - \left(\frac{13.867N_{CR}}{EI}\right) \left(\frac{11.667N_{CR}}{EI}\right) = 0$$

Solving the above quadratic equation,

$$N_{CR} = 0.02802EI \text{ vs. } 0.02467EI \text{ (exact)}$$

$$N_{CR} = 0.17728EI \text{ vs. } 0.09870EI \text{ (exact)}$$

The mode shapes may be computed from the sets of homogeneous linear equations upon substitution of the buckling loads. For the fundamental mode, in which $N_{CR} = 0.02802EI$, the linear equations are

$$(0.35488 - 1)X_{S1} + 0.38850X_{S2} = 0$$

$$0.32686X_{S1} + (0.80315 - 1)X_{S2} = 0$$

or,

$$\{X_S\} = \left\{\begin{array}{c} X_{S1} \\ X_{S2} \end{array}\right\} = \left\{\begin{array}{c} +0.6022 \\ +1.0000 \end{array}\right\}$$

For the second mode, in which $N_{CR} = 0.17728EI$, the equations are

$$(2.2456 - 1)X_{S1} + 2.4583X_{S2} = 0$$

$$2.0683X_{S1} + (5.0821 - 1)X_{S2} = 0$$

or,

$$\{X_S\} = \left\{\begin{array}{c} X_{S1} \\ X_{S2} \end{array}\right\} = \left\{\begin{array}{c} +1.00000 \\ -0.5066 \end{array}\right\}$$

In the superposition checks of Fig. 5.5.2d and e, the secondary end shears V_1, V_2, and V_3 are computed by considering the three segments as free bodies, and their opposites are made to act on the beam. The deflections are, for the fundamental mode,

$$\{X_S\} = [\delta_{SS}] \{P_S\} = \begin{bmatrix} +68.267/EI & +94.667/EI \\ +94.667/EI & +166.667/EI \end{bmatrix} \begin{Bmatrix} +2.3607EI \\ +4.6591EI \end{Bmatrix} = \begin{Bmatrix} +0.6022 \\ +1.0000 \end{Bmatrix}$$

and, for the second mode,

$$\{X_S\} = [\delta_{SS}] \{P_S\} = [\delta_{SS}] \begin{Bmatrix} +88.838EI \\ -53.500EI \end{Bmatrix} = \begin{Bmatrix} +1.0000 \\ -0.5066 \end{Bmatrix}$$

5.6. Iteration Solution of the Eigenvalue Equation

The buckling equation

$$\{X_S\} = N_{CR} [\delta_{SS}] [K_2] \{X_S\}$$

is analogous in all respects to the free-vibration equation

$$\{A\} = p^2 [\delta_m] [M] \{A\}$$

previously developed in Chapter 1. In the iteration solution of the free-vibration equation, the only requirement imposed on $[M]$ is that it be a symmetric matrix, even though it is actually a diagonal matrix. Since the $[K_2]$ matrix is, by its nature, always symmetric, the analogy is complete.

For sake of convenience, the procedure involved in the iteration solution of the buckling equation may be repeated here as follows:

1. Assume an initial $\{X_S\}$ vector in which every element is equal to +1.
2. Compute the $\{\delta_{SS} K_2 X_S\}$ vector and scale it to a new $\{X_S\}$ vector in which the element with the largest absolute value is equal to +1.
3. Repeat Step 2 until the absolute value of the difference between any two corresponding elements in two successive $\{X_S\}$ vectors is less than a preset tolerance such as 0.0001.
4. Compute the fundamental N_{CR} by dividing +1 in the last obtained $\{X_S\}$ vector (which is the buckling mode) by its corresponding $\{\delta_{SS} K_2 X_S\}$ value just before scaling.

5. If higher mode is required, obtain a new $[\delta_{SS}K_2]_{i+1}$ matrix by the following formula

$$[\delta_{SS}K_2]_{i+1} = [\delta_{SS}K_2]_i - \frac{1}{(N_{CR})_i X_{Si}^T K_2 X_{Si}} X_{Si}[K_2 X_{Si}]^T$$

and repeat Steps 1 to 4 above.
6. After all NPS modes are exhausted, a check may be made by showing that

$$[\delta_{SS}K_2]_{NPS+1} = 0$$

Since the proof for the above procedure has already been made in Chapter 1, it is only necessary to illustrate once more by solving Example 5.5.2 by the present method.

Example 5.6.1. Solve the eigenvalue equation in Example 5.5.2 by the iteration method.

Solution: From Example 5.5.2,

$$[\delta_{SS}K_2]_1 = \begin{bmatrix} +12.667/EI & +13.867/EI \\ +11.667/EI & +28.667/EI \end{bmatrix}$$

Let

$$\{X_S\} = \begin{Bmatrix} +1.0 \\ +1.0 \end{Bmatrix}$$

$$[\delta_{SS}K_2]_1 \begin{Bmatrix} +1.0 \\ +1.0 \end{Bmatrix} = \begin{Bmatrix} +26.53/EI \\ +40.33/EI \end{Bmatrix} \longrightarrow \begin{Bmatrix} +0.6578 \\ +1.0000 \end{Bmatrix}$$

$$[\delta_{SS}K_2]_1 \begin{Bmatrix} +0.6578 \\ +1.0000 \end{Bmatrix} = \begin{Bmatrix} +22.20/EI \\ +36.34/EI \end{Bmatrix} \longrightarrow \begin{Bmatrix} +0.6109 \\ +1.0000 \end{Bmatrix}$$

$$[\delta_{SS}K_2]_1 \begin{Bmatrix} +0.6109 \\ +1.0000 \end{Bmatrix} = \begin{Bmatrix} +21.60/EI \\ +35.79/EI \end{Bmatrix} \longrightarrow \begin{Bmatrix} +0.6036 \\ +1.0000 \end{Bmatrix}$$

$$[\delta_{SS}K_2]_1 \begin{Bmatrix} +0.6036 \\ +1.0000 \end{Bmatrix} = \begin{Bmatrix} +21.52/EI \\ +35.71/EI \end{Bmatrix} \longrightarrow \begin{Bmatrix} +0.6024 \\ +1.0000 \end{Bmatrix}$$

$$[\delta_{SS}K_2]_1 \begin{Bmatrix} +0.6024 \\ +1.0000 \end{Bmatrix} = \begin{Bmatrix} +21.50/EI \\ +35.70/EI \end{Bmatrix} \longrightarrow \begin{Bmatrix} +0.6022 \\ +1.0000 \end{Bmatrix}$$

$$[\delta_{SS}K_2]_1 \begin{Bmatrix} +0.6022 \\ +1.0000 \end{Bmatrix} = \begin{Bmatrix} +21.50/EI \\ +35.69/EI \end{Bmatrix} \longrightarrow \begin{Bmatrix} +0.6022 \\ +1.0000 \end{Bmatrix}$$

Thus,

$$(N_{CR})_1 = \frac{+1.0000}{35.69/EI} = 0.028017EI$$

For the second mode,

$$[\delta_{SS}K_2]_2 = [\delta_{SS}K_2]_1 - \frac{1}{(N_{CR})_1 X_{S1}^T K_2 X_{S1}} X_{S1}[K_2 X_{S1}]^T$$

$$= \begin{bmatrix} +4.3224/EI & -2.6032/EI \\ -2.1900/EI & +1.3183/EI \end{bmatrix}$$

$$[\delta_{SS}K_2]_2 \begin{Bmatrix} +1.0 \\ +1.0 \end{Bmatrix} = \begin{Bmatrix} +1.7192/EI \\ -0.8717/EI \end{Bmatrix} \longrightarrow \begin{Bmatrix} +1.0000 \\ -0.5070 \end{Bmatrix}$$

$$[\delta_{SS}K_2]_2 \begin{Bmatrix} +1.0000 \\ -0.5070 \end{Bmatrix} = \begin{Bmatrix} +5.6423/EI \\ -2.8584/EI \end{Bmatrix} \longrightarrow \begin{Bmatrix} +1.0000 \\ -0.5066 \end{Bmatrix}$$

$$[\delta_{SS}K_2]_2 \begin{Bmatrix} +1.0000 \\ -0.5066 \end{Bmatrix} = \begin{Bmatrix} +5.6412/EI \\ -2.8578/EI \end{Bmatrix} \longrightarrow \begin{Bmatrix} +1.0000 \\ -0.5066 \end{Bmatrix}$$

Thus,

$$(N_{CR})_2 = \frac{+1.0000}{+5.6412/EI} = 0.17727EI$$

$$[\delta_{SS}K_2]_3 = [\delta_{SS}K_2]_2 - \frac{1}{(N_{CR})_2 X_{S2} K_2 X_{S2}} X_{S2}[K_2 X_{S2}]^T$$

$$= \begin{bmatrix} +4.3224/EI & -2.6032/EI \\ -2.1900/EI & +1.3183/EI \end{bmatrix} - \begin{bmatrix} +4.3225/EI & -2.6030/EI \\ -2.1898/EI & +1.3187/EI \end{bmatrix}$$

$$\approx \begin{bmatrix} 0. & 0. \\ 0. & 0. \end{bmatrix} \text{ (Check)}$$

5.7. The Computer Program

A computer program using the iteration method of Sec. 5.6 is shown in Appendix E. The input data includes the statics matrix $[A]$, the second-order stiffness matrix $[K_2]$, and the EI/L values of the members (or segments) which may be considered uniform. It may be noted that, a prismatic member, even if it is under a uniform primary axial force, should be divided into segments in order to achieve small values of the stability angle ϕ. However, a prismatic member not under a primary axial force need not be subdivided at all.

It is mentioned in Sec. 5.3 that there are two ways of obtaining the sidesway flexibility matrix $[\delta_{SS}]$. In the computer program of Appendix E, an inversion of the total $[ASA^T]$ matrix is made, and the $[\delta_{SS}]$ matrix is taken from the lower right corner of the $[ASA^T]^{-1}$ matrix.

In the eigenvalue solution, any number of modes up to NPS may be called for. When the ith eigenvector $\{X_{Si}\}$ has been obtained satisfying a preset tolerance, especially in higher modes where the reduced $[\delta_{SS}K_2]_i$ matrix is used, it is most instructive to compute and print out a so-called "check eigenvector" from $[\delta_{SS}K_2]_1\{X_{Si}\}$ where $[\delta_{SS}K_2]_1$ means the original unreduced $[\delta_{SS}K_2]$ matrix. This is done in the computer program.

Also, if all the NPS modes are called, it would be interesting to reduce the $[\delta_{SS}K_2]$ matrix once more, and print out the $[\delta_{SS}K_2]_{NPS+1}$ matrix. An observation can then be made of the relative magnitudes of the elements in the final null matrix with those in the original unreduced matrix.

For purpose of illustration the input data for two more numerical examples† will be shown.

Example 5.7.1. Show the input data for the buckling analysis of the simple beam of Fig. 5.7.1a using four 10-ft segments.

Solution: The nonzero elements in the $[A]$ and $[K_2]$ matrices are shown in Tables 5.7.1 and 5.7.2. The buckling loads are found to be 3,895, 18,000, and 47,534 kips, which are, as expected, all higher than the theoretical values of 3,701, 14,804, and 33,310 kips.

---

†These two examples are identical with those used in the author's paper "Stability of Rigid Frames with Nonuniform Members," *Journal of Structural Division*, American Society of Civil Engineers, February 1967.

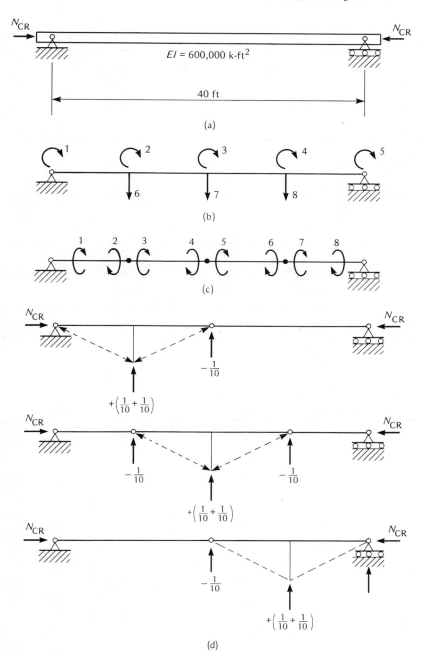

Figure 5.7.1. *Buckling analysis of a simple beam, Example 5.7.1.   (a) The given beam; (b) the P-X diagram; (c) the F-e diagram; (d) columns in* [K₂] *matrix.*

TABLE 5.7.1

Nonzero Elements in [A] of Example 5.7.1.

i	j	A(i, j)	i	j	A (i, j)	i	j	A (i, j)	i	j	A (i, j)
1	1	+1.	4	6	+1.	6	3	+0.1	7	6	+0.1
2	2	+1.	4	7	+1.	6	4	+0.1	8	5	-0.1
2	3	+1.	5	8	+1.	7	3	-0.1	8	6	-0.1
3	4	+1.	6	1	-0.1	7	4	-0.1	8	7	+0.1
3	5	+1.	6	2	-0.1	7	5	+0.1	8	8	+0.1

TABLE 5.7.2

Nonzero Elements in $[K_2]$ of Example 5.7.1.

i	j	K_2 (i, j)	i	j	K_2 (i, j)	i	j	K_2 (i, j)	i	j	K_2 (i, j)
1	1	+0.2	1	2	-0.1	3	2	-0.1	3	3	+0.2
2	1	-0.1	2	2	+0.2	2	3	-0.1			

Example 5.7.2. Show the input data for the buckling analysis of the rigid frame of Fig. 5.7.2a using six 2-ft segments for each column.

Solution: The nonzero elements in the [A] and $[K_2]$ matrices are shown in Tables 5.7.3 and 5.7.4. Only two modes are called for; the results are 1,625 and 5,673 kips. The theoretical results using the method of Chapter 4 give 1,613 and 5,400 kips.

TABLE 5.7.3

Nonzero Elements in [A] of Example 5.7.2.

i	j	A (i, j)	i	j	A (i, j)	i	j	A (i, j)	i	j	A (i, j)
1	2	+1.	9	19	+1.	15	7	+0.5	19	18	-0.5
1	3	+1.	10	20	+1.	15	8	+0.5	20	17	+0.5
2	4	+1.	10	21	+1.	16	7	-0.5	20	18	+0.5
2	5	+1.	11	22	+1.	16	8	-0.5	20	19	-0.5
3	6	+1.	11	23	+1.	16	9	+0.5	20	20	-0.5
3	7	+1.	12	24	+1.	16	10	+0.5	21	19	+0.5
4	8	+1.	12	25	+1.	17	9	-0.5	21	20	+0.5
4	9	+1.	13	1	-0.5	17	10	-0.5	21	21	-0.5
5	10	+1.	13	2	-0.5	17	11	+0.5	21	22	-0.5
5	11	+1.	13	3	+0.5	17	12	+0.5	22	21	+0.5
6	12	+1.	13	4	+0.5	18	11	-0.5	22	22	+0.5
6	13	+1.	14	3	-0.5	18	12	-0.5	22	23	-0.5
7	14	+1.	14	4	-0.5	18	15	-0.5	22	24	-0.5
7	15	+1.	14	5	+0.5	18	16	-0.5	23	23	+0.5
8	16	+1.	14	6	+0.5	19	15	+0.5	23	24	+0.5
8	17	+1.	15	5	-0.5	19	16	+0.5	23	25	-0.5
9	18	+1.	15	6	-0.5	19	17	-0.5	23	26	-0.5

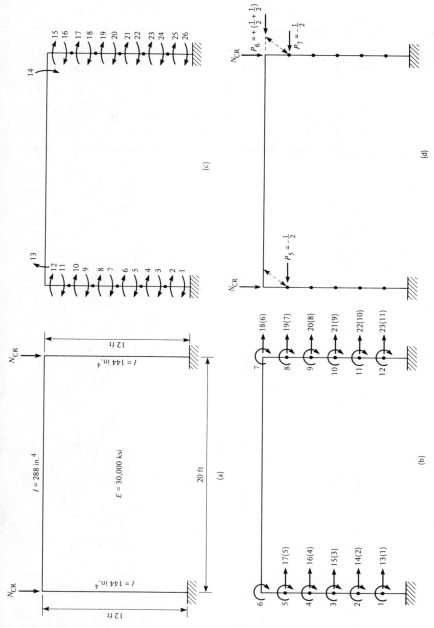

Figure 5.7.2. Buckling analysis of a rigid frame, Example 5.7.2. (a) The given frame; (b) the P-X diagram; (c) the F-e diagram; (d) sixth column in $[K_2]$ matrix.

TABLE 5.7.4

Nonzero Elements in [K₂] of Example 5.7.2.

i	j	$K_2(i, j)$	i	j	$K_2(i, j)$	i	j	$K_2(i, j)$	i	j	$K_2(i, j)$
1	1	+1.0	3	4	-0.5	7	6	-0.5	9	9	+1.0
2	1	-0.5	4	4	+1.0	6	7	-0.5	10	9	-0.5
1	2	-0.5	5	4	-0.5	7	7	+1.0	9	10	-0.5
2	2	+1.0	4	5	-0.5	8	7	-0.5	10	10	+1.0
3	2	-0.5	5	5	+1.0	7	8	-0.5	11	10	-0.5
2	3	-0.5	6	5	-0.5	8	8	+1.0	10	11	-0.5
3	3	+1.0	5	6	-0.5	9	8	-0.5	12	12	+1.0
4	3	-0.5	6	6	+1.0	8	9	-0.5			

CHAPTER 6

■

Second-Order Analysis of Rigid Frames

6.1. General Introduction

The difference between first-order and second-order analyses of rigid frames lies in whether the balance between the external and internal forces is in accord with the geometry of either the undeformed or the deformed structure. In order to simplify the treatment of a complex subject, the only external forces dealt with in this chapter are those acting on the joints. In a plane rigid frame, the six internal forces acting on each member are the two end axial forces, the two end shears, and the two end moments; however, only three of these six forces are independent unknowns, which are the magnitudes of the axial tensile force and of the two end moments acting clockwise on the member. The number of equations of equilibrium which must be satisfied at the joints has been defined as the degree of freedom.

With the rapidity in which a rigid frame may be analyzed by the displacement method on the computer, one can visualize the use of an iterative procedure of second-order analysis. A "first-cycle" second-order analysis can be made on the basis of the geometry described by the joint displacements of the first-order analysis. Then the "second-cycle" second-order analysis is made on the basis of the geometry described by the joint displacements of the first-cycle second-order

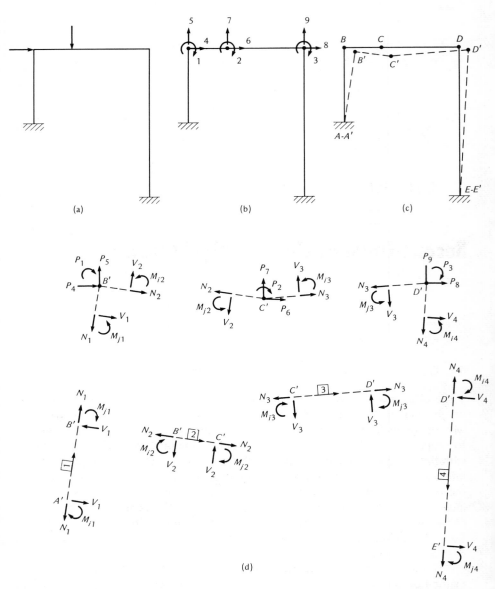

Figure 6.2.1. *Equilibrium in second-order analysis. (a) Applied loads; (b) the P-X diagram; (c) the displaced joints; (d) free-body diagrams of joints and members.*

analysis. The procedure may be repeated to any desired degree of accuracy, provided the loading is well below the buckling capacity.

The subject of second-order analysis of elastically behaving structures is a theoretical one, because in the elastic range of most engineering materials the joint displacements are usually very small in comparison with the original dimensions of the structure. As a matter of theoretical pursuit, no elastic limit is assumed in this chapter.

6.2. The Local [A'] Matrix

The number of joint equations of equilibrium is equal to the number of possible joint forces or of unknown joint displacements; and it has also been called the degree of freedom. For instance, the degree of freedom of the rigid frame in Fig. 6.2.1 is 9.

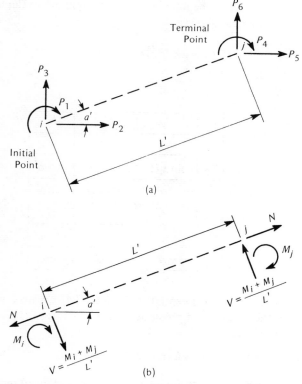

Figure 6.2.2. *The basis of the local* [A'] *matrix.* (a) *The local degrees of freedom,* (b) *the internal forces.*

Under the stipulation that external forces are applied only at the joints, the free-body diagrams of the 4 members in Fig. 6.2.1d are free of forces acting on the member proper. Calling the initial point the ith end and the terminal point the jth end, the six internal forces acting on a kth member may be defined by three independent quantities N_k, M_{ik}, and M_{jk}. Note that the directions of the axial and shear forces are those associated with the straight line joining the deflected joints.

In the iterative procedure of second-order analysis, it is first necessary to write the joint equations of equilibrium at the beginning of the first cycle according to the member directions obtained from the first-order analysis. Then in succession the joint equations of equilibrium at the beginning of the nth cycle are written according to the member directions obtained at the end of the $(n-1)$th cycle. With the ever-changing directions of the individual members, the use of the direct element method is most desirable. By designating the local degrees of freedom as shown in Fig. 6.2.2, in which α' and L' refer to the configuration of the rigid frame at the end of the $(n-1)$th cycle and N, M_i, and M_j are to be determined in the nth cycle, the joint equations of equilibrium can be described by the local $[A']$ matrix as follows:

$$\{P\}_{6 \times 1} = [A']_{6 \times 3} \{F\}_{3 \times 1} \tag{6.2.1a}$$

where

$$[A']_{6 \times 3} =$$

$P \diagdown F$	M_i	M_j	N
P_1	$+1$	0	0
P_2	$+\sin\alpha'/L'$	$+\sin\alpha'/L'$	$-\cos\alpha'$
P_3	$-\cos\alpha'/L'$	$-\cos\alpha'/L'$	$-\sin\alpha'$
P_4	0	$+1$	0
P_5	$-\sin\alpha'/L'$	$-\sin\alpha'/L'$	$+\cos\alpha'$
P_6	$+\cos\alpha'/L'$	$+\cos\alpha'/L'$	$+\sin\alpha'$

$$\tag{6.2.1b}$$

The symbol $[A']$ is used to differentiate it from the $[A_0]$ matrix, which will be used to represent the geometry of the undeformed structure.

6.3. Internal Deformations versus External Displacements

When large joint displacements are involved, it is important to reiterate clearly the definitions of internal deformations which are to be used in the second-order analysis of rigid frames. Consider a typical undeformed member AB in a rigid frame. It has gone through the external joint displacements X_1 to X_6 and taken the position and shape of the curve $A'B'$, as shown in Fig. 6.3.1a.

The three internal deformations corresponding with the three internal forces N, M_i, and M_j, are the increase in length Δ and the clockwise rotations ϕ_i and ϕ_j measured from the new member axis $A'B'$ to the elastic curve at the ith and jth ends respectively. Equations which express the internal deformations ϕ_i, ϕ_j, and Δ in terms of the external displacements X_1 to X_6 are commonly known as *compatibility equations*.

In first-order analysis, the counterclockwise rotation R of the member axis (see Fig. 6.3.1b) is taken as

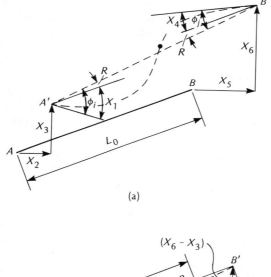

(a)

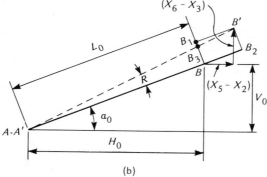

(b)

Figure 6.3.1. *Internal deformations vs. external displacements.*

$$R \text{ (first-order)} = \frac{BB_1}{L_0} = \frac{[(X_6 - X_3)\cos\alpha_0 - (X_5 - X_2)\sin\alpha_0]}{L_0} \quad (6.3.1)$$

In second-order analysis, the counterclockwise rotation R of the member axis (see also Fig. 6.3.1b) should be taken as

$$R \text{ (second-order)} = \frac{B_2 B'}{A'B_2} = \frac{BB_1}{L_0 + BB_2} \quad (6.3.2)$$

Since the difference between Eqs. 6.3.1 and 6.3.2 lies only in the denominator, it is assumed that Eq. 6.3.1 may also be used to represent the member rotation in the second-order analysis. Had this not been the case, the second-order member rotation may be expressed as the sum of the first-order member rotation and a corrective quantity equal to α_a, where α_a is caused essentially by the axial extension BB_2 in Fig. 6.3.1b, hence the subscript a for "axial." Thus,

$$R \text{ (second-order)} = \frac{BB_1 - B_1 B_3}{L_0} = \frac{BB_1}{L_0} - \frac{B_1 B_3}{L_0}$$

$$= R \text{ (first-order)} + \left\{ -\frac{1}{L_0}\left[(X_5 - X_2)\cos\alpha_0 + (X_6 - X_3)\sin\alpha_0\right]\sin R \right\}$$

$$= R \text{ (first-order)} + \alpha_a \quad (6.3.3a)$$

in which

$$\alpha_a = -\frac{1}{L_0}\left[(X_5 - X_2)\cos\alpha_0 + (X_6 - X_3)\sin\alpha_0\right]\sin R \quad (6.3.3b)$$

The fact that α_a may be dealt with in the same manner as Δ_t, as described in the next paragraph, could be a subject for further study.

In both first-order and second-order analyses,

$$\phi_i = X_1 + R \quad (6.3.4)$$

and

$$\phi_j = X_4 + R \quad (6.3.5)$$

The increase in length in the first-order analysis is, from Fig. 6.3.1b,

$$\Delta \text{ (first-order)} = BB_2 = (X_5 - X_2)\cos\alpha_0 + (X_6 - X_3)\sin\alpha_0 \quad (6.3.6)$$

More exactly, the increase in length should be

$$\Delta \text{ (second-order)} = A'B' - AB = \sqrt{(H_0 + X_5 - X_2)^2 + (V_0 + X_6 - X_3)^2} - L_0$$

Changing the above equation to the form

$$\Delta \text{ (second-order)} + L_0 = \sqrt{(H_0 + X_5 - X_2)^2 + (V_0 + X_6 - X_3)^2}$$

and squaring both sides,

$$[\Delta \text{ (second-order)}]^2 + 2L_0[\Delta \text{ (second-order)}] + L_0^2$$
$$= H_0^2 + 2H_0(X_5 - X_2) + (X_5 - X_2)^2 + V_0^2 + 2V_0(X_6 - X_3) + (X_6 - X_3)^2$$

from which

$$\Delta \text{ (second-order)} = \frac{(X_5 - X_2)H_0}{L_0} + \frac{(X_6 - X_3)V_0}{L_0}$$
$$+ \frac{(X_5 - X_2)^2 + (X_6 - X_3)^2 - [\Delta \text{ (second-order)}]^2}{2L_0}$$
$$= (X_5 - X_2) \cos\alpha_0 + (X_6 - X_3) \sin\alpha_0 + \Delta_t$$
$$= \Delta \text{ (first-order)} + \Delta_t \tag{6.3.7a}$$

where

$$\Delta_t = \frac{(X_5 - X_2)^2 + (X_6 - X_3)^2 - [\Delta \text{ (second-order)}]^2}{2L_0} \tag{6.3.7b}$$

Thus the second-order member length may be expressed as the sum of the first-order member length and a corrective quantity Δ_t, which is always a positive quantity since the transverse displacements of the member ends can only stretch the member. The subscript t is used to mean the effect of the "transverse" displacements. Upon solving a number of numerical examples it is found that the quantity Δ_t *must* be taken into account in second-order analysis.

Using Eqs. 6.3.1 and 6.3.7, the expressions for the internal deformations in second-order analysis become

$$\{e\}_{3 \times 1} = \begin{Bmatrix} \phi_i \\ \phi_j \\ \Delta \end{Bmatrix} = [B_0 = A_0^T] \{X\} + \begin{Bmatrix} 0 \\ 0 \\ \Delta_t \end{Bmatrix} \tag{6.3.8}$$

where $[A_0]$ and $[B_0]$ are the statics and deformation matrices based on the geometry of the undeformed structure.

6.4. Internal Force-Deformation Relationships

At any state of equilibrium and compatibility, the internal forces acting on a member in a rigid frame are M_i, M_j, and N (Fig. 6.2.2b) and the corresponding internal deformations are ϕ_i, ϕ_j, and Δ (Fig. 6.3.1b); thus,

$$\{F\} = \begin{Bmatrix} M_i \\ M_j \\ N \end{Bmatrix}$$

(6.4.1)

and

$$\{e\} = \begin{Bmatrix} \phi_i \\ \phi_j \\ \Delta \end{Bmatrix}$$

(6.4.2)

The relationship between the internal forces and deformations may be expressed by the member-stiffness matrix $[S]$; or,

$$[S] = \begin{array}{c|c|c|c} e \backslash F & \phi_i & \phi_j & \Delta \\ \hline M_i & S_{ii}\dfrac{EI_0}{L_0} & S_{ij}\dfrac{EI_0}{L_0} & 0 \\ \hline M_j & S_{ji}\dfrac{EI_0}{L_0} & S_{jj}\dfrac{EI_0}{L_0} & 0 \\ \hline N & 0 & 0 & \dfrac{EA_0}{L_0} \end{array}$$

(6.4.3)

Note that in the equation

$$N = \frac{EA_0}{L_0}\Delta$$

the axial forces N-N act in the direction of the straight line joining the displaced joints in the deformed structure; and, following the usual definition in Strength of Materials, the stiffness of the member in axial tension or compression is based on the original cross-sectional area A_0 and the original length L_0. The elongation Δ is expressed by Eq. 6.3.8, in which the value of Δ_t can only be based on the joint displacements obtained at the end of the previous cycle in the iteration procedure.

The derivation of the expressions for the flexural stiffness coefficients S_{ii}, S_{ij}, S_{ji}, and S_{jj} will be presented in the next section.

6.5. Stiffness and Flexibility Coefficients in Flexure

The flexural stiffness coefficients S_{ii}, $S_{ij} = S_{ji}$, and S_{jj} have been shown to be equal to +4, +2, and +4, if and only if the bending moment at any point *on* the elastic curve of Fig. 6.5.1 is considered to be unaffected by the axial forces N-N. Since relatively large forces and deformations are involved in second-order analysis, it will be necessary to determine the equation of the elastic curve on the basis of a more exact bending moment expression including the effect of the axial forces.

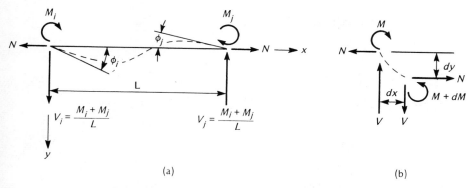

(a)   (b)

Figure 6.5.1. *A flexural member under axial tension.*

Consider first the case in which N is a tensile force. For moment equilibrium of the infinitesimal segment dx in Fig. 6.5.1b,

$$dM = V\,dx - N\,dy$$

Dividing the above equation through by dx,

$$\frac{dM}{dx} = V - N\frac{dy}{dx}$$

Differentiating again with respect to x,

$$\frac{d^2M}{dx^2} = \frac{dV}{dx} - N\frac{d^2y}{dx^2}$$

Without transverse load on the infinitesimal segment,

$$\frac{dV}{dx} = 0$$

and then

$$\frac{d^2M}{dx^2} = -N\frac{d^2y}{dx^2} \tag{6.5.1}$$

The change in slope of the elastic curve should be

$$\frac{d^2y}{dx^2} = -\frac{M}{EI} \tag{6.5.2}$$

Eliminating M between Eqs. 6.5.1 and 6.5.2,

$$\frac{d^4y}{dx^4} = +\frac{N}{EI}\frac{d^2y}{dx^2}$$

Using the notation

$$\phi = L\sqrt{\frac{N}{EI}} \tag{6.5.3}$$

the above equation becomes

$$\frac{d^4y}{dx^4} - \frac{\phi^2}{L^2}\frac{d^2y}{dx^2} = 0 \tag{6.5.4}$$

Equation 6.5.4 is the differential equation of the elastic curve in Fig. 6.5.1, where N is a tensile force.

The solution of the differential equation 6.5.4 is

$$y = A \sinh\frac{\phi}{L}x + B \cosh\frac{\phi}{L}x + Cx + D$$

The boundary conditions are:
(1) when $x = L$, $y = 0$; or

$$B + D = 0 \tag{6.5.5}$$

(2) when $x = L$, $y = 0$; or

$$A \sinh\phi + B \cosh\phi + CL + D = 0 \tag{6.5.6}$$

(3) when $x = 0$, $M = +M_i$; or

$$M_i = \left(-EI\frac{d^2y}{dx^2} \text{ at } x = 0\right) = -EI\left(A\frac{\phi^2}{L^2}\sinh\frac{\phi}{L}x + B\frac{\phi^2}{L^2}\cosh\frac{\phi}{L}x\right)$$

$$= -B\frac{\phi^2 EI}{L^2} \tag{6.5.7}$$

(4) when $x = L$, $M = -M_j$; or

$$M_j = \left(+EI\frac{d^2y}{dx^2} \text{ at } x = L\right) = +EI\left(A\frac{\phi^2}{L^2}\sinh\frac{\phi}{L}x + B\frac{\phi^2}{L^2}\cosh\frac{\phi}{L}x\right)$$

$$= +A\frac{\phi^2 EI}{L^2}\sinh\phi + B\frac{\phi^2 EI}{L^2}\cosh\phi \tag{6.5.8}$$

(5) when $x = 0$, $\frac{dy}{dx} = +\phi_i$; or

$$\phi_i = \left(+\frac{dy}{dx} \text{ at } x = 0\right) = A\frac{\phi}{L}\cosh\frac{\phi}{L}x + B\frac{\phi}{L}\sinh\frac{\phi}{L}x + C$$

$$= A\frac{\phi}{L} + C \tag{6.5.9}$$

(6) when $x = L$, $\frac{dy}{dx} = +\phi_j$; or

$$\phi_j = \left(+\frac{dy}{dx} \text{ at } x = L\right) = A\frac{\phi}{L}\cosh\frac{\phi}{L}x + B\frac{\phi}{L}\sinh\frac{\phi}{L}x + C$$

$$= A\frac{\phi}{L}\cosh\phi + B\frac{\phi}{L}\sinh\phi + C \tag{6.5.10}$$

Using Eqs. 6.5.5, 6.5.6, 6.5.7, and 6.5.8, the four arbitrary constants $A, B, C,$ and D can be solved in terms of the end moments M_i and M_j; thus,

$$A = +\frac{L^2 \cosh\phi}{\phi^2 EI \sinh\phi} M_i + \frac{L^2}{\phi^2 EI \sinh\phi} M_j \qquad (6.5.11a)$$

$$B = -\frac{L^2}{\phi^2 EI} M_i \qquad (6.5.11b)$$

$$C = -\frac{L}{\phi^2 EI} M_i - \frac{L}{\phi^2 EI} M_j \qquad (6.5.11c)$$

$$D = +\frac{L^2}{\phi^2 EI} M_i \qquad (6.5.11d)$$

Substituting Eq. 6.5.11 in Eqs. 6.5.9 and 6.5.10, the flexibility coefficients are found to be

$$[D] = \begin{array}{c|c|c} & M_i & M_j \\ \hline \phi_i & +\dfrac{\phi\cosh\phi - \sinh\phi}{\phi^2 \sinh\phi}\dfrac{L}{EI} & -\dfrac{\sinh\phi - \phi}{\phi^2 \sinh\phi}\dfrac{L}{EI} \\ \hline \phi_j & -\dfrac{\sinh\phi - \phi}{\phi^2 \sinh\phi}\dfrac{L}{EI} & +\dfrac{\phi\cosh\phi - \sinh\phi}{\phi^2 \sinh\phi}\dfrac{L}{EI} \end{array} \qquad (6.5.12)$$

And, for small values of ϕ,

$$[D] = \begin{array}{c|c|c} & M_i & M_j \\ \hline \phi_i & +\dfrac{1}{3}\dfrac{1+\phi^2/10}{1+\phi^2/6}\dfrac{L}{EI} & -\dfrac{1}{6}\dfrac{1+\phi^2/20}{1+\phi^2/6}\dfrac{L}{EI} \\ \hline \phi_j & -\dfrac{1}{6}\dfrac{1+\phi^2/20}{1+\phi^2/6}\dfrac{L}{EI} & +\dfrac{1}{3}\dfrac{1+\phi^2/10}{1+\phi^2/6}\dfrac{L}{EI} \end{array} \qquad (6.5.13)$$

Using Eqs. 6.5.5, 6.5.6, 6.5.9, and 6.5.10, the four arbitrary constants $A, B, C,$ and D can be solved in terms of the end rotations ϕ_i and ϕ_j; thus,

$$\frac{A}{L} = \frac{(1 - \cosh\phi + \phi\sinh\phi)\,\phi_i + (\cosh\phi - 1)\,\phi_j}{\phi(2 - 2\cosh\phi + \phi\sinh\phi)} \qquad (6.5.14a)$$

$$\frac{B}{L} = \frac{(\sinh\phi - \phi\cosh\phi)\,\phi_i + (\phi - \sinh\phi)\,\phi_j}{\phi\,(2 - 2\cosh\phi + \phi\sinh\phi)} \tag{6.5.14b}$$

$$C = \frac{(1 - \cosh\phi)\,\phi_i + (1 - \cosh\phi)\,\phi_j}{(2 - 2\cosh\phi + \phi\sinh\phi)} \tag{6.5.14c}$$

$$\frac{D}{L} = \frac{(\phi\cosh\phi - \sinh\phi)\,\phi_i + (\sinh\phi - \phi)\,\phi_j}{\phi\,(2 - 2\cosh\phi + \phi\sinh\phi)} \tag{6.5.14d}$$

Substituting Eq. 6.5.14 in Eqs. 6.5.7 and 6.5.8, the stiffness coefficients are found to be

		ϕ_i	ϕ_j
$[S] =$	M_i	$+\dfrac{\phi^2\cosh\phi - \phi\sinh\phi}{2 - 2\cosh\phi + \phi\sinh\phi}\dfrac{EI}{L}$	$+\dfrac{\phi\sinh\phi - \phi^2}{2 - 2\cosh\phi + \phi\sinh\phi}\dfrac{EI}{L}$
	M_j	$+\dfrac{\phi\sinh\phi - \phi^2}{2 - 2\cosh\phi + \phi\sinh\phi}\dfrac{EI}{L}$	$\dfrac{\phi^2\cosh\phi - \phi\sinh\phi}{2 - 2\cosh\phi + \phi\sinh\phi}\dfrac{EI}{L}$

$$\tag{6.5.15}$$

And, for small values of ϕ,

		ϕ_i	ϕ_j
$[S] =$	M_i	$\dfrac{4\,(1 + \phi^2/10)}{1 + \phi^2/15}\dfrac{EI}{L}$	$\dfrac{2\,(1 + \phi^2/20)}{1 + \phi^2/15}\dfrac{EI}{L}$
	M_j	$\dfrac{2\,(1 + \phi^2/20)}{1 + \phi^2/15}\dfrac{EI}{L}$	$\dfrac{4\,(1 + \phi^2/10)}{1 + \phi^2/15}\dfrac{EI}{L}$

$$\tag{6.5.16}$$

Now if the axial forces N-N are taken as positive if they are compressive, the differential equation of the elastic curve becomes

$$\frac{d^4y}{dx^4} + \frac{\phi^2}{L^2}\frac{d^2y}{dx^2} = 0$$

the solution of which is

$$y = A\,\sin\frac{\phi}{L}x + B\,\cos\frac{\phi}{L}x + Cx + D$$

The six boundary conditions are:

(1) When $x = L$, $y = 0$; or

$$B + D = 0 \qquad (6.5.17)$$

(2) When $x = L$, $y = 0$; or

$$A \sin\phi + B \cos\phi + CL + D = 0 \qquad (6.5.18)$$

(3) When $x = 0$, $M = +M_i$; or

$$M_i = +B\frac{\phi^2 EI}{L^2} \qquad (6.5.19)$$

(4) When $x = L$, $M = -M_j$; or

$$M_j = -A\frac{\phi^2 EI}{L^2} \sin\phi - B\frac{\phi^2 EI}{L^2} \cos\phi \qquad (6.5.20)$$

(5) When $x = 0$, $\dfrac{dy}{dx} = +\phi_i$; or

$$\phi_i = A\frac{\phi}{L} + C \qquad (6.5.21)$$

(6) When $x = L$, $\dfrac{dy}{dx} = +\phi_j$; or

$$\phi_j = A\frac{\phi}{L} \cos\phi - B\frac{\phi}{L} \sin\phi + C \qquad (6.5.22)$$

Using Eqs. 6.5.17, 6.5.18, 6.5.19, and 6.5.20, the four arbitrary constants A, B, C, and D can be solved in terms of the end moments M_i and M_j; thus,

$$A = -\frac{L^2 \cos\phi}{\phi^2 EI \sin\phi} M_i - \frac{L^2}{\phi^2 EI \sin\phi} M_j \qquad (6.5.23a)$$

$$B = +\frac{L^2}{\phi^2 EI} M_i \qquad (6.5.23b)$$

$$C = +\frac{L}{\phi^2 EI} M_i + \frac{L}{\phi^2 EI} M_j \qquad (6.5.23c)$$

$$D = -\frac{L^2}{\phi^2 EI} M_i \tag{6.5.23d}$$

Substituting Eq. 6.5.23 in Eqs. 6.5.21 and 6.5.22, the flexibility coefficients are found to be

$$[D] = \begin{array}{c|c|c} & M_i & M_j \\ \hline \phi_i & +\dfrac{\sin\phi - \phi\cos\phi}{\phi^2 \sin\phi}\dfrac{L}{EI} & -\dfrac{\phi - \sin\phi}{\phi^2 \sin\phi}\dfrac{L}{EI} \\ \hline \phi_j & -\dfrac{\phi - \sin\phi}{\phi^2 \sin\phi}\dfrac{L}{EI} & +\dfrac{\sin\phi - \phi\cos\phi}{\phi^2 \sin\phi}\dfrac{L}{EI} \end{array} \tag{6.5.24}$$

And, for small values of ϕ,

$$[D] = \begin{array}{c|c|c} & M_i & M_j \\ \hline \phi_i & +\dfrac{1}{3}\dfrac{1 - \phi^2/10}{1 - \phi^2/6}\dfrac{L}{EI} & -\dfrac{1}{6}\dfrac{1 - \phi^2/20}{1 - \phi^2/6}\dfrac{L}{EI} \\ \hline \phi_j & -\dfrac{1}{6}\dfrac{1 - \phi^2/20}{1 - \phi^2/6}\dfrac{L}{EI} & +\dfrac{1}{3}\dfrac{1 - \phi^2/10}{1 - \phi^2/6}\dfrac{L}{EI} \end{array} \tag{6.5.25}$$

Using Eqs. 6.5.17, 6.5.18, 6.5.21, and 6.5.22, the four arbitrary constants A, B, C, and D can be solved in terms of the end rotations ϕ_i and ϕ_j; thus,

$$\frac{A}{L} = \frac{(1 - \cos\phi - \phi\sin\phi)\,\phi_i + (\cos\phi - 1)\,\phi_j}{\phi\,(2 - 2\cos\phi - \phi\sin\phi)} \tag{6.5.26a}$$

$$\frac{B}{L} = \frac{(\sin\phi - \phi\cos\phi)\,\phi_i + (\phi - \sin\phi)\,\phi_j}{\phi\,(2 - \cos\phi - \phi\sin\phi)} \tag{6.5.25b}$$

$$C = \frac{(1 - \cos\phi)\,\phi_i + (1 - \cos\phi)\,\phi_j}{(2 - \cos\phi - \phi\sin\phi)} \tag{6.5.26c}$$

$$\frac{D}{L} = \frac{(\phi\cos\phi - \sin\phi)\,\phi_i + (\sin\phi - \phi)\,\phi_j}{\phi\,(2 - \cos\phi - \phi\sin\phi)} \tag{6.5.26d}$$

Substituting Eq. 6.5.26 in Eqs. 6.5.19 and 6.5.20, the stiffness coefficients are found to be

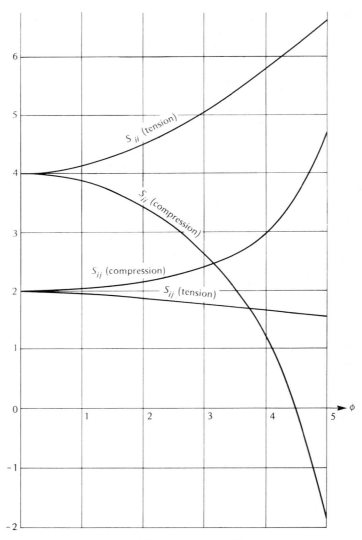

Figure 6.5.2. *Stiffness coefficients.*

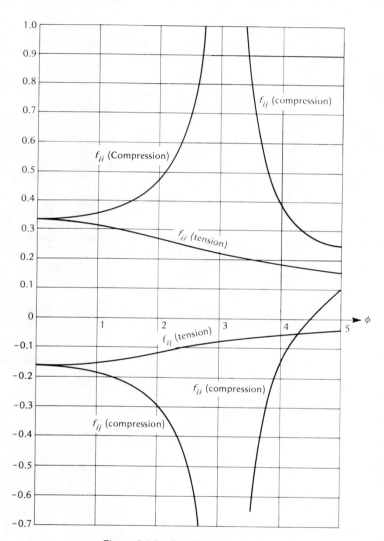

Figure 6.5.3. *Flexibility coefficients.*

TABLE 6.5.1

Stiffness and Flexibility Coefficients for a Member in Flexure.

	With Axial Compression				With Axial Tension			
ϕ	S_{ii}	S_{ij}	f_{ii}	f_{ij}	S_{ii}	S_{ij}	f_{ii}	f_{ij}
0.10	3.9987	2.0003	.33355	-.16686	4.0014	1.9997	.33311	-.16647
0.20	3.9947	2.0013	.33423	-.16745	4.0053	1.9987	.33245	-.16589
0.30	3.9880	2.0030	.33535	-.16843	4.0120	1.9970	.33135	-.16493
0.40	3.9786	2.0054	.33694	-.16983	4.0213	1.9947	.32983	-.16361
0.50	3.9665	2.0084	.33902	-.17166	4.0332	1.9917	.32791	-.16193
0.60	3.9518	2.0121	.34162	-.17394	4.0478	1.9881	.32560	-.15992
0.70	3.9342	2.0166	.34476	-.17671	4.0649	1.9839	.32293	-.15761
0.80	3.9139	2.0218	.34848	-.18001	4.0846	1.9791	.31992	-.15501
0.90	3.8908	2.0277	.35284	-.18388	4.1069	1.9737	.31662	-.15216
1.00	3.8649	2.0344	.35791	-.18840	4.1316	1.9677	.31304	-.14908
1.10	3.8360	2.0419	.36375	-.19362	4.1588	1.9611	.30921	-.14581
1.20	3.8043	2.0502	.37046	-.19965	4.1885	1.9540	.30517	-.14237
1.30	3.7695	2.0594	.37816	-.20661	4.2205	1.9465	.30095	-.13880
1.40	3.7317	2.0695	.38701	-.21463	4.2549	1.9384	.29658	-.13511
1.50	3.6907	2.0806	.39717	-.22390	4.2916	1.9299	.29208	-.13135
1.60	3.6466	2.0926	.40888	-.23464	4.3305	1.9210	.28749	-.12753
1.70	3.5991	2.1057	.42245	-.24716	4.3716	1.9116	.28283	-.12368
1.80	3.5483	2.1199	.43826	-.26183	4.4148	1.9019	.27813	-.11982
1.90	3.4940	2.1353	.45682	-.27917	4.4602	1.8919	.27339	-.11596
2.00	3.4361	2.1519	.47883	-.29988	4.5076	1.8815	.26866	-.11214
2.10	3.3745	2.1699	.50526	-.32489	4.5569	1.8708	.26393	-.10836
2.20	3.3090	2.1893	.53747	-.35560	4.6082	1.8599	.25923	-.10463
2.30	3.2395	2.2102	.57751	-.39401	4.6613	1.8488	.25458	-.10097
2.40	3.1659	2.2328	.62848	-.44325	4.7163	1.8374	.24997	-.09738
2.50	3.0878	2.2572	.69546	-.50837	4.7730	1.8259	.24543	-.09389
2.60	3.0052	2.2834	.78725	-.59817	4.8314	1.8142	.24095	-.09048
2.70	2.9178	2.3118	.92065	-.72943	4.8915	1.8024	.23656	-.08717
2.80	2.8254	2.3425	1.1321	-.93858	4.9531	1.7905	.23224	-.08395
2.90	2.7276	2.3756	1.5183	-1.3224	5.0162	1.7785	.22802	-.08084
3.00	2.6242	2.4114	2.4495	-2.2509	5.0809	1.7665	.22388	-.07784
3.10	2.5148	2.4503	7.8553	-7.6539	5.1469	1.7544	.21983	-.07494
3.20	2.3990	2.4924	-5.2466	5.4510	5.2143	1.7424	.21588	-.07214
3.30	2.2763	2.5382	-1.80513	2.01283	5.2830	1.7303	.21203	-.06944
3.40	2.1463	2.5880	-1.02624	1.23746	5.3530	1.7183	.20827	-.06685
3.50	2.0083	2.6424	-.68112	.89614	5.4242	1.7063	.20460	-.06436
3.60	1.8618	2.7017	-.48575	.70488	5.4966	1.6944	.20103	-.06197
3.70	1.7060	2.7668	-.35957	.58315	5.5701	1.6825	.19755	-.05967
3.80	1.5400	2.8382	-.27094	.49935	5.6447	1.6708	.19417	-.05747
3.90	1.3627	2.9168	-.20489	.43856	5.7203	1.6591	.19087	-.05536
4.00	1.1731	3.0037	-.15342	.39284	5.7968	1.6476	.18767	-.05334
4.10	.96976	3.1001	-.11185	.35746	5.8744	1.6362	.18455	-.05140
4.20	.75101	3.2074	-.07724	.32987	5.9528	1.6249	.18151	-.04955
4.30	.51494	3.3273	-.04766	.30792	6.0321	1.6138	.17856	-.04777
4.40	.25919	3.4619	-.02175	.29048	6.1122	1.6028	.17569	-.04607
4.50	-.01910	3.6140	.00146	.27671	6.1931	1.5920	.17289	-.04444
4.60	-.32344	3.7866	.02272	.26603	6.2748	1.5814	.17018	-.04289
4.70	-.65819	3.9839	.04263	.25805	6.3572	1.5709	.16753	-.04140
4.80	-1.0289	4.2112	.06170	.25254	6.4403	1.5606	.16496	-.03997
4.90	-1.4427	4.4751	.08039	.24938	6.5240	1.5505	.16245	-.03861
5.00	-1.9087	4.7845	.09916	.24857	6.6084	1.5406	.16002	-.03730

152

$$[S] = \begin{array}{c|c|c}
 & \phi_i & \phi_j \\
\hline
M_i & +\dfrac{\phi\sin\phi - \phi^2\cos\phi}{2 - 2\cos\phi - \phi\sin\phi}\dfrac{EI}{L} & +\dfrac{\phi^2 - \phi\sin\phi}{2 - 2\cos\phi - \phi\sin\phi}\dfrac{EI}{L} \\
\hline
M_j & +\dfrac{\phi^2 - \phi\sin\phi}{2 - 2\cos\phi - \phi\sin\phi}\dfrac{EI}{L} & +\dfrac{\phi\sin\phi - \phi^2\cos\phi}{2 - 2\cos\phi - \phi\sin\phi}\dfrac{EI}{L}
\end{array} \qquad (6.5.27)$$

And, for small values of ϕ,

$$\begin{array}{c|c|c}
 & \phi_i & \phi_j \\
\hline
M_i & +\dfrac{4\,(1 - \phi^2/10)}{1 - \phi^2/15}\dfrac{EI}{L} & +\dfrac{2\,(1 - \phi^2/20)}{1 - \phi^2/15}\dfrac{EI}{L} \\
\hline
M_j & +\dfrac{2\,(1 - \phi^2/20)}{1 - \phi^2/15}\dfrac{EI}{L} & +\dfrac{4\,(1 - \phi^2/10)}{1 - \phi^2/15}\dfrac{EI}{L}
\end{array} \qquad (6.5.28)$$

Tabulated values of stiffness and flexibility coefficients for values of $\phi = 0$ to $\phi = 5.00$ are shown in Table 6.5.1; and the corresponding graphs are shown in Figs. 6.5.2 and 6.5.3. Note that, in comparison with the case under no axial load, a flexural member is stiffer with axial tension but more flexible with axial compression. Particularly note that the flexibility coefficients are discontinuous when the Euler's buckling load ($\phi = \pi$) is present.

6.6. The Displacement Method of Second-Order Analysis

The displacement method of second-order analysis follows the same pattern as for first-order analysis, except that the axial forces and joint displacements obtained by the first-order analysis are needed at the beginning of the "first-cycle" second-order analysis, and, subsequently, these same values obtained at the end of the "nth cycle" second-order analysis are needed at the beginning of the "$(n + 1)$th cycle" second-order analysis. The iteration procedure should be continued until a criterion for convergence is satisfied, such as the values in two successive cycles, either of axial forces and bending moments or of joint displacements, should not differ by a preset tolerance.

The direct-element method is conveniently used in the computer program described in Appendix F. Using this concept, the equilibrium equations are

$$\{P\}_{6\times 1} = [A']_{6\times 3}\{F\}_{3\times 1} \qquad (6.6.1)$$

where

$$
\{P\} = \begin{bmatrix} P_1 \\ P_2 \\ P_3 \\ P_4 \\ P_5 \\ P_6 \end{bmatrix}
\qquad
[A'] =
\begin{bmatrix}
+1 & 0 & 0 \\
+\sin\alpha'/L' & +\sin\alpha'/L' & -\cos\alpha' \\
-\cos\alpha'/L' & -\cos\alpha'/L' & -\sin\alpha' \\
0 & +1 & 0 \\
-\sin\alpha'/L' & -\sin\alpha'/L' & +\cos\alpha' \\
+\cos\alpha'/L' & +\cos\alpha'/L' & +\sin\alpha'
\end{bmatrix}
\qquad
\{F\} = \begin{bmatrix} M_i \\ M_j \\ N \end{bmatrix}
$$

The compatibility equations are

$$
\{e\}_{3\times1} = [A_0^T]_{3\times6}\,\{X\}_{6\times1} + \begin{Bmatrix} 0 \\ 0 \\ \Delta_t \end{Bmatrix}
\tag{6.6.2}
$$

where

$$
\{e\} = \begin{bmatrix} \phi_i \\ \phi_j \\ \Delta \end{bmatrix}
\qquad
[A_0] =
\begin{bmatrix}
+1 & 0 & 0 \\
+\sin\alpha_0/L_0 & +\sin\alpha_0/L_0 & -\cos\alpha_0 \\
-\cos\alpha_0/L_0 & -\cos\alpha_0/L_0 & -\sin\alpha_0 \\
0 & +1 & 0 \\
-\sin\alpha_0/L_0 & -\sin\alpha_0/L_0 & -\cos\alpha_0 \\
+\cos\alpha_0/L_0 & +\cos\alpha_0/L_0 & +\sin\alpha_0
\end{bmatrix}
\qquad
\{X\} = \begin{bmatrix} X_1 \\ X_2 \\ X_3 \\ X_4 \\ X_5 \\ X_6 \end{bmatrix}
$$

and,

$$
\Delta_t = \frac{(X_5 - X_2)^2 + (X_6 - X_3)^2 - \Delta^2}{2L_0}
$$

The internal force-deformation relationships are

$$
\{F\}_{3\times1} = [S]_{3\times3}\,\{e\}_{3\times1}
\tag{6.6.3}
$$

where

$$
\{F\} = \begin{bmatrix} M_i \\ M_j \\ N \end{bmatrix}
\qquad
[S] = \begin{bmatrix} S_{ii}\dfrac{EI_0}{L_0} & S_{ij}\dfrac{EI_0}{L_0} & 0 \\[2mm] S_{ji}\dfrac{EI_0}{L_0} & S_{ii}\dfrac{EI_0}{L_0} & 0 \\[2mm] 0 & 0 & \dfrac{EA_0}{L_0} \end{bmatrix}
\qquad
\{e\} = \begin{bmatrix} \phi_j \\ \phi_j \\ \Delta \end{bmatrix}
$$

Combining Eqs. 6.6.1, 6.6.2, and 6.6.3, the two important equations required in any one cycle of the displacement method of second-order analysis may be obtained as

$$
\{X\} = [A'SA_0^T]^{-1}\left\{ P - A'\left\{ \begin{array}{c} 0 \\ 0 \\ EA_0\Delta_t/L_0 \end{array} \right\} \right\}
\tag{6.6.4}
$$

and

$$
\{F\} = [SA_0^T]\{X\} + \left\{ \begin{array}{c} 0 \\ 0 \\ EA_0\Delta_t/L_0 \end{array} \right\}
\tag{6.6.5}
$$

In the application of Eqs. 6.6.4 and 6.6.5, the following may be noted:

1. The $[A']$ matrix is based on the geometry of the deformed structure at the end of the preceding cycle.
2. The flexural stiffness coefficients in the $[S]$ matrix are based on the kind and amount of the axial forces obtained at the end of the preceding article.
3. The value of Δ_t for each member is based on the values of the joint displacements obtained at the end of the preceding cycle.
4. The $\{X\}$ matrix in Eq. 6.6.5 are the joint displacements just computed from Eq. 6.6.4 within the present cycle.
5. The dividing value of ϕ for using the trigometric or the series expansion formulas of the stiffness coefficients is found to be $\phi = 0.01$. However, this value may vary depending on the computer software.

6.7. Numerical Example.

In this section the complete output checks of the results of the second-order analysis of a typical rigid frame will be shown. Through making the statics checks, equal in number to the degree of freedom, and the deformation checks,

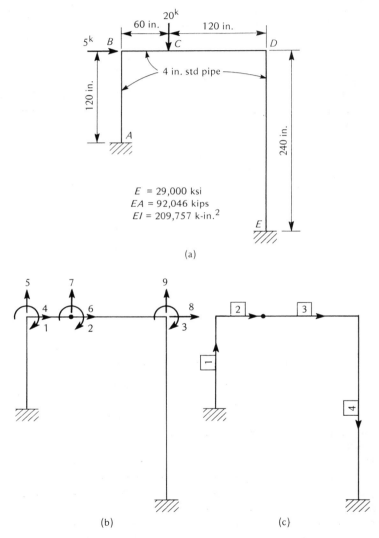

(a)

(b)   (c)

Figure 6.7.1. *Data for Example 6.7.1. (a) The rigid frame; (b) the global P-X numbers; (c) the member numbers.*

equal in number to three times the number of members, one can become more clearly aware of the implications and assumptions made in the development of Eqs. 6.6.4 and 6.6.5, which constitute the two main steps in any one cycle of second-order analysis.

Example 6.7.1. For the rigid frame shown in Fig. 6.7.1, obtain and list the results of the first-order analysis and three cycles of second-order analysis by using the computer program shown in Appendix F. Make the statics and deformation checks of the output of the "second-cycle" second-order analysis, on the basis of the shape of the deformed structure obtained at the end of the "first-cycle" second-order analysis.

Solution: The results of the first-order analysis and the three cycles of second-order analysis are summarized in Table 6.7.1. Since the purpose of this study is to investigate the effect of joint displacements on the internal forces, no proportional limit and no elastic limit have been imposed on the material properties. Thus the joint rotations in radians and the linear joint displacements in

TABLE 6.7.1.

Second-order Analysis of a Rigid Frame

	First-Order	Second-Order 1st Cycle	2nd Cycle	3rd Cycle
X_1, radians	+ 0.12169861	+ 0.13597050	+ 0.13673310	+ 0.13673021
X_2, radians	+ 0.03995068	+ 0.04116531	+ 0.04063736	+ 0.04054997
X_3, radians	− 0.04343808	− 0.04879604	− 0.04922205	− 0.04925081
X_4, inches	+ 8.9631282	+ 10.5111800	+ 10.6654321	+ 10.6741527
X_5, inches	− 0.0153543	− 0.3488736	− 0.4752522	− 0.4893401
X_6, inches	+ 8.9614463	+ 10.2247931	+ 10.3318926	+ 10.3403474
X_7, inches	− 5.8755022	− 6.6613872	− 6.7878199	− 6.7982396
X_8, inches	+ 8.9580825	+ 10.0794141	+ 10.1547004	+ 10.1586807
X_9, inches	− 0.0214393	− 0.1893439	− 0.2340061	− 0.2372217
N_1, kips	− 11.777498	− 11.165378	− 11.078868	− 11.072135
N_2, kips	− 2.580202	− 1.350659	− 1.240681	− 1.238494
N_3, kips	− 2.580203	− 2.046443	− 1.976797	− 1.969193
N_4, kips	− 8.222502	− 8.516349	− 8.543795	− 8.544700
V_1, kips	− 2.419797	− 3.371997	− 3.536099	− 3.552557
V_2, kips	− 11.777498	− 11.571651	− 11.540189	− 11.538404
V_3, kips	+ 8.222502	+ 8.724531	+ 8.773540	+ 8.776581
V_4, kips	− 2.580203	− 2.788758	− 2.808258	− 2.809662
M_{i1}, in.-kips	−357.91396	−424.29664	−435.90447	−436.81006
M_{j1}, in.-kips	+ 67.53828	+ 18.58150	+ 11.17673	+ 10.50445
M_{i2}, in.-kips	− 67.53828	− 18.58150	− 11.17673	− 10.50445
M_{j2}, in.-kips	−639.11159	−679.00186	−681.76945	−681.79356
M_{i3}, in.-kips	+639.11159	+679.00186	+681.76945	+681.79356
M_{j3}, in.-kips	+347.58866	+369.15760	+371.31191	+371.41292
M_{i4}, in.-kips	−347.58866	−369.15760	−371.31191	−371.41292
M_{j4}, in.-kips	−271.65998	−300.55073	−302.73289	−302.85250

inches are designed to show significance when compared with the original dimensions of the structure. The positive direction of the end shears is such that they tend to rotate the member in the counterclockwise direction. As for end moments, the arrows on Fig. 6.7.1c are supposed to go from the "*i*-end" to the "*j*-end." Note that the value of the end shears is equal to the sum of the end moments within the same cycle divided by the length of the member at the end of the preceding cycle.

The free-body diagrams of the four members and the three joints are shown in Fig. 6.7.2., where the axial forces, end shears, and end moments are those at the end of the second cycle, but the lengths of the horizontal and vertical projections of the members are those existing at the end of the first cycle. To make sure that the computer program is functioning correctly, the end shears are recomputed by hand from the end moments, and the new member length are found to check exactly with the computer output to the 6th decimal place.

Since the degree of freedom of this rigid frame is 9, there should be 9 statics checks. These are the three conditions of equilibrium at each of the joints B, C, and D, as shown in Fig. 6.7.2. Details of the checks will not be shown, but the degree of accuracy of the solution may be indicated by the following:

$$\Sigma F_x \text{ at joint } B = +5.9695287 - 5.9695286$$
$$\Sigma F_y \text{ at joint } B = +11.4762430 - 11.4762421$$
$$\Sigma F_x \text{ at joint } C = +2.4469955 - 2.4469957$$
$$\Sigma F_y \text{ at joint } C = +20.2370190 - 20.2370195$$
$$\Sigma F_x \text{ at joint } D = +2.8057807 - 2.8057808$$
$$\Sigma F_y \text{ at joint } D = +8.7607769 - 8.7607769$$

There should be three deformation checks for each member. First, the change in length of a member due to the axial force must be equal to the sum of two parts, one due to the axial components of the joint displacements and the other due to the increase in length arisen from the transverse displacements of the member ends (see Fig. 6.7.3). In equation form,

$$\frac{[N]_2 L_0}{A_0 E} = [(X_5 - X_2) \cos \alpha_0 + (X_6 - X_3) \sin \alpha_0]_2 + [\Delta_t]_1$$

where

$$[\Delta_t]_1 = \frac{[(X_5 - X_2)^2 + (X_6 - X_3)^2 - \Delta^2]_1}{2L_0}$$

In the above equation, the subscripts of the X's refer to the local degree of

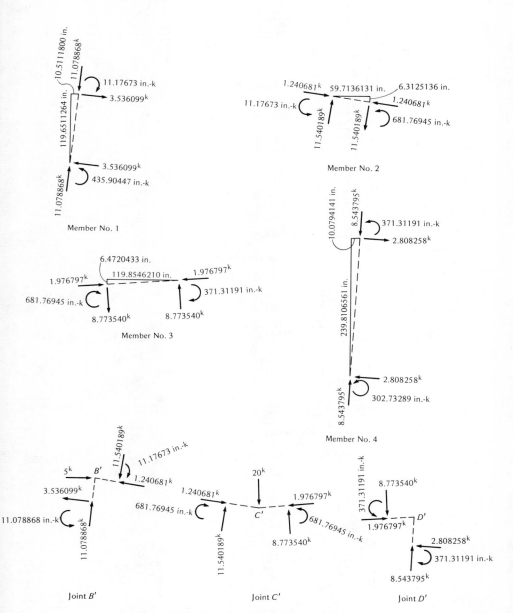

Figure 6.7.2. *Statics checks for Example 6.7.1.*

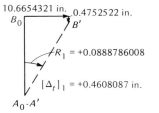

10.6654321 in.   0.4752522 in.

B_0

B'

$R_1 = +0.0888786008$

$[\Delta_t]_1 = +0.4608087$ in.

$A_0 \cdot A'$

$X_1 = +0.13673310$

ϕ_j

ϕ_i

A'

Member No. 1

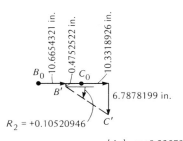

10.6654321 in.

0.4752522 in.

10.3318926 in.

B_0 C_0

B'

6.7878199 in.

$R_2 = +0.10520946$ C'

$[\Delta_t]_1 = +0.3327308$ in.

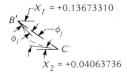

$X_1 = +0.13673310$

B'

ϕ_i ϕ_j

C'

$X_2 = +0.04063736$

Member No. 2

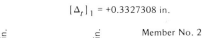

10.3318926 in.

10.1547004 in.

C_0 -10.3318926 in. D_0 10.1547004 in.   0.2340061 in.

D'

6.7878199 in.

C' $R_3 = -0.05461512$

$[\Delta_t]_1 = +0.1746151$ in.

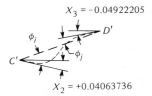

$X_3 = -0.04922205$

ϕ_i D'

ϕ_j

C'

$X_2 = +0.04063736$

Member No. 3

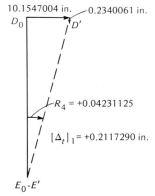

10.1547004 in.   0.2340061 in.

D_0 D'

$R_4 = +0.04231125$

$[\Delta_t]_1 = +0.2117290$ in.

$E_0 \cdot E'$

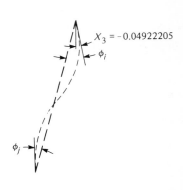

$X_3 = -0.04922205$

ϕ_i

ϕ_j

Member No. 4

Figure 6.7.3. *Deformation checks for Example 6.7.1.*

freedom and the subscripts 1 and 2 outside of the brackets refer to the ends of the first and second cycles of the second-order analysis.

For member No. 1,

$$\frac{(-11.078868)(120)}{92,046} = [-0.4752522]$$

$$+ \left[\frac{(10.5111800)^2 + (0.3488736)^2 - (0.1119351)^2}{2(120)}\right]$$

$$- 0.0144435 = -0.0144435$$

For member No. 2,

$$\frac{(-1.240681)(60)}{92,046} = [10.3318926 - 10.6654321]$$

$$+ \left[\frac{(0.2863869)^2 + (6.3125136)^2 - (0.0463439)^2}{2(60)}\right]$$

$$- 0.0008087 = -0.0008087$$

For member No. 3,

$$\frac{(-1.976797)(120)}{92,046} = [10.1547004 - 10.3318926]$$

$$+ \left[\frac{(0.1453790)^2 + (6.4720432)^2 - (0.0292361)^2}{2(120)}\right]$$

$$- 0.0025771 = -0.0025771$$

For member No. 4,

$$\frac{(-8.543795)(240)}{92,046} = [-0.2340061]$$

$$+ \left[\frac{(10.0794141)^2 + (0.1893439)^2 - (0.0223851)^2}{2(240)}\right]$$

$$- 0.0222770 = -0.0222770$$

The remaining two deformation checks for each member should concern the continuity of the rigid connection at its two ends. The rotation from the displaced member axis to the tangent to the elastic curve as caused by the end moments must be equal to that caused by the external displacements. In equation form, for member ij,

$$\frac{[f_{ii}]_1 [M_i]_2 L_0}{EI_0} + \frac{[f_{ij}]_1 [M_j]_2 L_0}{EI_0} = [X_i]_2 - [R_{ij}]_2$$

and,

$$\frac{[f_{ji}]_1 [M_i]_2 L_0}{EI_0} + \frac{[f_{jj}]_1 [M_j]_2 L_0}{EI_0} = [X_j]_2 - [R_{ij}]_2$$

where $[f_{ii}]_1 = [f_{jj}]_1$ and $[f_{ij}]_1 = [f_{ji}]_1$ are the flexibility coefficients associated with the axial forces existing at the end of the first cycle, but $[M_i, M_j]_2$, $[X_i, X_j]_2$, and $[R_{ij}]_2$ are the end moments, the external joint rotations, and the rotation of the member axis at the end of the second cycle.

For member No. 1,

$$N = -11.165378$$

$$\phi = 120 \sqrt{\frac{11.165378}{209,757}} = 0.8755072$$

$$\frac{f_{ii}L_0}{EI_0} = +201.21211 \times 10^{-6} \qquad \frac{f_{ij}L_0}{EI_0} = -104.62292 \times 10^{-6}$$

$$M_i = -435.90447 \qquad\qquad M_j = +11.17673$$

$$X_i = 0 \qquad\qquad\qquad X_j = +0.13673310$$

$$R_{ij} = +\frac{10.6654321}{120} = +0.0888786$$

$$-0.08887860 = -0.08887860 \qquad (\text{at } i)$$

$$+0.04785449 = +0.04785449 \qquad (\text{at } j)$$

For member No. 2,

$$N = -1.350659$$

$$\phi = 60 \sqrt{\frac{1.350659}{209,757}} = 0.1494083$$

$$\frac{f_{ii}L_0}{EI_0} = +95.49619 \times 10^{-6} \qquad \frac{f_{ij}L_0}{EI_0} = -47.80350 \times 10^{-6}$$

$$M_i = -11.17673 \qquad\qquad M_j = -681.76945$$

$X_i = +0.13673310$ $X_j = +0.04063736$

$$R_{ij} = \frac{6.7878199 - 0.4752522}{60} = +0.1052095$$

$\qquad +0.0315236 = +0.0315236$ (at i)

$\qquad -0.0645721 = -0.0645721$ (at j)

For member No. 3,

$$N = -2.046443$$

$$\phi = 120 \sqrt{\frac{2.046443}{209{,}757}} = 0.3748201$$

$\dfrac{f_{ii}L_0}{EI_0} = +192.50715 \times 10^{-6}$ $\dfrac{f_{ij}L_0}{EI_0} = -96.93472 \times 10^{-6}$

$\qquad M_i = +681.76945$ $M_j = +371.31191$

$\qquad X_i = +0.04063736$ $X_j = -0.04922205$

$$R_{ij} = \frac{-6.7878199 + 0.2340061}{120} = -0.0546151$$

$\qquad +0.0952525 = +0.0952525$ (at i)

$\qquad +0.0053931 = +0.0053931$ (at j)

For member No. 4,

$$N = -8.516349$$

$$\phi = 240 \sqrt{\frac{8.516349}{209{,}757}} = 1.5292544$$

$\dfrac{f_{ii}L_0}{EI_0} = +458.15566 \times 10^{-6}$ $\dfrac{f_{ij}L_0}{EI_0} = -259.58643 \times 10^{-6}$

$\qquad M_i = -371.31191$ $M_j = -302.73289$

$\qquad X_i = -0.04922205$ $X_j = 0$

$$R_{ij} = \frac{+10.1547004}{240} = +0.04231125$$

$\qquad -0.0915333 = -0.0915333$ (at i)

$\qquad -0.0423112 = -0.0423112$ (at j)

CHAPTER 7

■

Treatment of Prismatic Beam Element by the Energy Method

7.1. General Introduction

Traditionally a distinction has been made between structural analysis and stress analysis; the former deals with framed structures that consist of members connected at joints, and the latter with plates and shells subjected to membrane or transverse loads. Because of the fact that the displacement method may be applied as well to the stress analysis of plate and shell structures as to the structural analysis of framed structures, many have called the two subjects interchangeably by the names *matrix methods* or *finite-element* methods. Actually a framed structure has only *natural*, or actual, finite elements, whereas a plate or shell structure can only have *artificial*, or imaginary, finite elements (which are pieces connected with their neighbors at points or lines). In most cases of natural finite elements it is possible to obtain exact expressions for the element-stiffness matrix and for the fixed-condition forces due to distributed loads on the element, but in almost all cases of artificial finite elements only approximate expressions may be derived and then used.

The approximate solutions for the element-stiffness matrix or the fixed-condition forces are most conveniently obtainable by means of energy principles. The purpose of this chapter is to show the use of energy methods in treating prismatic beam elements in axial compression and free vibration, thus providing a transition from matrix analysis of framed structures to the bona fide finite-element method of plate and shell analysis.

7.2. The Reciprocal Energy Theorem†

The reciprocal energy theorem, simply stated, is as follows: The virtual work done by a P-force system acting on a linear elastic structure, in going through the displacements due to a Q-force system, is equal to the virtual work done by the Q-force system in going through the displacements due to the P-force system. Symbolically,

$$P * \Delta Q = Q * \Delta P \tag{7.2.1}$$

The key to the proof of this theorem is the principle of superposition which holds true for a linear elastic structure. If the P-force system is applied first and the Q-force system added, the work done is

$$W_1 = \frac{1}{2}P * \Delta P + \frac{1}{2}Q * \Delta Q + P * \Delta Q$$

but if the Q-force system is applied first and the P-force system added, the work done is

$$W_2 = \frac{1}{2}Q * \Delta Q + \frac{1}{2}P * \Delta P + Q * \Delta P$$

W_1 and W_2 should be equal since the total elastic response must be identical regardless of the order of application of the two force systems; thus

$$P * \Delta Q = Q * \Delta P$$

In all linear elastic finite elements, the displacement equation (such as the expression for the transverse displacement in a beam element as a function of distance along the element) is most basic, from which internal forces and internal deformations (such as bending moments and curvatures in a beam element) and external forces and displacements (such as moments, shears, slopes, and deflections at both ends of the beam element) may be derived. Thus, when a

†This theorem is known historically as Betti's Theorem (*Nuovo cimento*, vols. 7–8, 1872).

displacement equation of certain form is arbitrarily chosen for a *fictitious Q-force system*, using only the external displacements at the boundary points of the finite element in the as yet undetermined constants, the expressions for the internal forces and deformations can be obtained. The fundamental assumption in the approximate solution of an *actual P-force system* acting on the same finite element is that the form of the unknown displacement equation is similar to the chosen form of the Q-force system. Exactly how the reciprocal energy theorem is used will now be developed.

7.3. Four Basic Q-Y Modes of a Prismatic Beam Element

Consider that a prismatic beam element is subjected to a fictitious Q-force system as shown in Fig. 7.3.1a, due to which the slopes and deflections at the ends of the element are the Y-values shown in Fig. 7.3.1b. Note that the positive

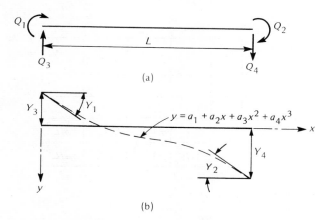

Figure 7.3.1. *The fictitious Q-Y system.*

directions of the Q's and Y's are consistently the same. Choose the cubic form

$$y = a_1 + a_2x + a_3x^2 + a_4x^3$$

as the equation of the elastic curve. It is important to note here that the number of arbitrary constants a_1 to a_4 in this displacement equation is exactly equal to the number of boundary displacements Y_1 to Y_4. From the displacement equation,

$$\frac{dy}{dx} = a_2 + 2a_3x + 3a_4x^2$$

Using the conditions

(1) $\left(\dfrac{dy}{dx} \text{ at } x = 0\right) = a_2 = Y_1$

(2) $\left(\dfrac{dy}{dx} \text{ at } x = L\right) = a_2 + 2a_3 L + 3a_4 L^2 = Y_2$

(3) $(y \text{ at } x = 0) = a_1 = -Y_3$

(4) $(y \text{ at } x = L) = a_1 + a_2 L + a_3 L^2 + a_4 L^3 = Y_4$

the constants a_1 to a_4 may be expressed in terms of Y_1 to Y_4 as

$$\{a\} = [C]\{Y\} \qquad (7.3.1a)$$

in which

$$[C]_{4\times4} = \quad$$

a \ Y	1	2	3	4
1			$-1.$	
2	$+1.$			
3	$-2/L$	$-1/L$	$+3/L^2$	$+3/L^2$
4	$+1/L^2$	$+1/L^2$	$-2/L^3$	$-2/L^3$

$(7.3.1b)$

Thus the equation of the elastic curve is

$$y = \left(+x - \frac{2x^2}{L} + \frac{x^3}{L^2}\right) Y_1 + \left(-\frac{x^2}{L} + \frac{x^3}{L^2}\right) Y_2$$

$$+ \left(-1 + \frac{3x^2}{L^2} - \frac{2x^3}{L^3}\right) Y_3 + \left(+\frac{3x^2}{L^2} - \frac{2x^3}{L^3}\right) Y_4 \qquad (7.3.2)$$

It has been shown in Strength of Materials that the curvature ϕ and the bending moment M in a beam element of Fig. 7.3.2 are equal to

$$\phi = -\frac{d^2y}{dx^2} \qquad (7.3.3)$$

and

$$M = EI\phi \qquad (7.3.4)$$

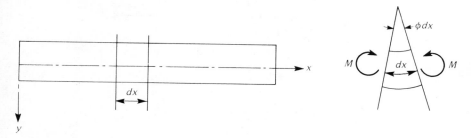

Figure 7.3.2. *Bending moment and curvature.*

Using the nomenclature in the displacement method, the ϕ is equivalent to internal deformation; the M, to internal force; and the EI, to stiffness.

The four basic Q-Y modes shown in Fig. 7.3.3 can thus be derived from Eqs. 7.3.2, 7.3.3, and 7.3.4 by letting

(1) $Y_1 \neq 0$, $Y_2 = Y_3 = Y_4 = 0$
(2) $Y_2 \neq 0$, $Y_1 = Y_3 = Y_4 = 0$
(3) $Y_3 \neq 0$, $Y_1 = Y_2 = Y_4 = 0$
(4) $Y_4 \neq 0$, $Y_1 = Y_2 = Y_3 = 0$

At this point it should be noted that although the expressions for the Q-forces are not shown in Fig. 7.3.3, they can nevertheless be obtained by finding the shear forces and bending moments at the ends of the beam element.

7.4. Stiffness Matrix of an Ordinary Beam Element

Let it be required to find the stiffness matrix $[K]$ of an ordinary beam element, of which the P-X diagram is as shown in Fig. 7.4.1a; or

$$[K] = \begin{array}{c|cccc} \diagdown\!\!\!{}^{X}_{P} & 1 & 2 & 3 & 4 \\ \hline 1 & K_{11} & K_{12} & K_{13} & K_{14} \\ 2 & K_{21} & K_{22} & K_{23} & K_{24} \\ 3 & K_{31} & K_{32} & K_{33} & K_{34} \\ 4 & K_{41} & K_{42} & K_{43} & K_{44} \end{array} \qquad (7.4.1)$$

The 16 elements in the $[K]$ matrix are indicated in the four P-X basic modes shown in Fig. 7.4.1bcde. If an *assumption* is made here that the displacement

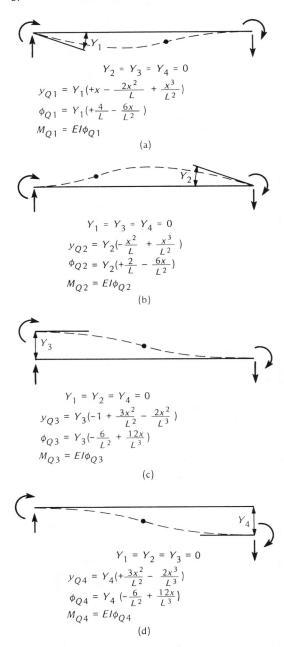

$$Y_2 = Y_3 = Y_4 = 0$$
$$y_{Q1} = Y_1(+x - \frac{2x^2}{L} + \frac{x^3}{L^2})$$
$$\phi_{Q1} = Y_1(+\frac{4}{L} - \frac{6x}{L^2})$$
$$M_{Q1} = EI\phi_{Q1}$$

(a)

$$Y_1 = Y_3 = Y_4 = 0$$
$$y_{Q2} = Y_2(-\frac{x^2}{L} + \frac{x^3}{L^2})$$
$$\phi_{Q2} = Y_2(+\frac{2}{L} - \frac{6x}{L^2})$$
$$M_{Q2} = EI\phi_{Q2}$$

(b)

$$Y_1 = Y_2 = Y_4 = 0$$
$$y_{Q3} = Y_3(-1 + \frac{3x^2}{L^2} - \frac{2x^2}{L^3})$$
$$\phi_{Q3} = Y_3(-\frac{6}{L^2} + \frac{12x}{L^3})$$
$$M_{Q3} = EI\phi_{Q3}$$

(c)

$$Y_1 = Y_2 = Y_3 = 0$$
$$y_{Q4} = Y_4(+\frac{3x^2}{L^2} - \frac{2x^3}{L^3})$$
$$\phi_{Q4} = Y_4(-\frac{6}{L^2} + \frac{12x}{L^3})$$
$$M_{Q4} = EI\phi_{Q4}$$

(d)

Figure 7.3.3. *The four basic* Q-Y *modes of a beam element. (a) First* Q-Y *basic mode; (b) second* Q-Y *basic mode; (c) third* Q-Y *basic mode; (d) fourth* Q-Y *basic mode.*

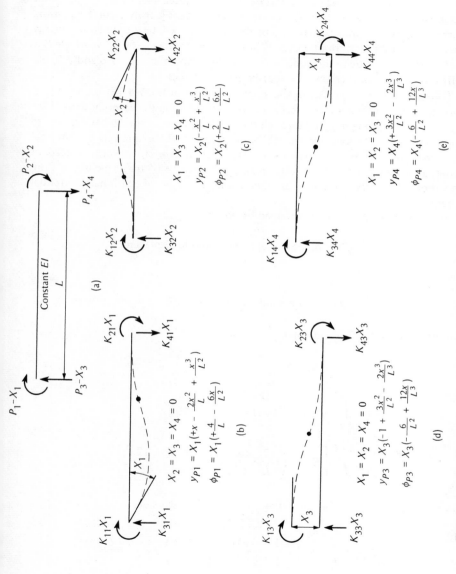

Figure 7.4.1. The four basic P-X modes of a beam element. (a) The given beam element; (b) first P-X basic mode; (c) second P-X basic mode; (d) third P-X basic mode; (e) fourth P-X basic mode.

$X_2 = X_3 = X_4 = 0$

$y_{P1} = X_1(+x - \frac{2x^2}{L} + \frac{x^3}{L^2})$

$\phi_{P1} = X_1(+\frac{4}{L} - \frac{6x}{L^2})$

$X_1 = X_3 = X_4 = 0$

$y_{P2} = X_2(-\frac{x^2}{L} + \frac{x^3}{L^2})$

$\phi_{P2} = X_2(+\frac{2}{L} - \frac{6x}{L^2})$

$X_1 = X_2 = X_4 = 0$

$y_{P3} = X_3(-1 + \frac{3x^2}{L^2} - \frac{2x^3}{L^3})$

$\phi_{P3} = X_3(-\frac{6}{L^2} + \frac{12x}{L^3})$

$X_1 = X_2 = X_3 = 0$

$y_{P4} = X_4(+\frac{3x^2}{L^2} - \frac{2x^3}{L^3})$

$\phi_{P4} = X_4(-\frac{6}{L^2} + \frac{12x}{L^3})$

equation of the actual *P-X* modes is in the same form as that of the fictitious *Q-Y* modes in the previous section, then the expressions for y_{p1} to y_{p4} and ϕ_{p1} to ϕ_{p4} shown in Fig. 7.4.1 can be directly quoted from Fig. 7.3.3. Since the elastic curve of an unloaded ordinary beam element is truly a cubic equation, there is *in fact* no approximation and the $[K]$ matrix later obtained by energy method is truly exact. In other cases, however, when the elastic curve of the *P-X* system should not be in the cubic form as will be shown in Secs. 7.6 and 7.7, the stiffness matrix can then only be approximately correct.

To obtain the element K_{ij} in the stiffness matrix of Eq. 7.4.1 it is only necessary to apply the reciprocal energy theorem by equating the external work done by the P_j basic mode in going through the displacements of the Q_i basic mode, to the *internal work* done by the Q_i basic mode in going through the internal deformations of the P_j basic mode. The fact that internal work, instead of external work, is used in the latter makes definite use of the Principle of Conservation of Energy, or under another name, the Law of Stationary Potential Energy.

As an example, K_{23} can be obtained by equating

$$W_{\text{ext}} = (P_3 - \text{mode force}) * (Q_2 - \text{mode displacement})$$

and

$$W_{\text{int}} = (Q_2 - \text{mode bending moment}) * (P_3 - \text{mode curvature})$$

Referring to Figs. 7.3.3 and 7.4.1,

$$W_{\text{ext}} = (K_{23}X_3)(Y_2)$$

$$W_{\text{int}} = \int_0^L (EI\phi_{Q2})(\phi_{P3}) \, dx$$

$$= \int_0^L \left[EIY_2 \left(+\frac{2}{L} - \frac{6x}{L^2} \right) \right] \left[X_3 \left(-\frac{6}{L^2} + \frac{12x}{L^3} \right) \right] dx$$

Equating W_{ext} to W_{int} and cancelling (X_3Y_2) from each side,

$$K_{23} = \int_0^L EI \left(+\frac{2}{L} - \frac{6x}{L^2} \right) \left(-\frac{6}{L^2} + \frac{12x}{L^3} \right) dx = -\frac{6EI}{L^2}$$

By defining ϕ_{Q1} to ϕ_{Q4} as used in Fig. 7.3.3 as $\phi_{Q1} = Y_1\phi_1$, $\phi_{Q2} = Y_2\phi_2$, $\phi_{Q3} = Y_3\phi_3$, and $\phi_{Q4} = Y_4\phi_4$, ϕ_{P1} to ϕ_{P4} can also be expressed as $\phi_{P1} = X_1\phi_1$,

$\phi_{P2} = X_2\phi_2$, $\phi_{P3} = X_3\phi_3$, and $\phi_{P4} = X_4\phi_4$; thus

$$\{\phi\} = \begin{Bmatrix} \phi_1 \\ \phi_2 \\ \phi_3 \\ \phi_4 \end{Bmatrix} = \begin{Bmatrix} \left(+\dfrac{4}{L} - \dfrac{6x}{L^2}\right) \\ \left(+\dfrac{2}{L} - \dfrac{6x}{L^2}\right) \\ \left(-\dfrac{6}{L^2} + \dfrac{12x}{L^3}\right) \\ \left(-\dfrac{6}{L^2} + \dfrac{12x}{L^3}\right) \end{Bmatrix}$$

Since

$$K_{ij} = \int_0^L EI\,(\phi_i)(\phi_j)\,dx$$

it follows that

$$[K] = EI \int_0^L \{\phi\}\,\{\phi\}^T\,dx \qquad (7.4.2)$$

Carrying out the operations involved in Eq. 7.4.2 gives

$$[K] =$$

X \\ P	1	2	3	4
1	$+4EI/L$	$+2EI/L$	$-6EI/L^2$	$-6EI/L^2$
2	$+2EI/L$	$+4EI/L$	$-6EI/L^2$	$-6EI/L^2$
3	$-6EI/L^2$	$-6EI/L^2$	$+12EI/L^3$	$+12EI/L^3$
4	$-6EI/L^2$	$-6EI/L^2$	$+12EI/L^3$	$+12EI/L^3$

$$(7.4.3)$$

It may be noted that, for equilibrium of the free body shown in Fig. 7.4.1a,

$$P_3 = P_4 = -\frac{P_1 + P_2}{L}$$

which is true for each column in Eq. 7.4.3. Thus the rank of the stiffness matrix

$[K]$ in Eq. 7.4.3 is 2 and it has no inverse. If rotations $X_1 - \dfrac{X_3 + X_4}{L}$ and

$X_2 - \dfrac{X_3 + X_4}{L}$ are used as member-end deformations, then

$$P_1 = \frac{4EI}{L}\left(X_1 - \frac{X_3 + X_4}{L}\right) + \frac{2EI}{L}\left(X_2 - \frac{X_3 + X_4}{L}\right)$$

$$P_2 = \frac{2EI}{L}\left(X_1 - \frac{X_3 + X_4}{L}\right) + \frac{4EI}{L}\left(X_2 - \frac{X_3 + X_4}{L}\right)$$

which is consistent with the 2 X 2 member-stiffness matrix for a prismatic beam element.

7.5. Fixed-Condition Forces for an Ordinary Beam Element

The displacement method of analysis requires not only the stiffness matrix of the finite element but also the equivalent forces at the nodes due to loads acting on the element when all nodal displacements are equal to zero. These equivalent nodal forces will be called *fixed-condition forces.*

The fixed-condition forces P_{01} to P_{04} for the two types of loads acting on a prismatic beam element shown in Fig. 7.5.1 may be conveniently determined by

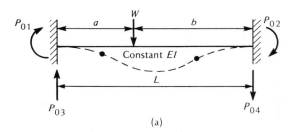

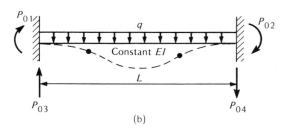

Figure 7.5.1. *Fixed-condition forces on a beam element.*

applying the reciprocal energy theorem between the fixed condition and each of the four fictitious Q-Y basic modes shown in Fig. 7.3.3. For example, for the loading of Fig. 7.5.1a, P_{03} may be obtained by equating the external work done by the forces in Fig. 7.5.1a in going through the displacements in Fig. 7.3.3c, to the external work done by the forces in Fig. 7.3.3c in going through the displacements in Fig. 7.5.1a. The former is equal to

$$P_{03} * Y_3 + W Y_3 \left(-1 + \frac{3a^2}{L^2} - \frac{2a^3}{L^3}\right)$$

but the latter is equal to zero; thus

$$P_{03} = -W \left(-1 + \frac{3a^2}{L^2} - \frac{2a^3}{L^3}\right) = +\frac{Wb^2}{L^3}(3a + b)$$

In general,

$$\{P_0\} \text{ in Fig. 7.5.1a} = \begin{Bmatrix} P_{01} \\ P_{02} \\ P_{03} \\ P_{04} \end{Bmatrix} = - \begin{Bmatrix} W\left(+a - \dfrac{2a^2}{L} + \dfrac{a^3}{L^2}\right) \\[2mm] W\left(-\dfrac{a^2}{L} + \dfrac{a^3}{L^2}\right) \\[2mm] W\left(-1 + \dfrac{3a^2}{L^2} - \dfrac{2a^3}{L^3}\right) \\[2mm] W\left(+\dfrac{3a^2}{L^2} - \dfrac{2a^3}{L^3}\right) \end{Bmatrix} = \begin{Bmatrix} -\dfrac{Wab^2}{L^2} \\[2mm] +\dfrac{Wba^2}{L^2} \\[2mm] +\dfrac{Wb^2}{L^3}(3a + b) \\[2mm] -\dfrac{Wa^2}{L^3}(3b + a) \end{Bmatrix}$$

$$(7.5.1)$$

$$\{P_0\} \text{ in Fig. 7.5.1b} = \begin{Bmatrix} P_{01} \\ P_{02} \\ P_{03} \\ P_{04} \end{Bmatrix} = \begin{Bmatrix} \displaystyle\int_0^L \left(+x - \dfrac{2x^2}{L} + \dfrac{x^3}{L^2}\right) q\, dx \\[3mm] \displaystyle\int_0^L \left(-\dfrac{x^2}{L} + \dfrac{x^3}{L^2}\right) q\, dx \\[3mm] \displaystyle\int_0^L \left(-1 + \dfrac{3x^2}{L^2} - \dfrac{2x^3}{L^3}\right) q\, dx \\[3mm] \displaystyle\int_0^L \left(+\dfrac{3x^2}{L^2} - \dfrac{2x^3}{L^3}\right) q\, dx \end{Bmatrix} = \begin{Bmatrix} -\dfrac{qL^2}{12} \\[3mm] +\dfrac{qL^2}{12} \\[3mm] +\dfrac{qL}{2} \\[3mm] -\dfrac{qL}{2} \end{Bmatrix}$$

$$(7.5.2)$$

Since the equation of the elastic curve of an unloaded beam element is truly cubic as is chosen in the Q-Y basic modes, Eqs. 7.5.1 and 7.5.2 are truly exact.

7.6. Stiffness Matrix of a Prismatic Beam Element in Axial Compression

When a prismatic beam element as shown in Fig. 7.6.1 is subjected to an axial compression, and if the secondary moment (or the product of the axial compression and the transverse deflection) is to be considered in the equilibrium

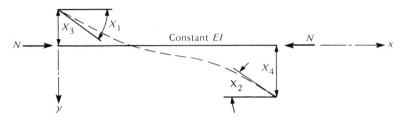

Figure 7.6.1. *Prismatic beam element under axial compression.*

equation, the solution of the differential equation of the elastic curve has been found, in Chapter 6, to be

$$y = A \sin \frac{\phi}{L} x + B \cos \frac{\phi}{L} x + Cx + D \qquad (7.6.1)$$

where

$$\phi = L \sqrt{\frac{N}{EI}}$$

The stiffness matrix of this beam element under axial compression, as defined by the four P-X basic modes in Fig. 7.6.2, may be expressed as

$$[K] =$$

P \ X	1	2	3	4
1	K_{11}	K_{12}	K_{13}	K_{14}
2	K_{21}	K_{22}	K_{23}	K_{24}
3	K_{31}	K_{32}	K_{33}	K_{34}
4	K_{41}	K_{42}	K_{43}	K_{44}

$\overset{X}{\diagdown}_{P}$	1	2	3	4
1	TEMP1	TEMP2	TEMP3	TEMP3
2	TEMP2	TEMP1	TEMP3	TEMP3
3	TEMP3	TEMP3	TEMP4	TEMP4
4	TEMP3	TEMP3	TEMP4	TEMP4

$$= \qquad\qquad\qquad\qquad (7.6.2)$$

On the basis of the exact solution, which is Eq. 7.6.1,

$$TEMP1 = + \frac{\phi \sin \phi - \phi^2 \cos \phi}{2 - 2 \cos \phi - \phi \sin \phi} \frac{EI}{L} \qquad (7.6.3a)$$

$$TEMP2 = + \frac{\phi^2 - \phi \sin \phi}{2 - 2 \cos \phi - \phi \sin \phi} \frac{EI}{L} \qquad (7.6.3b)$$

$$TEMP3 = - \frac{\phi^2 (1 - \cos \phi)}{2 - 2 \cos \phi - \phi \sin \phi} \frac{EI}{L^2} \qquad (7.6.3c)$$

$$TEMP4 = + \frac{2\phi^2 (1 - \cos \phi)}{2 - 2 \cos \phi - \phi \sin \phi} \frac{EI}{L^3} \qquad (7.6.3d)$$

It should be observed that, because of the terms $(Cx + D)$ in Eq. 7.6.1, the rank of the $[K]$ matrix in Eq. 7.6.2 is 2. Consequently, as it is the case in Eq. 7.4.3, the third and fourth rows in the $[K]$ matrix are identical, each being equal to the sum of the first and second rows divided by L, in the opposite sign. Note also, (1) that TEMP1 and TEMP2 in Eq. 7.6.3ab are the same as in Eq. 6.5.27, and (2) that TEMP4, the shear force at either end of the element balances only the end moments but not the couple arisen out of the noncollinear axial compressive forces at the ends. The reactions due to this moment couple should be considered separately, for instance, in stability analysis.

For small values of ϕ, by using the series expressions,

$$\sin \phi = \phi - \frac{\phi^3}{3!} + \frac{\phi^5}{5!} - \frac{\phi^7}{7!} + \cdots$$

$$\cos \phi = 1 - \frac{\phi^2}{2!} + \frac{\phi^4}{4!} - \frac{\phi^6}{6!} + \cdots$$

Equations 7.6.3abcd can be alternately expressed as

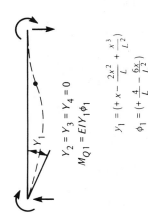

$Y_2 = Y_3 = Y_4 = 0$

$M_{Q1} = EIY_1\phi_1$

$y_1 = (+x - \frac{2x^2}{L} + \frac{x^3}{L^2})$

$\phi_1 = (+\frac{4}{L} - \frac{6x}{L^2})$

$Y_1 = Y_3 = Y_4 = 0$

$M_{Q2} = EIY_2\phi_2$

$y_2 = (-\frac{x^2}{L} + \frac{x^3}{L^2})$

$\phi_2 = (+\frac{2}{L} - \frac{6x}{L^2})$

(a)

(b)

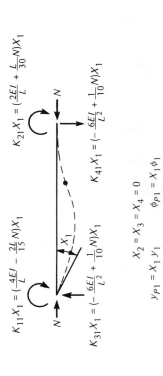

$K_{11}X_1 = (\frac{4EI}{L} - \frac{2L}{15}N)X_1$

$K_{21}X_1 = (\frac{2EI}{L} + \frac{L}{30}N)X_1$

$K_{41}X_1 = (-\frac{6EI}{L^2} + \frac{1}{10}N)X_1$

$K_{31}X_1 = (-\frac{6EI}{L^2} + \frac{1}{10}N)X_1$

$X_2 = X_3 = X_4 = 0$

$\phi_{P1} = X_1\phi_1$

$y_{P1} = X_1 y_1$

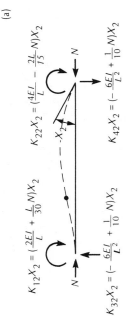

$K_{12}X_2 = (\frac{2EI}{L} + \frac{L}{30}N)X_2$

$K_{22}X_2 = (\frac{4EI}{L} - \frac{2L}{15}N)X_2$

$K_{42}X_2 = (-\frac{6EI}{L^2} + \frac{1}{10}N)X_2$

$K_{32}X_2 = (-\frac{6EI}{L^2} + \frac{1}{10}N)X_2$

$X_1 = X_3 = X_4 = 0$

$\phi_{P2} = X_2\phi_2$

$y_{P2} = X_2 y_2$

178

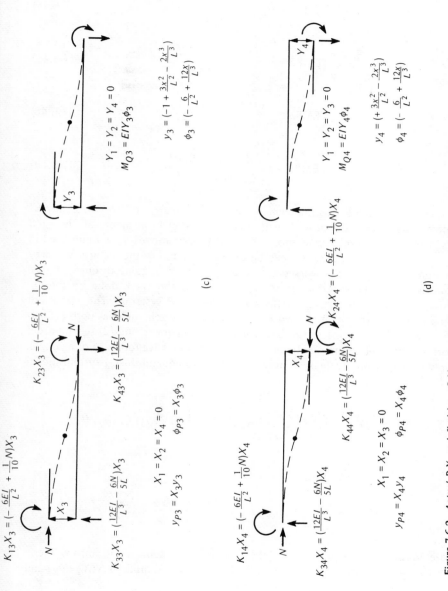

$$K_{13}X_3 = (-\frac{6EI}{L^2} + \frac{1}{10}N)X_3$$

$$K_{23}X_3 = (-\frac{6EI}{L^2} + \frac{1}{10}N)X_3$$

$$K_{33}X_3 = (\frac{12EI}{L^3} - \frac{6N}{5L})X_3$$

$$K_{43}X_3 = (\frac{12EI}{L^3} - \frac{6N}{5L})X_3$$

$$X_1 = X_2 = X_4 = 0$$

$$y_{P3} = X_3 y_3 \qquad \phi_{P3} = X_3 \phi_3$$

$$Y_1 = Y_2 = Y_4 = 0$$

$$M_{Q3} = EI Y_3 \phi_3$$

$$y_3 = (-1 + \frac{3x^2}{L^2} - \frac{2x^3}{L^3})$$

$$\phi_3 = (-\frac{6}{L^2} + \frac{12x}{L^3})$$

(c)

$$K_{14}X_4 = (-\frac{6EI}{L^2} + \frac{1}{10}N)X_4$$

$$K_{24}X_4 = (-\frac{6EI}{L^2} + \frac{1}{10}N)X_4$$

$$K_{34}X_4 = (\frac{12EI}{L^3} - \frac{6N}{5L})X_4$$

$$K_{44}X_4 = (\frac{12EI}{L^3} - \frac{6N}{5L})X_4$$

$$X_1 = X_2 = X_3 = 0$$

$$y_{P4} = X_4 y_4 \qquad \phi_{P4} = X_4 \phi_4$$

$$Y_1 = Y_2 = Y_3 = 0$$

$$M_{Q4} = EI Y_4 \phi_4$$

$$y_4 = (+\frac{3x^2}{L^2} - \frac{2x^3}{L^3})$$

$$\phi_4 = (-\frac{6}{L^2} + \frac{12x}{L^3})$$

(d)

Figure 7.6.2. Actual P-X and fictitious Q-Y systems of a beam element under axial compression. (a) First P-X and Q-Y basic modes; (b) second P-X and Q-Y basic modes; (c) third P-X and Q-Y basic modes; (d) fourth P-X and Q-Y basic modes.

$$\text{TEMP1} = + \frac{4(1 - \phi^2/10)}{(1 - \phi^2/15)} \frac{EI}{L} \tag{7.6.4a}$$

$$\text{TEMP2} = + \frac{2(1 - \phi^2/20)}{(1 - \phi^2/15)} \frac{EI}{L} \tag{7.6.4b}$$

$$\text{TEMP3} = - \frac{6(1 - \phi^2/12)}{(1 - \phi^2/15)} \frac{EI}{L^2} \tag{7.6.4c}$$

$$\text{TEMP4} = + \frac{12(1 - \phi^2/12)}{(1 - \phi^2/15)} \frac{EI}{L^3} \tag{7.6.4d}$$

Approximate values for the elements in the $[K]$ matrix of Eq. 7.6.2 may be obtained by assuming that the elastic curves in the P-X basic modes of Fig. 7.6.2 are in the cubic form, just as those of the Q-Y basic modes, now duplicated in Fig. 7.6.2 from Fig. 7.3.3. K_{ij} can be obtained by use of the reciprocal energy theorem in equating the work done by the P_j-system in going through the displacement and deformation of the Q_i-system, to the work done by the Q_i-system in going through the deformation of the P_j-system. The important thing to note here is that the work done by the P_j-system includes both (1) external work of the forces acting at the ends of the element, and (2) second-order work of the bending moment due to the axial compressive forces. For example, applying the reciprocal theorem between the P_2-system and the Q_3-system shown in Fig. 7.6.2,

$$(K_{32}X_2)(Y_3) + \int \left(Y_3 \frac{dy_3}{dx}\right)(NX_2 \, dy_2) = \int (EIY_3\phi_3)(X_2\phi_2) \, dx$$

from which

$$K_{32} = \int EI\phi_3 \phi_2 \, dx - N \int \frac{dy_3}{dx} \frac{dy_2}{dx} \, dx$$

Note in the above equation that the clockwise moment acting on any incremental length dx by the axial forces in the second P-X mode is $N(X_2 \, dy_2)$ and the clockwise slope in the third Q-Y mode is $\left(Y_3 \frac{dy_3}{dx}\right)$.

In general,

$$[K] = EI \; \begin{Bmatrix} \phi_1 \\ \phi_2 \\ \phi_3 \\ \phi_4 \end{Bmatrix} \; [\phi_1 \; \phi_2 \; \phi_3 \; \phi_4] \; dx \; - \; N \; \begin{Bmatrix} \dfrac{dy_1}{dx} \\[2ex] \dfrac{dy_2}{dx} \\[2ex] \dfrac{dy_3}{dx} \\[2ex] \dfrac{dy_4}{dx} \end{Bmatrix} \; \left[\dfrac{dy_1}{dx} \; \dfrac{dy_2}{dx} \; \dfrac{dy_3}{dx} \; \dfrac{dy_4}{dx} \right] \; dx$$

$$(7.6.5)$$

Substituting in Eq. 7.6.5 the expressions for ϕ_1 to ϕ_4 and $\dfrac{dy_1}{dx}$ to $\dfrac{dy_4}{dx}$ shown in Fig. 7.6.2 and evaluating the integrals, the TEMP1 to TEMP4 values in the $[K]$ matrix are found to be

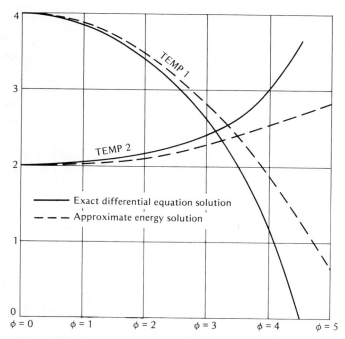

Figure 7.6.3. *Elements in the stiffness matrix of a beam element under axial compression.*

$$\text{TEMP1} = +\frac{4EI}{L} - \frac{2L}{15}N = +\left(4 - \frac{2\phi^2}{15}\right)\frac{EI}{L} \qquad (7.6.6a)$$

$$\text{TEMP2} = +\frac{2EI}{L} + \frac{L}{30}N = +\left(2 + \frac{\phi^2}{30}\right)\frac{EI}{L} \qquad (7.6.6b)$$

$$\text{TEMP3} = -\frac{6EI}{L^2} + \frac{1}{10}N = -\left(6 - \frac{\phi^2}{10}\right)\frac{EI}{L^2} \qquad (7.6.6c)$$

$$\text{TEMP4} = +\frac{12EI}{L^3} - \frac{1}{5L}N = +\left(12 - \frac{\phi^2}{5}\right)\frac{EI}{L^3} \qquad (7.6.6d)$$

Since TEMP3 and TEMP4 values are dependent on TEMP1 and TEMP2 values by the relationships (1) TEMP3 = $-$ (TEMP1 + TEMP2)$/L$ and (2) TEMP4 = $-$ 2(TEMP3)$/L$, a comparison of TEMP1 and TEMP2 values only as determined by the exact and energy solutions, respectively, would be sufficiently indicative. It can be seen from such a comparison in Fig. 7.6.3 that for values of ϕ well under 3, the energy solution yields good approximation indeed.

7.7. Stiffness Matrix of a Prismatic Beam Element in Free Vibration

When a prismatic beam element of uniform mass per unit distance as shown in Fig. 7.7.1 is in free vibration, the differential equation of the elastic curve yields

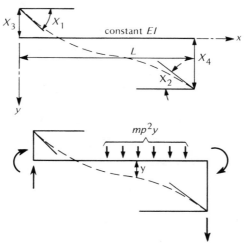

Figure 7.7.1. *Prismatic beam element in free vibration.*

the solution, as derived in Chapter 2,

$$y = A \sin \frac{\phi}{L} x + B \cos \frac{\phi}{L} x + C \sinh \frac{\phi}{L} x + D \cosh \frac{\phi}{L} x \qquad (7.7.1)$$

where

$$\phi = L \sqrt[4]{\frac{mp^2}{EI}}$$

p = circular frequency, rad/sec

m = mass per unit length

In fact, as explained by Eq. 2.3.6, Eq. 7.7.1 is the elastic curve of a statically equivalent beam subjected to a varying distributed load of mp^2y per unit distance in the positive y-direction.

The stiffness matrix of this beam element in free vibration as defined by the four P-X basic modes in Fig. 7.7.2, may be expressed as

$$[K] =$$

P \ X	1	2	3	4
1	K_{11}	K_{12}	K_{13}	K_{14}
2	K_{21}	K_{22}	K_{23}	K_{24}
3	K_{31}	K_{32}	K_{33}	K_{34}
4	K_{41}	K_{42}	K_{43}	K_{44}

$$=$$

P \ X	1	2	3	4
1	TEMP1	TEMP2	TEMP3	TEMP4
2	TEMP2	TEMP1	TEMP4	TEMP3
3	TEMP3	TEMP4	TEMP5	TEMP6
4	TEMP4	TEMP3	TEMP6	TEMP5

$$(7.7.2)$$

On the basis of the exact solution, which is Eq. 7.7.1,

$$\text{TEMP1} = +\frac{\phi \left(sc' - cs'\right)}{1 - cc'} \frac{EI}{L}$$

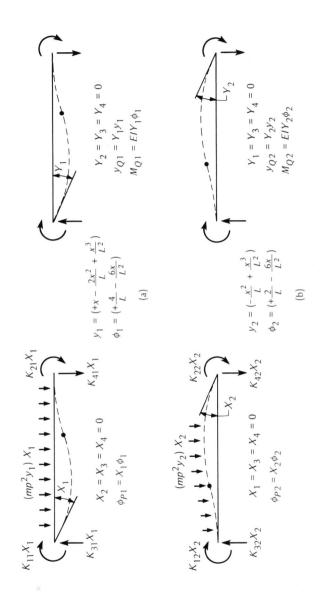

$$Y_2 = Y_3 = Y_4 = 0$$
$$y_{Q1} = Y_1 y_1$$
$$M_{Q1} = EIY_1\phi_1$$

$$Y_1 = Y_3 = Y_4 = 0$$
$$y_{Q2} = Y_2 y_2$$
$$M_{Q2} = EIY_2\phi_2$$

$$y_1 = \left(+x - \frac{2x^2}{L} + \frac{x^3}{L^2}\right)$$
$$\phi_1 = \left(+\frac{4}{L} - \frac{6x}{L^2}\right)$$

(a)

$$y_2 = \left(-\frac{x^2}{L} + \frac{x^3}{L^2}\right)$$
$$\phi_2 = \left(+\frac{2}{L} - \frac{6x}{L^2}\right)$$

(b)

$K_{21}X_1$

$K_{11}X_1$ $K_{41}X_1$

$(mp^2 y_1) X_1$

$K_{31}X_1$

$$X_2 = X_3 = X_4 = 0$$
$$\phi_{P1} = X_1\phi_1$$

$K_{22}X_2$

$K_{12}X_2$ $K_{42}X_2$

$(mp^2 y_2) X_2$

$K_{32}X_2$

$$X_1 = X_3 = X_4 = 0$$
$$\phi_{P2} = X_2\phi_2$$

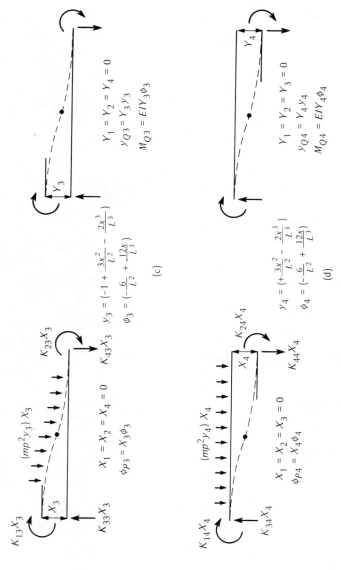

Figure 7.7.2. *Actual P-X and fictitious Q-Y systems of a beam element in free vibration. (a) First P-X and Q-Y basic modes; (b) second P-X and Q-Y basic modes; (c) third P-X and Q-Y basic modes; (d) fourth P-X and Q-Y basic modes.*

The equations appearing in panel (c):

$$Y_1 = Y_2 = Y_4 = 0$$
$$y_{Q3} = Y_3 y_3$$
$$M_{Q3} = EI Y_3 \phi_3$$

$$X_1 = X_2 = X_4 = 0$$
$$\phi_{P3} = X_3 \phi_3$$

$$y_3 = \left(-1 + \frac{3x^2}{L^2} - \frac{2x^3}{L^3}\right)$$
$$\phi_3 = \left(-\frac{6}{L^2} + \frac{12x}{L^3}\right)$$

$$(mp^2 y_3)\, X_3$$

Labels in panel (c): $K_{13}X_3$, $K_{23}X_3$, $K_{43}X_3$, $K_{33}X_3$, X_3, Y_3

(c)

The equations appearing in panel (d):

$$Y_1 = Y_2 = Y_3 = 0$$
$$y_{Q4} = Y_4 y_4$$
$$M_{Q4} = EI Y_4 \phi_4$$

$$X_1 = X_2 = X_3 = 0$$
$$\phi_{P4} = X_4 \phi_4$$

$$y_4 = \left(+\frac{3x^2}{L^2} - \frac{2x^3}{L^3}\right)$$
$$\phi_4 = \left(-\frac{6}{L^2} + \frac{12x}{L^3}\right)$$

$$(mp^2 y_4)\, X_4$$

Labels in panel (d): $K_{24}X_4$, $K_{44}X_4$, $K_{14}X_4$, $K_{34}X_4$, X_4, Y_4

(d)

$$\text{TEMP2} = + \frac{\phi \ (s' - s)}{1 - cc'} \frac{EI}{L}$$

$$\text{TEMP3} = - \frac{\phi^2 \ ss'}{1 - cc'} \frac{EI}{L}$$

$$\text{TEMP4} = - \frac{\phi^2 \ (c' - c)}{1 - cc'} \frac{EI}{L^2}$$ (7.7.3)

$$\text{TEMP5} = + \frac{\phi^3 \ (sc' + cs')}{1 - cc'} \frac{EI}{L^3}$$

$$\text{TEMP6} = + \frac{\phi^3 \ (s' + s)}{1 - cc'} \frac{EI}{L^3}$$

where $s = \sin \phi$, $c = \cos \phi$, $s' = \sinh \phi$, and $c' = \cosh \phi$. Equation 7.73 has been derived in Chapter 2.

Approximate values for the elements in the $[K]$ matrix of Eq. 7.7.2 may be obtained by assuming that the elastic curves in the P-X basic modes of Fig. 7.7.2 are in the cubic form, just as those of the Q-Y basic modes, again duplicated in Fig. 7.7.2 from Fig. 7.3.3. K_{ij} can be obtained by use of the reciprocal energy theorem in equating the external work done by the P_j-system in going through the displacement of the Q_j-system, to the internal work done by the Q_j-system in going through the deformation of the P_j-system. The important thing to note here is that the external work done by the P_j-system should include both (1) of the forces acting at the ends of the element, and (2) of the statical equivalent inertia force (mp^2y) acting throughout the element. For example, applying the reciprocal energy theorem between the P_2-system and the Q_3-system shown in Fig. 7.7.2,

$$(K_{32}X_2)(Y_3) + \int (mp^2y_2X_2)(y_3Y_3) \ dx = \int (EI\phi_3 Y_3)(\phi_2X_2) \ dx$$

from which

$$K_{32} = EI \int \phi_3\phi_2 \ dx - mp^2 \int y_3y_2 \ dx$$

In general,

$$[K] = EI\int \begin{Bmatrix} \phi_1 \\ \phi_2 \\ \phi_3 \\ \phi_4 \end{Bmatrix} [\phi_1 \ \phi_2 \ \phi_3 \ \phi_4] \ dx - mp^2\int \begin{Bmatrix} y_1 \\ y_2 \\ y_3 \\ y_4 \end{Bmatrix} [y_1 \ y_2 \ y_3 \ y_4] \ dx$$ (7.7.4)

Substituting in Eq. 7.7.4 the expressions for ϕ_1 to ϕ_4 and y_1 to y_4 shown in Fig. 7.7.2 and evaluating the integrals, the TEMP1 to TEMP6 values in the $[K]$ matrix are found to be

$$TEMP1 = + \frac{4EI}{L} - mp^2 \frac{L^3}{105} = + \left(4 - \frac{\phi^4}{105}\right) \frac{EI}{L}$$

$$TEMP2 = + \frac{2EI}{L} + mp^2 \frac{L^3}{140} = + \left(2 + \frac{\phi^4}{140}\right) \frac{EI}{L}$$

$$TEMP3 = - \frac{6EI}{L^2} + mp^2 \frac{11L^2}{210} = - \left(6 - \frac{11\phi^4}{210}\right) \frac{EI}{L^2}$$

$$TEMP4 = - \frac{6EI}{L^2} - mp^2 \frac{13L^2}{420} = - \left(6 + \frac{13\phi^4}{420}\right) \frac{EI}{L^2}$$

$$TEMP5 = + \frac{12EI}{L^3} - mp^2 \frac{13L}{35} = + \left(12 - \frac{13\phi^4}{35}\right) \frac{EI}{L^3}$$

$$TEMP6 = + \frac{12EI}{L^3} - mp^2 \frac{9L}{70} = + \left(12 + \frac{9\phi^4}{70}\right) \frac{EI}{L^3}$$

(7.7.5)

A plotting of the exact vs. approximate values of TEMP1 to TEMP6, respectively given by Eqs. 7.7.3 and 7.7.5, shows that there is very little difference when $\phi < 2$, some appreciable difference when $2 < \phi < 3$, and large divergence when $\phi > 3$.

7.8. Eigenvalue Solution of Stability and Free Vibration Problems

The approximate stiffness matrices, as obtained by the energy method for a prismatic beam element in axial compression or in free vibration, may be regarded as consisting of two parts: one principal part (Eq. 7.4.3) identical to that of an ordinary beam element and another supplementary part having $\alpha_i N_{CR}$ or $m_i p^2$ as a common multiplier (Eqs. 7.6.6 or 7.7.5), where $\alpha_i N_{CR}$ is the axial compression and m_i is the uniform mass per unit length of the ith beam element. It can be shown that in the eigenvalue solution of stability and free vibration problems, the effect of the supplementary global stiffness matrix resulting from the supplementary stiffness matrices of the elements may be combined with the second-order stiffness matrix in stability analysis or the sidesway inertia-force matrix in free vibration analysis.

Calling the principal global stiffness matrix $[K_P]_{NP \times NP}$ and the supplementary global stiffness matrix $N_{CR}[K_S]_{NP \times NP}$ wherein N_{CR} is the buckling load factor, the governing equation in stability analysis is

$$\begin{Bmatrix} P_R \\ P_S \end{Bmatrix} = \left[[K_P] + N_{CR}[K_S] \right] \begin{Bmatrix} X_R \\ X_S \end{Bmatrix} - N_{CR} \begin{bmatrix} 0 & 0 \\ 0 & K_2 \end{bmatrix} \begin{Bmatrix} X_R \\ X_S \end{Bmatrix} \tag{7.8.1}$$

in which $[K_2]_{NPS \times NPS}$ is the second-order stiffness matrix as defined in Eq. 5.2.2. Since the external force matrix is zero at bifurcation, Eq. 7.8.1 may be rewritten as

$$\begin{Bmatrix} X_R \\ X_S \end{Bmatrix} = N_{CR} [K_P^{-1}] \left[\begin{bmatrix} 0 & 0 \\ 0 & K_2 \end{bmatrix} - [K_S] \right] \begin{Bmatrix} X_R \\ X_S \end{Bmatrix} \tag{7.8.2}$$

Equation 7.8.2 may be solved by the iterative procedure for the eigenvalue problem outlined in Chapter 5.

Similarly, in free vibration analysis, calling the supplementary global stiffness matrix $p^2[K_S]_{NP \times NP}$ where p is the circular frequency, the governing equation is

$$\begin{Bmatrix} P_R \\ P_S \end{Bmatrix} = \left[[K_P] + p^2 [K_S] \right] \begin{Bmatrix} X_R \\ X_S \end{Bmatrix} - p^2 \begin{bmatrix} 0 & 0 \\ 0 & G \end{bmatrix} \begin{Bmatrix} X_R \\ X_S \end{Bmatrix} \tag{7.8.3}$$

in which $[G]_{NPS \times NPS}$ is the sidesway inertia-force matrix as defined in Eq. 2.8.1. Since again the external-force matrix is zero in free vibration, Eq. 7.8.3 may be rewritten as

$$\begin{Bmatrix} X_R \\ X_S \end{Bmatrix} = p^2 [K_P^{-1}] \left[\begin{bmatrix} 0 & 0 \\ 0 & G \end{bmatrix} - [K_S] \right] \begin{Bmatrix} X_R \\ X_S \end{Bmatrix} \tag{7.8.4}$$

Equation 7.8.4 can then be solved by the iterative procedure for the eigenvalue problem outlined in Chapter 1.

The use of the supplementary matrices obtained by the energy method in the eigenvalue solution would generally yield fairly accurate results so long as the ϕ_i values ($\phi_i = L_i \sqrt{\alpha_i N_{CR}/(EI_i)}$) in stability analysis or $\phi_i = L_i \sqrt[4]{m_i p^2/(EI_i)}$ in free vibration analysis) are well under 3. Consequently for the same accuracy, much longer beam elements may be used than those permitted in Chapter 5 wherein only the principal part of the stiffness matrix is used, or in Chapter 1 wherein the mass inertia forces are simply lumped in a diagonal mass matrix.

CHAPTER 8

■

Finite-Element Formulation of Plane Stress Analysis

8.1. Plane Stress versus Plane Strain Analysis

Plane stress and strain analysis is one of the elementary topics in Theory of Elasticity. The three sets of basic equations are: (1) the differential equations of equilibrium, (2) the differential equations of compatibility, and (3) the relationships between stresses and strains.

Consistent with the positive x and y axes shown in Fig. 8.1.1a and denoting the normal stresses by σ_1 and σ_2, the shear stress by σ_3, and the body forces by q_x and q_y per unit volume, the differential equations of equilibrium can be established by equating to zero the sum of the forces in the x and y directions acting on the free body of Fig. 8.1.1b; thus,

$$\frac{\partial \sigma_1}{\partial x} + \frac{\partial \sigma_3}{\partial y} + q_x = 0 \tag{8.1.1a}$$

$$\frac{\partial \sigma_2}{\partial y} + \frac{\partial \sigma_3}{\partial x} + q_y = 0 \tag{8.1.1b}$$

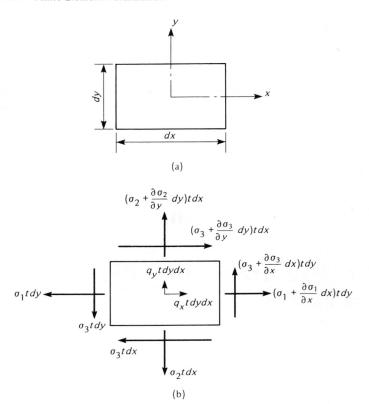

Figure 8.1.1. *Equilibrium of a differential element.*

The differential equations of compatibility express the normal strains e_1 and e_2 and the shear strain e_3, corresponding respectively to the normal stresses σ_1 and σ_2 and the shear stress σ_3, in terms of the displacements u and v in the positive x and y directions; these are

$$e_1 = \frac{\partial u}{\partial x} \qquad (8.1.2a)$$

$$e_2 = \frac{\partial v}{\partial y} \qquad (8.1.2b)$$

$$e_3 = \frac{\partial u}{\partial y} + \frac{\partial v}{\partial x} \qquad (8.1.2c)$$

The relationships between stresses and strains are

$$e_1 = \frac{\sigma_1}{E} - \frac{\mu\sigma_2}{E} - \frac{\mu\sigma_z}{E} \qquad (8.1.3a)$$

$$e_2 = \frac{\sigma_2}{E} - \frac{\mu\sigma_1}{E} - \frac{\mu\sigma_z}{E} \qquad (8.1.3b)$$

$$e_3 = \frac{2(1+\mu)}{E}\sigma_3 \qquad (8.1.3c)$$

where E is the modulus of elasticity, μ is the Poisson's ratio, and σ_z is the stress normal to the xy-plane.

Since $\sigma_z = 0$ in plane stress analysis, Eq. 8.1.3 gives directly the "particle-flexibility matrix" $[D]$ as

$$[D] =$$

$\overset{\sigma}{\underset{e}{\diagdown}}$	1	2	3
1	$+\dfrac{1}{E}$	$-\dfrac{\mu}{E}$	0.
2	$-\dfrac{\mu}{E}$	$+\dfrac{1}{E}$	0.
3	0.	0.	$+\dfrac{2(1+\mu)}{E}$

$$(8.1.4a)$$

The name *particle-flexibility matrix* is used here to differentiate it from the "member-flexibility matrix" in framed structures. The "particle-stiffness matrix $[S]$ is then

$$[S] = [D^{-1}] =$$

$\overset{e}{\underset{\sigma}{\diagdown}}$	1	2	3
1	$+\dfrac{E}{1-\mu^2}$	$+\dfrac{\mu E}{1-\mu^2}$	0.
2	$+\dfrac{\mu E}{1-\mu^2}$	$+\dfrac{E}{1-\mu^2}$	0.
3	0.	0.	$+\dfrac{E}{2(1+\mu)}$

$$(8.1.4b)$$

In plane strain analysis,

$$e_z = \frac{\sigma_z}{E} - \frac{\mu \sigma_1}{E} - \frac{\mu \sigma_2}{E} = 0$$

from which

$$\sigma_z = +\mu \left(\sigma_1 + \sigma_2\right)$$

Substituting the above equation in Eq. 8.1.3ab,

$$e_1 = \frac{1 - \mu^2}{E} \sigma_1 - \frac{\mu \left(1 + \mu\right)}{E} \sigma_2 \tag{8.1.5a}$$

$$e_2 = \frac{1 - \mu^2}{E} \sigma_2 - \frac{\mu \left(1 + \mu\right)}{E} \sigma_1 \tag{8.1.5b}$$

The particle-flexibility matrix $[D]$ now becomes, from Eqs. 8.1.5ab and 8.1.3c,

$$[D] =$$

e \\ σ	1	2	3
1	$+\dfrac{1 - \mu^2}{E}$	$-\dfrac{\mu \left(1 + \mu\right)}{E}$	0.
2	$-\dfrac{\mu \left(1 + \mu\right)}{E}$	$+\dfrac{1 - \mu^2}{E}$	0.
3	0.	0.	$+\dfrac{2 \left(1 + \mu\right)}{E}$

$$\tag{8.1.6a}$$

and the particle-stiffness matrix $[S]$ is

$$[S] = [D^{-1}] =$$

σ \\ e	1	2	3
1	$+\dfrac{E \left(1 - \mu\right)}{\left(1 + \mu\right)\left(1 - 2\mu\right)}$	$+\dfrac{\mu E}{\left(1 + \mu\right)\left(1 - 2\mu\right)}$	0.
2	$+\dfrac{\mu E}{\left(1 + \mu\right)\left(1 - 2\mu\right)}$	$+\dfrac{E \left(1 - \mu\right)}{\left(1 + \mu\right)\left(1 - 2\mu\right)}$	0.
3	0.	0.	$+\dfrac{E}{2 \left(1 + \mu\right)}$

$$\tag{8.1.6b}$$

It can be shown that the particle-flexibility and particle-stiffness matrices in plane strain analysis can be obtained from the same matrices in plane stress analysis by replacing the E and μ in the latter expressions by

$$E' = \frac{E}{1 - \mu^2} \tag{8.1.7a}$$

$$\mu' = \frac{\mu}{1 - \mu} \tag{8.1.7b}$$

For example,

$$\frac{E'}{1 - \mu'^2} = \frac{E/(1 - \mu^2)}{1 - \mu^2/(1 - \mu)^2} = \frac{E\,(1 - \mu)}{(1 + \mu)(1 - 2\mu)}$$

$$\frac{\mu'E'}{1 - \mu'^2} = \frac{[\mu/(1 - \mu)]\,[E/(1 - \mu^2)]}{1 - \mu^2/(1 - \mu)^2} = \frac{\mu E}{(1 + \mu)(1 - 2\mu)}$$

$$\frac{E'}{2\,(1 + \mu')} = \frac{E/(1 - \mu^2)}{2[1 + \mu/(1 - \mu)]} = \frac{E}{2\,(1 + \mu)}$$

Thus in the remainder of this chapter only plane stress analysis will be treated. In case of plane strain analysis, it is only necessary to replace E and μ in the plane stress formulation by $E/(1 - \mu^2)$ and $\mu/(1 - \mu)$.

8.2. General Description of Finite-Element Method

Although the finite-element method is generally applicable to many problems in the theory of elasticity or of plates and shells, it is expedient to describe the general concept by taking plane stress analysis as a frame of reference.

In plane stress analysis when the boundaries, whether single or multiple, are irregular, or when the loadings are unsymmetrical, closed solutions obeying the three sets of basic equations described in the previous section are usually not obtainable. The finite-element method can afford an approximate solution. The plate may be divided into a *finite* number of pieces (or *elements*), which are connected to each other only at points (or *nodes*). The basic unknowns in the analysis are the horizontal and vertical displacements (u and v) at each node. Following the notations in the matrix displacement method, these unknown displacements are numbered from $X(1)$ to $X(NP)$ where NP is the degree of freedom.

While the imposition on the plate may arise from body forces, distributed loads at the boundaries, or temperature changes, it has to take the form of a set of equivalent forces $P(1)$ to $P(NP)$ in the directions of the degrees of freedom.

Using the direct element approach the global stiffness matrix is the summation of the stiffness matrices of all the finite elements. It will be shown that the reciprocal energy theorem, as previously discussed in Sec. 7.2, plays a major role in the formulation of the stiffness matrix of a finite element.

8.3. Stiffness Matrix of a Finite Element

The stiffness matrix of a finite element expresses the nodal forces in terms of the nodal displacements. In plane stress analysis each nodal point can have two unknown nodal displacements, usually one in the horizontal direction and the other in the vertical direction; thus a triangular element would have six nodal displacements and a rectangular element, eight nodal displacements. Define NPE as the degree of freedom of an element, or the number of nodal displacements which may be present on an element.

Now if the number of arbitrary constants, called α's, in the chosen form of the displacement equation is also NPE, then NPE linear equations may be established by expressing the nodal displacements $X(1)$ to $X(NPE)$ in terms of the arbitrary constants $\alpha(1)$ to $\alpha(NPE)$ in the displacement equation; thus

$$\{X\}_{NPE \times 1} = [C]_{NPE \times NPE} \{\alpha\}_{NPE \times 1} \tag{8.3.1}$$

Care must be taken so that the $[C]$ matrix is not singular; thus

$$\{\alpha\}_{NPE \times 1} = [C^{-1}]_{NPE \times NPE} \{X\}_{NPE \times 1} \tag{8.3.2}$$

Since $\alpha(1)$ to $\alpha(NPE)$ are the only undetermined arbitrary constants in the displacement equation, expressions for the three strains (in plane stress analysis) in terms of the arbitrary constants $\alpha(1)$ to $\alpha(NPE)$ may be obtained from the differential equations of compatibility; thus

$$\{e\}_{3 \times 1} = [G]_{3 \times NPE} \{\alpha\}_{NPE \times 1} \tag{8.3.3}$$

Note, however, that the contents of the $[G]$ matrix may be expressions, usually involving x and y which are the coordinates of the point.

Substituting Eq. 8.3.2 in Eq. 8.3.3,

$$\{e\}_{3 \times 1} = [GC^{-1}]_{3 \times NPE} \{X\}_{NPE \times 1} = [B]_{3 \times NPE} \{X\}_{NPE \times 1} \tag{8.3.4}$$

where

$$[B] = [GC^{-1}] \tag{8.3.5}$$

The $[B]$ matrix, then, expresses the internal deformations in terms of the NPE nodal displacements. It is one of the most crucial matrices in the finite element formulation processes.

Having had the $[B]$ matrix, the K_{ij} term in the stiffness matrix $[K]$ of the finite element may be conveniently obtained by applying the reciprocal energy theorem between the actual jth P-X basic mode and the fictitious ith Q-Y basic mode. Although the names actual P-X and fictitious Q-Y basic modes have been defined in Chapter 7, the reader may be reminded that the fundamental assumption is that the displacement equation in the actual P-X modes is identical in form to that which has been chosen for the fictitious Q-Y modes. Equating the external work done by the P_j-system in going through the displacements of the Q_i-system, to the internal work done by the Q_i-system is going through the internal deformations in the P_j-system,

$$(K_{ij}X_j)(Y_i) = \int [(\sigma_{1i}Y_i)(e_{1j}X_j) + (\sigma_{2i}Y_i)(e_{2j}X_j) + (\sigma_{3i}Y_i)(e_{3j}X_j)] \, t \, dA \quad (8.3.6)$$

in which σ_{1i}, σ_{2i}, and σ_{3i} are the three stresses due to a unit ith nodal displacement, and e_{1j}, e_{2j}, and e_{3j} are the three strains due to a unit jth nodal displacement.

Cancelling $(X_j Y_i)$ from every term in Eq. 8.3.6,

$$K_{ij} = \int [\sigma_{1i} \ \sigma_{2i} \ \sigma_{3i}] \begin{Bmatrix} e_{1j} \\ e_{2j} \\ e_{3j} \end{Bmatrix} t \, dA \quad (8.3.7)$$

But, by definition of the $[B]$ matrix,

$$\begin{Bmatrix} \sigma_{1i} \\ \sigma_{2i} \\ \sigma_{3i} \end{Bmatrix} = [S] \begin{Bmatrix} e_{1i} \\ e_{2i} \\ e_{3i} \end{Bmatrix} = [S] \begin{Bmatrix} B_{1i} \\ B_{2i} \\ B_{3i} \end{Bmatrix} \quad (8.3.8)$$

in which $[S]$ is the particle-stiffness matrix. Similarly,

$$\begin{Bmatrix} e_{1j} \\ e_{2j} \\ e_{3j} \end{Bmatrix} = \begin{Bmatrix} B_{1j} \\ B_{2j} \\ B_{3j} \end{Bmatrix} \quad (8.3.9)$$

Substituting Eqs. 8.3.8 and 8.3.9 in Eq. 8.3.7 and noting that $[S] = [S^T]$,

$$K_{ij} = \int [B_{1i}\ B_{2i}\ B_{3i}]\ [S] \begin{Bmatrix} B_{1j} \\ B_{2j} \\ B_{3j} \end{Bmatrix} t\, dA \qquad (8.3.10)$$

and, in general,

$$[K] = \int [B^T]\,[S]\,[B]\, t\, dA \qquad (8.3.11)$$

Equation 8.3.11 is the all-important formula which yields the stiffness matrix of a finite element. Applications of this equation will be shown in the subsequent sections of this chapter.

8.4. Triangular Finite Element

A useful shape for a finite element is the triangle because it may fit well into irregular situations of practical importance. Let the three vertices be numbered 1, 2, and 3, counterclockwise around the perimeter (Fig. 8.4.1a); and let

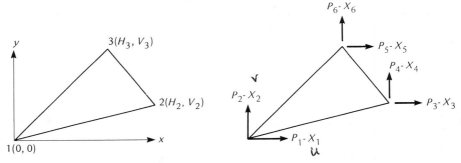

Figure 8.4.1. *A triangular finite element in plane stress analysis.*

(H_2, V_2) and (H_3, V_3) be the coordinates of points 2 and 3 referred to point 1 as origin. In plane stress analysis, the six conditions expressing the nodal displacements X_1 to X_6 (Fig. 8.4.1b) are:

$$
\begin{aligned}
&(1)\ X_1 = u \quad \text{at} \quad (0,0) \\
&(2)\ X_2 = v \quad \text{at} \quad (0,0) \\
&(3)\ X_3 = u \quad \text{at} \quad (H_2, V_2) \\
&(4)\ X_4 = v \quad \text{at} \quad (H_2, V_2) \\
&(5)\ X_5 = u \quad \text{at} \quad (H_3, V_3) \\
&(6)\ X_6 = v \quad \text{at} \quad (H_3, V_3)
\end{aligned}
\qquad (8.4.1)
$$

wherein u and v are the horizontal and vertical displacements.

Choosing the displacement equations for u and v in the form

$$u = \alpha_1 + \alpha_2 x + \alpha_3 y$$
$$v = \alpha_4 + \alpha_5 x + \alpha_6 y \tag{8.4.2}$$

not only fixes the number of arbitrary constants at 6, but also insures compatible horizontal and vertical displacements at all points on the perimeter. Since complete equilibrium and compatibility at all points on the perimeter would mean exact solution, the attainment of which is an exception rather than the rule, finite element solution based on Eq. 8.4.2 would not generally produce equilibrium along the perimeter of the triangle.

The matrix $[C]$, which expresses the X's in terms of the α's may be constructed by observing Eqs. 8.4.1 and 8.4.2, thus:

(∂)
$[C] =$

α / X	1	2	3	4	5	6
1	+1					
2				+1		
3	+1	$+H_2$	$+V_2$			
4				+1	$+H_2$	$+V_2$
5	+1	$+H_3$	$+V_3$			
6				+1	$+H_3$	$+V_3$

$$(8.4.3)$$

Applying the differential equations of compatibility in plane stress analysis to the displacement equations of Eq. 8.4.2,

$$e_1 = \frac{\partial u}{\partial x} = +\alpha_2$$

$$e_2 = \frac{\partial v}{\partial y} = +\alpha_6 \tag{8.4.4}$$

$$e_3 = \frac{\partial u}{\partial y} + \frac{\partial v}{\partial x} = +\alpha_3 + \alpha_5$$

Because the matrix $[G]$ expresses the internal deformations (strains in this case) in terms of the α's, it is

$[G] =$

e \ α	1	2	3	4	5	6
1		+1				
2						+1
3			+1	+1		

(8.4.5)

It may be seen from Eq. 8.4.4 that each of the three strains, and consequently the stresses, is of a constant value at all points within the triangle.

Inverting Eq. 8.4.3 gives

$$[C^{-1}] = \frac{1}{(H_2 V_3 - H_3 V_2)}$$

α \ X	1	2	3	4	5	6
1	$H_2 V_3 - H_3 V_2$					
2	$V_2 - V_3$		$+V_3$		$-V_2$	
3	$H_3 - H_2$		$-H_3$		$+H_2$	
4		$H_2 V_3 - H_3 V_2$				
5		$V_2 - V_3$		$+V_3$		$-V_2$
6		$H_3 - H_2$		$-H_3$		$+H_2$

(8.4.6)

Using the formula $[B] = [GC^{-1}]$ gives

strain-displacement

$[D]$

$$[B] = \frac{1}{(H_2 V_3 - H_3 V_2)} *$$

e \ X	1	2	3	4	5	6
1	$V_2 - V_3$		$+V_3$		$-V_2$	
2		$H_3 - H_2$		$-H_3$		$+H_2$
3	$H_3 - V_2$	$V_2 - V_3$	$-H_3$	$+V_3$	$+H_2$	$-V_2$

(8.4.7)

The particle-stiffness matrix has been shown previously as

$$[S] = \overset{[E]}{[D]}$$

σ \ e	1	2	3
1	$+\dfrac{E}{1-\mu^2}$	$+\dfrac{\mu E}{1-\mu^2}$	0.
2	$+\dfrac{\mu E}{1-\mu^2}$	$+\dfrac{E}{1-\mu^2}$	0.
3	0.	0.	$+\dfrac{E}{2(1+\mu)}$

Thus,

$$[SB] = \frac{E}{(1-\mu^2)(H_2 V_3 - H_3 V_2)} \quad *$$

σ \ X	1	2	3	4	5	6
1	$+(V_2 - V_3)$	$+\mu(H_3 - H_2)$	$+V_3$	$-\mu H_3$	$-V_2$	$+\mu H_2$
2	$+\mu(V_2 - V_3)$	$+(H_3 - H_2)$	$+\mu V_3$	$-H_3$	$-\mu V_2$	$+H_2$
3	$+\dfrac{(1-\mu)}{2}(H_3 - H_2)$	$+\dfrac{(1-\mu)}{2}(V_2 - V_3)$	$-\dfrac{(1-\mu)}{2}H_3$	$+\dfrac{(1-\mu)}{2}V_3$	$+\dfrac{(1-\mu)}{2}H_2$	$-\dfrac{(1-\mu)}{2}V_2$

$$(8.4.8)$$

Finally, the stiffness matrix $[K]$ of the triangular element is

$$[K] = \int [B^T] [SB] \, t \, dA$$

or

$$[K] =$$

P \ X	1	2	3	4	5	6
1	K_{11}					
2	K_{21}	K_{22}		(Symmetrical)		
3	K_{31}	K_{32}	K_{33}			
4	K_{41}	K_{42}	K_{43}	K_{44}		
5	K_{51}	K_{52}	K_{53}	K_{54}	K_{55}	
6	K_{61}	K_{62}	K_{63}	K_{64}	K_{65}	K_{66}

$$(8.4.9)$$

in which

$$K_{11} = \frac{Et}{2(1 - \mu^2)(H_2 V_3 - H_3 V_2)} [+(V_2 - V_3)^2 + (1 - \mu)(H_3 - H_2)^2/2]$$

$$K_{21} = \frac{Et}{2(1 - \mu^2)(H_2 V_3 - H_3 V_2)} [+(1 + \mu)(H_3 - H_2)(V_2 - V_3)/2]$$

$$K_{31} = \frac{Et}{2(1 - \mu^2)(H_2 V_3 - H_3 V_2)} [+V_3(V_2 - V_3) - (1 - \mu)H_3(H_3 - H_2)/2]$$

$$K_{41} = \frac{Et}{2(1 - \mu^2)(H_2 V_3 - H_3 V_2)} [-\mu H_3(V_2 - V_3) + (1 - \mu)V_3(H_3 - H_2)/2]$$

$$K_{51} = \frac{Et}{2(1 - \mu^2)(H_2 V_3 - H_3 V_2)} [-V_2(V_2 - V_3) + (1 - \mu)H_2(H_3 - H_2)/2]$$

$$K_{61} = \frac{Et}{2(1 - \mu^2)(H_2 V_3 - H_3 V_2)} [+\mu H_2(V_2 - V_3) - (1 - \mu)V_2(H_3 - H_2)/2]$$

$$K_{22} = \frac{Et}{2(1 - \mu^2)(H_2 V_3 - H_3 V_2)} [+(H_3 - H_2)^2 + (1 - \mu)(V_2 - V_3)^2/2]$$

$$K_{32} = \frac{Et}{2(1 - \mu^2)(H_2 V_3 - H_3 V_2)} [+\mu V_3(H_3 - H_2) - (1 - \mu)H_3(V_2 - V_3)/2]$$

$$K_{42} = \frac{Et}{2(1 - \mu^2)(H_2 V_3 - H_3 V_2)} [-H_3(H_3 - H_2) + (1 - \mu)V_3(V_2 - V_3)/2]$$

$$K_{52} = \frac{Et}{2(1 - \mu^2)(H_2 V_3 - H_3 V_2)} [-\mu V_2(H_3 - H_2) + (1 - \mu)H_2(V_2 - V_3)/2]$$

$$K_{62} = \frac{Et}{2(1 - \mu^2)(H_2 V_3 - H_3 V_2)} [+H_2(H_3 - H_2) - (1 - \mu)V_2(V_2 - V_3)/2]$$

$$K_{33} = \frac{Et}{2(1 - \mu^2)(H_2 V_3 - H_3 V_2)} [+V_3^2 + (1 - \mu)H_3^2/2]$$

$$K_{43} = \frac{Et}{2(1 - \mu^2)(H_2 V_3 - H_3 V_2)} [-(1 + \mu)H_3 V_3/2]$$

$$K_{53} = \frac{Et}{2(1 - \mu^2)(H_2 V_3 - H_3 V_2)} [-V_2 V_3 - (1 - \mu)H_2 H_3/2]$$

$$K_{63} = \frac{Et}{2(1 - \mu^2)(H_2 V_3 - H_3 V_2)} [+\mu H_2 V_3 + (1 - \mu)H_3 V_2/2]$$

$$K_{44} = \frac{Et}{2(1-\mu^2)(H_2V_3 - H_3V_2)}\,[+H_3^2 + (1-\mu)V_3^2/2]$$

$$K_{54} = \frac{Et}{2(1-\mu^2)(H_2V_3 - H_3V_2)}\,[+\mu H_3V_2 + (1-\mu)H_2V_3/2]$$

$$K_{64} = \frac{Et}{2(1-\mu^2)(H_2V_3 - H_3V_2)}\,[-H_2H_3 - (1-\mu)V_2V_3/2]$$

$$K_{55} = \frac{Et}{2(1-\mu^2)(H_2V_3 - H_3V_2)}\,[+V_3^2 + (1-\mu)H_3^2/2]$$

$$K_{65} = \frac{Et}{2(1-\mu^2)(H_2V_3 - H_3V_2)}\,[-(1+\mu)H_2V_2/2]$$

$$K_{66} = \frac{Et}{2(1-\mu^2)(H_2V_3 - H_3V_2)}\,[+H_2^2 + (1-\mu)V_2^2/2]$$

8.5. Rectangular Finite Element

Another useful shape for a finite element is the rectangle because many common plate structures have rectangular boundaries. After placing the origin of the reference x and y axes at the center of the element and numbering the four corner points as shown in Fig. 8.5.1a, the eight degrees of freedom in plane stress analysis are numbered as shown in Fig. 8.5.1b. The nodal displacements X_1 to X_8 are (1) $X_1 = u$ at $(+a/2, +b/2)$; (2) $X_2 = v$ at $(+a/2, +b/2)$; (3) $X_3 = u$ at $(-a/2, +b/2)$; (4) $X_4 = v$ at $(-a/2, +b/2)$; (5) $X_5 = u$ at $(-a/2, -b/2)$; (6) $X_6 = v$ at $(-a/2, -b/2)$; (7) $X_7 = u$ at $(+a/2, -b/2)$; and $X_8 = v$ at $(+a/2, -b/2)$. u and v are the horizontal and vertical displacements, respectively.

To be consistent with the 8 nodal displacements at the four corners of the rectangle, the displacement equations to be chosen for the fictitious Q-Y systems should contain 8 arbitrary constants. If these equations are such that both u and v vary linearly with y when x is constant and linearly with x when y is constant, then there would be compatible horizontal and vertical displacements at all points of each edge between two adjacent rectangles. The above conditions are met when

$$u = \alpha_1 x + \alpha_2 xy + \alpha_3 y + \alpha_4 \tag{8.5.1a}$$

and

$$v = \alpha_5 x + \alpha_6 xy + \alpha_7 y + \alpha_8 \tag{8.5.1b}$$

The nodal displacements X_1 to X_8 are now expressible in terms of the constants α_1 to α_8 by the $[C]$ matrix; thus

$$[C] =$$

X \ α	1	2	3	4	5	6	7	8
1	$+a/2$	$+ab/4$	$+b/2$	$+1$				
2					$+a/2$	$+ab/4$	$+b/2$	$+1$
3	$-a/2$	$-ab/4$	$+b/2$	$+1$				
4					$-a/2$	$-ab/4$	$+b/2$	$+1$
5	$-a/2$	$+ab/4$	$-b/2$	$+1$				
6					$-a/2$	$+ab/4$	$-b/2$	$+1$
7	$+a/2$	$-ab/4$	$-b/2$	$+1$				
8					$+a/2$	$-ab/4$	$-b/2$	$+1$

(8.5.2)

and, vice versa,

$$[C^{-1}] =$$

α \ X	1	2	3	4	5	6	7	8
1	$+\dfrac{1}{2a}$		$-\dfrac{1}{2a}$		$-\dfrac{1}{2a}$		$+\dfrac{1}{2a}$	
2	$+\dfrac{1}{ab}$		$-\dfrac{1}{ab}$		$+\dfrac{1}{ab}$		$-\dfrac{1}{ab}$	
3	$+\dfrac{1}{2b}$		$+\dfrac{1}{2b}$		$-\dfrac{1}{2b}$		$-\dfrac{1}{2b}$	
4	$+\dfrac{1}{4}$		$+\dfrac{1}{4}$		$+\dfrac{1}{4}$		$+\dfrac{1}{4}$	
5		$+\dfrac{1}{2a}$		$-\dfrac{1}{2a}$		$-\dfrac{1}{2a}$		$+\dfrac{1}{2a}$
6		$+\dfrac{1}{ab}$		$-\dfrac{1}{ab}$		$+\dfrac{1}{ab}$		$-\dfrac{1}{ab}$
7		$+\dfrac{1}{2b}$		$+\dfrac{1}{2b}$		$-\dfrac{1}{2b}$		$-\dfrac{1}{2b}$
8		$+\dfrac{1}{4}$		$+\dfrac{1}{4}$		$+\dfrac{1}{4}$		$+\dfrac{1}{4}$

(8.5.3)

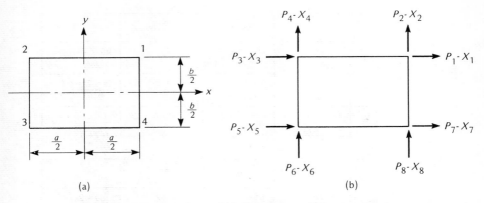

Figure 8.5.1. *A rectangular finite element in plane stress analysis.*

The differential equations of compatibility in plane stress analysis give

$$e_1 = \frac{\partial u}{\partial x} = \alpha_1 + \alpha_2 y \tag{8.5.4a}$$

$$e_2 = \frac{\partial v}{\partial y} = \alpha_6 x + \alpha_7 \tag{8.5.4b}$$

$$e_3 = \frac{\partial u}{\partial y} + \frac{\partial v}{\partial x} = \alpha_2 x + \alpha_3 + \alpha_5 + \alpha_6 y \tag{8.5.4c}$$

Rewriting Eq. 8.5.4 in matrix form,

$$[G] =$$

e \ α	1	2	3	4	5	6	7	8
1	+1	+y						
2					+x	+1		
3		+x	+1		+1	+y		

$$(8.5.5)$$

Then

$$[B] = [GC^{-1}] =$$

e \ X	1	2	3	4	5	6	7	8
1	$+\frac{1}{2a}+\frac{y}{ab}$		$-\frac{1}{2a}-\frac{y}{ab}$		$+\frac{1}{2a}+\frac{y}{ab}$		$+\frac{1}{2a}-\frac{y}{ab}$	
2		$+\frac{1}{2b}+\frac{x}{ab}$		$+\frac{1}{2b}-\frac{x}{ab}$		$-\frac{1}{2b}+\frac{x}{ab}$		$-\frac{1}{2b}-\frac{x}{ab}$
3	$+\frac{1}{2b}+\frac{x}{ab}$	$+\frac{1}{2a}+\frac{y}{ab}$	$+\frac{1}{2b}-\frac{x}{ab}$	$-\frac{1}{2a}-\frac{y}{ab}$	$-\frac{1}{2b}+\frac{x}{ab}$	$+\frac{1}{2a}-\frac{y}{ab}$	$-\frac{1}{2b}-\frac{y}{ab}$	$+\frac{1}{2a}-\frac{y}{ab}$

$$(8.5.6)$$

$$[SB] = \frac{E}{1 - u^2} *$$

σ \ X	1	2	3	4
1	$+\dfrac{b + 2y}{2ab}$	$+\dfrac{\mu(a + 2x)}{2ab}$	$-\dfrac{b + 2y}{2ab}$	$+\dfrac{\mu(a - 2x)}{2ab}$
2	$+\dfrac{\mu(b + 2y)}{2ab}$	$+\dfrac{a + 2x}{2ab}$	$-\dfrac{\mu(b + 2y)}{2ab}$	$+\dfrac{(a - 2x)}{2ab}$
3	$+\dfrac{(1 - \mu)(a + 2x)}{4ab}$	$+\dfrac{(1 - \mu)(b + 2y)}{4ab}$	$+\dfrac{(1 - \mu)(a - 2x)}{4ab}$	$-\dfrac{(1 - \mu)(b + 2y)}{4ab}$

σ \ X	5	6	7	8
1	$-\dfrac{b - 2y}{2ab}$	$-\dfrac{\mu(a - 2x)}{2ab}$	$+\dfrac{b - 2y}{2ab}$	$-\dfrac{\mu(a + 2x)}{2ab}$
2	$-\dfrac{\mu(b - 2y)}{2ab}$	$-\dfrac{a - 2x}{2ab}$	$+\dfrac{\mu(b - 2y)}{2ab}$	$-\dfrac{a + 2x}{2ab}$
3	$-\dfrac{(1 - \mu)(a - 2x)}{4ab}$	$-\dfrac{(1 - \mu)(b - 2y)}{4ab}$	$-\dfrac{(1 - \mu)(a + 2x)}{4ab}$	$+\dfrac{(1 - \mu)(b - 2y)}{4ab}$

$$(8.5.7)$$

$$[K] = \int [B^T] \, [SB] \, t \, dA$$

P \ X	1	2	3	4	5	6	7	8
1	$T1$	$T11$	$T3$	$T9$	$T5$	$-T12$	$T7$	$-T10$
2	$T11$	$T2$	$-T9$	$T8$	$-T12$	$T6$	$T10$	$T4$
3	$T3$	$-T9$	$T1$	$-T11$	$T7$	$T10$	$T5$	$T12$
4	$T9$	$T8$	$-T11$	$T2$	$-T10$	$T4$	$T12$	$T6$
5	$T5$	$-T12$	$T7$	$-T10$	$T1$	$T11$	$T3$	$T9$
6	$-T12$	$T6$	$T10$	$T4$	$T11$	$T2$	$-T9$	$T8$
7	$T7$	$T10$	$T5$	$T12$	$T3$	$-T9$	$T1$	$-T11$
8	$-T10$	$T4$	$T12$	$T6$	$T9$	$T8$	$-T11$	$T2$

$$(8.5.8)$$

in which

$$T1 = \frac{Et}{12(1 - \mu^2)}\left[+\frac{4b}{a} + \frac{2a}{b}(1 - \mu)\right] \qquad T2 = \frac{Et}{12(1 - \mu^2)}\left[+\frac{4a}{b} + \frac{2b}{a}(1 - \mu)\right]$$

$$T3 = \frac{Et}{12(1-\mu^2)}\left[-\frac{4b}{a}+\frac{a}{b}(1-\mu)\right] \qquad T4 = \frac{Et}{12(1-\mu^2)}\left[-\frac{4a}{b}+\frac{b}{a}(1-\mu)\right]$$

$$T5 = \frac{Et}{12(1-\mu^2)}\left[-\frac{2b}{a}-\frac{a}{b}(1-\mu)\right] \qquad T6 = \frac{Et}{12(1-\mu^2)}\left[-\frac{2a}{b}-\frac{b}{a}(1-\mu)\right]$$

$$T7 = \frac{Et}{12(1-\mu^2)}\left[+\frac{2b}{a}-\frac{2a}{b}(1-\mu)\right] \qquad T8 = \frac{Et}{12(1-\mu^2)}\left[+\frac{2a}{b}-\frac{2b}{a}(1-\mu)\right]$$

$$T9 = \frac{Et}{12(1-\mu^2)}\left[+\frac{3}{2}(3\mu-1)\right] \qquad T10 = T9$$

$$T11 = \frac{Et}{12(1-\mu^2)}\left[+\frac{3}{2}(1+\mu)\right] \qquad T12 = T11$$

8.6. Arbitrary Stress Functions

As a general procedure, the stiffness matrix of a finite element may only be obtained when some specific form of displacement equations has been chosen. On occasions it may be convenient to choose arbitrary forms for the internal force equations (e.g., the normal stresses σ_1 and σ_2 and shear stress σ_3 in plane stress analysis), and from these are then derived the forms of the displacement equations. This is satisfactory so long as the number of arbitrary constants finally involved in the displacement equations is equal to the number of nodal displacements on the finite element.

For the rectangular finite element in plane stress analysis shown in Fig. 8.5.1, assume the following arbitrary stress functions:

$$\sigma_1 = \alpha_1 + \alpha_2 y$$
$$\sigma_2 = \alpha_3 + \alpha_4 x$$
$$\sigma_3 = \alpha_5 \qquad (8.6.1)$$

where σ_1 and σ_2 are the normal stresses and σ_3 is the shear stress as defined in Fig. 8.1.1. Note that σ_1 is constant across the width of the rectangle but varies linearly with y, σ_2 is constant across the depth of the rectangle but varies linearly with x, and σ_3 is constant at all points in the rectangle. Also note that there are 5 arbitrary constants in the chosen stress functions.

The displacement equations consistent with Eq. 8.6.1 may be derived by using the particle-flexibility matrix of Eq. 8.1.4a and the differential equations of compatibility Eq. 8.1.2; thus

$$e_1 = \frac{\partial u}{\partial x} = \frac{\sigma_1}{E} - \frac{\mu\sigma_2}{E} = \frac{1}{E}(\alpha_1 + \alpha_2 y - \mu\alpha_3 - \mu\alpha_4 x) \tag{8.6.2}$$

$$e_2 = \frac{\partial v}{\partial y} = \frac{\sigma_2}{E} - \frac{\mu\sigma_1}{E} = \frac{1}{E}(-\mu\alpha_1 - \mu\alpha_2 y + \alpha_3 + \alpha_4 x) \tag{8.6.3}$$

$$e_3 = \frac{\partial v}{\partial y} + \frac{\partial v}{\partial x} = \frac{2(1 + \mu)}{E}\sigma_3 = \frac{2(1 + \mu)}{E}\sigma_5 \tag{8.6.4}$$

Integrating Eqs. 8.6.2 and 8.6.3,

$$u = \frac{1}{E}[\alpha_1 x + \alpha_2 xy - \mu\alpha_3 x - \mu\alpha_4 x^2/2 + f(y)] \tag{8.6.5}$$

$$v = \frac{1}{E}[-\mu\alpha_1 y - \mu\alpha_2 y^2/2 + \alpha_3 y + \alpha_4 xy + f(x)] \tag{8.6.6}$$

Substituting Eqs. 8.6.5 and 8.6.6 into Eq. 8.6.4,

$$\alpha_2 x + f'(y) + \alpha_4 y + f'(x) = 2(1 + \mu)\,\alpha_5 \tag{8.6.7}$$

Separating Eq. 8.6.7 into expressions of x and y and equating each to a new constant α_6,

$$f'(y) + \alpha_4 y = 2(1 + \mu)\,\alpha_5 - \alpha_2 x - f'(x) = \alpha_6 \tag{8.6.8}$$

Integrating Eq. 8.6.8,

$$f(y) = -\alpha_4 y^2/2 + \alpha_6 y + \alpha_7 \tag{8.6.9}$$

$$f(x) = -\alpha_2 x^2/2 + 2(1 + \mu)\,\alpha_5 x - \alpha_6 x + \alpha_8 \tag{8.6.10}$$

Substituting Eqs. 8.6.9 and 8.6.10 in Eqs. 8.6.5 and 8.6.6,

$$u = \frac{1}{E}[\alpha_1 x + \alpha_2 xy - \mu\alpha_3 x - \alpha_4(\mu x^2 + y^2)/2 + \alpha_6 y + \alpha_7] \tag{8.6.11}$$

$$v = \frac{1}{E}[-\mu\alpha_1 y - \alpha_2(x^2 + \mu y^2)/2 + \alpha_3 y + \alpha_4 xy + 2(1 + \mu)\,\alpha_5 x - \alpha_6 x + \alpha_8]$$

$$\tag{8.6.12}$$

Since it happens that there are, in Eqs. 8.6.11 and 8.6.12, three more arbitrary constants in addition to the five in the stress function, the [C] matrix expressing the 8 X's in terms of the 8 α's may be established by equating the nodal displacements to the u and v values at the corners of the rectangle; thus

$[C] = \dfrac{1}{E}$ *

X \ α	1	2	3	4	5	6	7	8
1	$+\dfrac{a}{2}$	$+\dfrac{ab}{4}$	$-\dfrac{\mu a}{2}$	$-\dfrac{\mu a^2 + b^2}{8}$		$+\dfrac{b}{2}$	$+1$	
2	$-\dfrac{\mu b}{2}$	$-\dfrac{a^2 + \mu b^2}{8}$	$+\dfrac{b}{2}$	$+\dfrac{ab}{4}$	$+(1+\mu)a$	$-\dfrac{a}{2}$		$+1$
3	$-\dfrac{a}{2}$	$-\dfrac{ab}{4}$	$+\dfrac{\mu a}{2}$	$-\dfrac{\mu a^2 + b^2}{8}$		$+\dfrac{b}{2}$	$+1$	
4	$-\dfrac{\mu b}{2}$	$\dfrac{a^2 + \mu b^2}{8}$	$+\dfrac{b}{2}$	$-\dfrac{ab}{4}$	$-(1+\mu)a$	$+\dfrac{a}{2}$		$+1$
5	$-\dfrac{a}{2}$	$+\dfrac{ab}{4}$	$+\dfrac{\mu a}{2}$	$-\dfrac{\mu a^2 + b^2}{8}$		$-\dfrac{b}{2}$	$+1$	
6	$+\dfrac{\mu b}{2}$	$-\dfrac{a^2 + \mu b^2}{8}$	$-\dfrac{b}{2}$	$+\dfrac{ab}{4}$	$-(1+\mu)a$	$+\dfrac{a}{2}$		$+1$
7	$+\dfrac{a}{2}$	$-\dfrac{ab}{4}$	$-\dfrac{\mu a}{2}$	$-\dfrac{\mu a^2 + b^2}{8}$		$-\dfrac{b}{2}$	$+1$	
8	$+\dfrac{\mu b}{2}$	$-\dfrac{a^2 + \mu b^2}{8}$	$-\dfrac{b}{2}$	$-\dfrac{ab}{4}$	$+(1+\mu)a$	$-\dfrac{a}{2}$		$+1$

(8.6.13)

$[C^{-1}] = E$ *

α \ X	1	2	3	4	5	6	7	8
1	$+\dfrac{1}{2a(1-\mu^2)}$	$+\dfrac{\mu}{2b(1-\mu^2)}$	$-\dfrac{1}{2a(1-\mu^2)}$	$+\dfrac{\mu}{2b(1-\mu^2)}$	$-\dfrac{1}{2a(1-\mu^2)}$	$-\dfrac{\mu}{2b(1-\mu^2)}$	$+\dfrac{1}{2a(1-\mu^2)}$	$-\dfrac{\mu}{2b(1-\mu^2)}$
2	$+\dfrac{1}{ab}$		$-\dfrac{1}{ab}$		$+\dfrac{1}{ab}$		$-\dfrac{1}{ab}$	
3	$+\dfrac{\mu}{2a(1-\mu^2)}$	$+\dfrac{1}{2b(1-\mu^2)}$	$-\dfrac{\mu}{2a(1-\mu^2)}$	$+\dfrac{1}{2b(1-\mu^2)}$	$-\dfrac{\mu}{2a(1-\mu^2)}$	$-\dfrac{1}{2b(1-\mu^2)}$	$+\dfrac{\mu}{2a(1-\mu^2)}$	$-\dfrac{1}{2b(1-\mu^2)}$
4		$+\dfrac{1}{ab}$		$-\dfrac{1}{ab}$		$+\dfrac{1}{ab}$		$-\dfrac{1}{ab}$
5	$+\dfrac{1}{4b(1+\mu)}$	$+\dfrac{1}{4a(1+\mu)}$	$+\dfrac{1}{4b(1+\mu)}$	$-\dfrac{1}{4a(1+\mu)}$	$-\dfrac{1}{4b(1+\mu)}$	$-\dfrac{1}{4a(1+\mu)}$	$-\dfrac{1}{4b(1+\mu)}$	$+\dfrac{1}{4a(1+\mu)}$
6	$+\dfrac{1}{2b}$		$+\dfrac{1}{2b}$		$-\dfrac{1}{2b}$		$-\dfrac{1}{2b}$	
7	$+\dfrac{1}{4}$	$+\dfrac{\mu a^2 + b^2}{8ab}$	$+\dfrac{1}{4}$	$-\dfrac{\mu a^2 + b^2}{8ab}$	$+\dfrac{1}{4}$	$+\dfrac{\mu a^2 + b^2}{8ab}$	$+\dfrac{1}{4}$	$-\dfrac{\mu a^2 + b^2}{8ab}$
8	$+\dfrac{a^2 + \mu b^2}{8ab}$	$+\dfrac{1}{4}$	$-\dfrac{a^2 + \mu b^2}{8ab}$	$+\dfrac{1}{4}$	$+\dfrac{a^2 + \mu b^2}{8ab}$	$+\dfrac{1}{4}$	$-\dfrac{a^2 + \mu b^2}{8ab}$	$+\dfrac{1}{4}$

(8.6.14)

$$[G] = \frac{1}{E} *$$

e \ α	1	2	3	4	5	6	7	8
1	$+1$	$+y$	$-\mu$	$-\mu x$				
2	$-\mu$	$-\mu y$	$+1$	$+x$				
3					$+2(1+\mu)$			

(8.6.15)

$$[B] = [GC^{-1}]$$

$$=$$

e \ X	1	2	3	4	5	6	7	8
1	$+\dfrac{b+2y}{2ab}$	$-\dfrac{\mu x}{ab}$	$-\dfrac{b+2y}{2ab}$	$+\dfrac{\mu x}{ab}$	$-\dfrac{b-2y}{2ab}$	$-\dfrac{\mu x}{ab}$	$+\dfrac{b-2y}{2ab}$	$+\dfrac{\mu x}{ab}$
2	$-\dfrac{\mu y}{ab}$	$+\dfrac{a+2x}{2ab}$	$+\dfrac{\mu y}{ab}$	$+\dfrac{a-2x}{2ab}$	$-\dfrac{\mu y}{ab}$	$-\dfrac{a-2x}{2ab}$	$+\dfrac{\mu y}{ab}$	$-\dfrac{a+2x}{2ab}$
3	$+\dfrac{1}{2b}$	$+\dfrac{1}{2a}$	$+\dfrac{1}{2b}$	$-\dfrac{1}{2a}$	$-\dfrac{1}{2b}$	$-\dfrac{1}{2a}$	$-\dfrac{1}{2b}$	$+\dfrac{1}{2a}$

(8.6.16)

$$[SB] = E$$

$$*$$

σ \ X	1	2	3	4
1	$+\dfrac{y}{ab} + \dfrac{1}{2a(1-\mu^2)}$	$+\dfrac{\mu}{2b(1-\mu^2)}$	$-\dfrac{y}{ab} - \dfrac{1}{2a(1-\mu^2)}$	$+\dfrac{\mu}{2b(1-\mu^2)}$
2	$+\dfrac{\mu}{2a(1-\mu^2)}$	$+\dfrac{x}{2b} + \dfrac{1}{2b(1-\mu^2)}$	$-\dfrac{\mu}{2a(1-\mu^2)}$	$-\dfrac{x}{2b} + \dfrac{1}{2b(1-\mu^2)}$
3	$+\dfrac{1}{4b(1+\mu)}$	$+\dfrac{1}{4a(1+\mu)}$	$+\dfrac{1}{4b(1+\mu)}$	$-\dfrac{1}{4a(1+\mu)}$

σ \ X	5	6	7	8
1	$+\dfrac{y}{ab} - \dfrac{1}{2a(1-\mu^2)}$	$-\dfrac{\mu}{2b(1-\mu^2)}$	$-\dfrac{y}{ab} + \dfrac{1}{2a(1-\mu^2)}$	$-\dfrac{\mu}{2b(1-\mu^2)}$
2	$-\dfrac{\mu}{2a(1-\mu^2)}$	$+\dfrac{x}{2b} - \dfrac{1}{2b(1-\mu^2)}$	$+\dfrac{\mu}{2a(1-\mu^2)}$	$-\dfrac{x}{2b} - \dfrac{1}{2b(1-\mu^2)}$
3	$-\dfrac{1}{4b(1+\mu)}$	$-\dfrac{1}{4a(1+\mu)}$	$-\dfrac{1}{4b(1+\mu)}$	$+\dfrac{1}{4a(1+\mu)}$

$$(8.6.17)$$

$$[K] = \int [B^T][SB]\, t\, dA$$

$$= \quad (8.6.18)$$

P \ X	1	2	3	4	5	6	7	8
1	$T1$	$T11$	$T3$	$T9$	$T5$	$-T12$	$T7$	$-T10$
2	$T11$	$T2$	$-T9$	$T8$	$-T12$	$T6$	$T10$	$T4$
3	$T3$	$-T9$	$T1$	$-T11$	$T7$	$T10$	$T5$	$T12$
4	$T9$	$T8$	$-T11$	$T2$	$-T10$	$T4$	$T12$	$T6$
5	$T5$	$-T12$	$T7$	$-T10$	$T1$	$T11$	$T3$	$T9$
6	$-T12$	$T6$	$T10$	$T4$	$T11$	$T2$	$-T9$	$T8$
7	$T7$	$T10$	$T5$	$T12$	$T3$	$-T9$	$T1$	$-T11$
8	$-T10$	$T4$	$T12$	$T6$	$T9$	$T8$	$-T11$	$T2$

in which

$$T1 = \frac{Et}{12(1-\mu^2)}\left[+(4-\mu^2)\frac{b}{a} + \frac{3}{2}(1-\mu)\frac{a}{b}\right]$$

$$T2 = \frac{Et}{12(1-\mu^2)}\left[+(4-\mu^2)\frac{a}{b} + \frac{3}{2}(1-\mu)\frac{b}{a}\right]$$

$$T3 = \frac{Et}{12(1 - \mu^2)} \left[-(4 - \mu^2) \frac{b}{a} + \frac{3}{2} (1 - \mu) \frac{a}{b} \right]$$

$$T4 = \frac{Et}{12(1 - \mu^2)} \left[-(4 - \mu^2) \frac{a}{b} + \frac{3}{2} (1 - \mu) \frac{b}{a} \right]$$

$$T5 = \frac{Et}{12(1 - \mu^2)} \left[-(2 + \mu^2) \frac{b}{a} - \frac{3}{2} (1 - \mu) \frac{a}{b} \right]$$

$$T6 = \frac{Et}{12(1 - \mu^2)} \left[-(2 + \mu^2) \frac{a}{b} - \frac{3}{2} (1 - \mu) \frac{b}{a} \right]$$

$$T7 = \frac{Et}{12(1 - \mu^2)} \left[+(2 + \mu^2) \frac{b}{a} - \frac{3}{2} (1 - \mu) \frac{a}{b} \right]$$

$$T8 = \frac{Et}{12(1 - \mu^2)} \left[+(2 + \mu^2) \frac{a}{b} - \frac{3}{2} (1 - \mu) \frac{b}{a} \right]$$

$$T9 = \frac{Et}{12(1 - \mu^2)} \left[+\frac{3}{2} (3\mu - 1) \right]$$

$$T10 = T9$$

$$T11 = \frac{Et}{12(1 - \mu^2)} \left[+\frac{3}{2} (1 + \mu) \right]$$

$$T12 = T11$$

8.7. Compatible Edge Displacement versus Compatible Edge Stress

It has been said before that in a general situation, the finite elements are considered to be connected at the nodal points only. The displacements of these nodal points are the basic unknowns in the so-called *displacement method* of finite-element analysis.

When it may so happen that the displacements at all points are always identical at an edge common to two adjacent finite elements, the formulation is one of compatible edge displacement. Likewise, if the internal forces, such as the three stresses in plane stress analysis, are always identical at all points of a common edge, the formulation is one of compatible edge stress.

If a finite-element model has compatible edge displacement but incompatible edge stress, the nodal displacements resulting from any external imposition should be smaller than the true values, because there would have been supporting stresses at the edges to maintain equilibrium. On the other hand, should a finite element have compatible edge stress but incompatible edge displacement, the nodal displacements in any analysis would be larger than the true values, because the relative gaps and overlaps at the edges could be taken as "cutting loose" the structure.

The triangular finite element derived for plane stress analysis in Sec. 8.4, and the rectangular element derived in Sec. 8.5, both have compatible edge displacement. Within the triangle each of the three stresses has a constant value at all points but may differ from the corresponding values of the adjacent triangles. In the rectangular element of compatible edge displacement, the stresses vary with y when x is constant, and vary with x when y is constant; but they do not match at a common edge.

The rectangular finite element derived for plane stress analysis in Sec. 8.6 has both incompatible edge displacement and incompatible edge stress. While incompatible edge displacement tends to yield nodal displacements larger than true values, incompatible edge stress will tend to cancel at least some of this effect. Some numerical examples will be shown later in the chapter.

8.8. Principal Stress Modes

Frequently it is highly desirable to test the appropriateness of a finite-element model by substituting the principal stress modes in the stiffness matrix of the element obtained from application of the reciprocal energy theorem. In plane stress analysis the three principal stress modes are: (1) $\sigma_1 \neq 0$, $\sigma_2 = 0$; $\sigma_3 = 0$; (2) $\sigma_1 = 0$, $\sigma_2 \neq 0$, $\sigma_3 = 0$; and (3) $\sigma_1 = 0$, $\sigma_2 = 0$, $\sigma_3 \neq 0$. For a rectangular element, the lumped forces at the nodes, as well as the nodal displacements, in each principal stress mode may be conveniently obtained by visual inspection, as shown in Fig. 8.8.1. Note that in the pure shear state of Fig. 8.8.1d, the horizontal and vertical displacements at each corner are related by an arbitrary ratio k such that

$$v_3 = ku_3 \qquad (8.8.1)$$

From the stress-strain relationship,

$$\sigma_3 = \frac{E}{2(1+\mu)} e_3 = \frac{E}{2(1+\mu)}\left(\frac{2u_3}{b} + \frac{2v_3}{a}\right) \qquad (8.8.2)$$

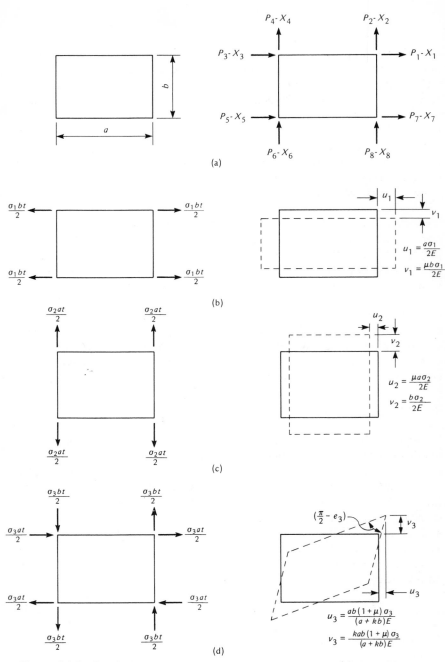

Figure 8.8.1. *Principal stress modes in plane stress analysis. (a) Rectangular finite element in plane stress analysis. (b) $\sigma_1 \neq 0$, $\sigma_2 = 0$, $\sigma_3 = 0$; (c) $\sigma_1 = 0$, $\sigma_2 \neq 0$, $\sigma_3 = 0$; (d) $\sigma_1 = 0$, $\sigma_2 = 0$, $\sigma_3 \neq 0$.*

Solving Eqs. 8.8.1 and 8.8.2 for u_3 and v_3,

$$u_3 = \frac{ab\,(1 + \mu)\,\sigma_3}{(a + kb)\,E} \qquad (8.8.3a)$$

$$v_3 = \frac{kab\,(1 + \mu)\,\sigma_3}{(a + kb)\,E} \qquad (8.8.3b)$$

The nodal forces and displacements corresponding to the three principal stress modes may be summarized as follows:

Principal Stress Mode		1	2	3	4	5	6	7	8
				Local Degree of Freedom Numbers					
1	P	$+\frac{\sigma_1 bt}{2}$	0	$-\frac{\sigma_1 bt}{2}$	0	$-\frac{\sigma_1 bt}{2}$	0	$+\frac{\sigma_1 bt}{2}$	0
	X	$+\frac{a\sigma_1}{2E}$	$-\frac{\mu b\sigma_1}{2E}$	$-\frac{a\sigma_1}{2E}$	$-\frac{\mu b\sigma_1}{2E}$	$-\frac{a\sigma_1}{2E}$	$+\frac{\mu b\sigma_1}{2E}$	$+\frac{a\sigma_1}{2E}$	$+\frac{\mu b\sigma_1}{2E}$
2	P	0	$+\frac{\sigma_2 at}{2}$	0	$+\frac{\sigma_2 at}{2}$	0	$-\frac{\sigma_2 at}{2}$	0	$-\frac{\sigma_2 at}{2}$
	X	$-\frac{\mu a\sigma_2}{2E}$	$+\frac{b\sigma_2}{2E}$	$+\frac{\mu a\sigma_2}{2E}$	$+\frac{b\sigma_2}{2E}$	$+\frac{\mu a\sigma_2}{2E}$	$+\frac{b\sigma_2}{2E}$	$-\frac{\mu a\sigma_2}{2E}$	$+\frac{b\sigma_2}{2E}$
3	P	$+\frac{\sigma_3 at}{2}$	$+\frac{\sigma_3 bt}{2}$	$+\frac{\sigma_3 at}{2}$	$-\frac{\sigma_3 bt}{2}$	$-\frac{\sigma_3 bt}{2}$	$\frac{\sigma_3 at}{2}$	$\frac{\sigma_3 bt}{2}$	$\frac{\sigma_3 at}{2}$
	X	$+TEMP1$	$+TEMP2$	$+TEMP1$	$-TEMP2$	$-TEMP1$	$-TEMP2$	$-TEMP1$	$+TEMP2$

$$TEMP1 = \frac{ab(1 + \mu)\sigma_3}{(a + kb)\,E} \qquad TEMP2 = \frac{kab(1 + \mu)\sigma_3}{(a + kb)\,E}$$

The appropriateness of the two $[K]$ matrices, obtained for the rectangular finite element in Eqs. 8.5.8 and 8.6.18, is in fact ascertained because the equation $\{P\} = [K]\{X\}$ is satisfied by all three sets of P-X vectors in the three principal stress modes.

8.9. Effects of Symmetrical Finite Element

When a finite element is symmetrical about two orthogonal reference axes through its geometric center such as in the case of a rectangle, the interrelationships between the sets of nodal forces and the sets of nodal displacements must satisfy a good number of common sense observations. As an illustration, for the rectangular element in plane stress analysis shown in Fig. 8.9.1, the elements K_{11}, K_{33}, K_{55}, and K_{77} in the stiffness matrix $[K]$ must be equal; and the elements K_{22}, K_{44}, K_{66}, and K_{88}, should not only be equal to each other but must be identical in form to that of $K_{11} = K_{33} = K_{55} = K_{77}$ except with a and b interchanged. By this kind of reasoning it is found that only 12 different ele-

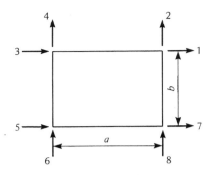

Figure 8.9.1. *Rectangular finite element in plane stress analysis.*

ment values, denoted by $T1$ to $T12$, should appear in the stiffness matrix $[K]$ as shown:

$$[K] =$$

P \ X	1	2	3	4	5	6	7	8
1	$T1$	$T11$	$T3$	$T9$	$T5$	$-T12$	$T7$	$-T10$
2	$T11$	$T2$	$-T9$	$T8$	$-T12$	$T6$	$T10$	$T4$
3	$T3$	$-T9$	$T1$	$-T11$	$T7$	$T10$	$T5$	$T12$
4	$T9$	$T8$	$-T11$	$T2$	$-T10$	$T4$	$T12$	$T6$
5	$T5$	$-T12$	$T7$	$-T10$	$T1$	$T11$	$T3$	$T9$
6	$-T12$	$T6$	$T10$	$T4$	$T11$	$T2$	$-T9$	$T8$
7	$T7$	$T10$	$T5$	$T12$	$T3$	$-T9$	$T1$	$-T11$
8	$-T10$	$T4$	$T12$	$T6$	$T9$	$T8$	$-T11$	$T2$

$$(8.9.1)$$

The locations of elements which should have the common values are listed in the following table.

Element Value	Element Locations			
$T1$	1-1	3-3	5-5	7-7
$T2$	2-2	4-4	6-6	8-8
$T3$	1-3	3-1	5-7	7-5
$T4$	2-8	8-2	4-6	6-4
$T5$	1-5	5-1	3-7	7-3
$T6$	2-6	6-2	4-8	8-4
$T7$	1-7	7-1	3-5	5-3

Table (cont.)

Element Value	Element Locations			
T8	2-4	4-2	6-8	8-6
T9	1-4	4-1	5-8	8-5
-T9	2-3	3-2	6-7	7-6
T10	2-7	7-2	3-6	6-3
-T10	1-8	8-1	4-5	5-4
T11	1-2	2-1	5-6	6-5
-T11	3-4	4-3	7-8	8-7
T12	3-8	8-3	4-7	7-4
-T12	1-6	6-1	2-5	5-2

8.10. Independent Elements in the Stiffness Matrix of Rectangular Finite Elements

It can be shown that only $T1$ and $T2$ of the 12 values $T1$ to $T12$ in the stiffness matrix (Eq. 8.9.1) of a rectangular finite element in plane stress analysis are independent. The values of $T3$ to $T8$ are expressible in terms of $T1$ and $T2$, and the values of $T9 = T10$ and $T11 = T12$ are dependent only on the modulus of elasticity E, the Poisson's ratio μ, and the thickness of plate t. These relationships may be determined (1) by substituting the three principal stress modes in the first two rows of the $[K]$ matrix (the other 6 rows will give identical information), and (2) by applying the three equations of equilibrium to the 8 nodal forces in the first and second columns of the $[K]$ matrix (the other 6 columns will give identical information).

Substituting the three principal stress modes in the first two rows of the $[K]$ matrix,

$$+\frac{\sigma_1 bt}{2} = \frac{a\sigma_1}{2E}(T1 - T3 - T5 + T7) + \frac{\mu b\sigma_1}{2E}(-T11 - T9 - T12 - T10) \quad (8.10.1)$$

$$0 = \frac{a\sigma_1}{2E}(T11 + T9 + T12 + T10) + \frac{\mu b\sigma_1}{2E}(-T2 - T8 + T6 + T4) \quad (8.10.2)$$

$$0 = \frac{\mu a\sigma_2}{2E}(-T1 + T3 + T5 - T7) + \frac{b\sigma_2}{2E}(T11 + T9 + T12 + T10) \quad (8.10.3)$$

$$+\frac{\sigma_2 at}{2} = \frac{\mu a\sigma_2}{2E}(-T11 - T9 - T12 - T10) + \frac{b\sigma_2}{2E}(T2 + T8 - T6 - T4) \quad (8.10.4)$$

$$+\frac{\sigma_3 at}{2} = \frac{ab(1+\mu)\sigma_3}{(a+kb)E}(T1 + T3 - T5 - T7) + \frac{kab(1+\mu)\sigma_3}{(a+kb)E}(T11 - T9 + T12 - T10)$$
$$(8.10.5)$$

$$+ \frac{\sigma_3 bt}{2} = \frac{ab(1 + \mu)\sigma_3}{(a + kb)E}(T11 - T9 + T12 - T10) + \frac{kab(1 + \mu)\sigma_3}{(a + kb)E}(T2 - T8 - T6 + T4)$$

$$(8.10.6)$$

Applying the three equations of equilibrium to each of the two free-body

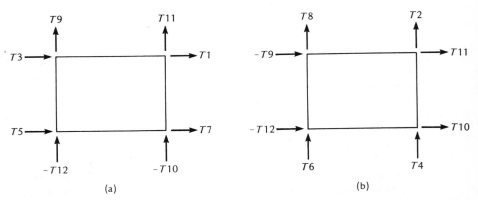

(a)   (b)

Figure 8.10.1. *Free-body diagrams of rectangular finite element.   (a) First column in* [K] *matrix; (b) second column in* [K] *matrix.*

diagrams in Fig. 8.10.1 for the first two columns of the $[K]$ matrix,

$$T1 + T3 + T5 + T7 = 0 \qquad (8.10.7)$$

$$T11 + T9 - T12 - T10 = 0 \qquad (8.10.8)$$

$$(T1 + T3)b = (T11 - T10)a \qquad (8.10.9)$$

$$T11 - T9 - T12 + T10 = 0 \qquad (8.10.10)$$

$$T2 + T8 + T6 + T4 = 0 \qquad (8.10.11)$$

$$(T11 - T9)b = (T2 + T4)a \qquad (8.10.12)$$

After careful and systematic manipulations of the 12 equations as listed in Eqs. 8.10.1 to 8.10.12, it is found that

$$T9 = T10 = \frac{Et(3\mu - 1)}{8(1 - \mu^2)} \qquad (8.10.13)$$

$$T11 = T12 = \frac{Et}{8(1 - \mu)} \qquad (8.10.14)$$

In addition, $T3$, $T5$, and $T7$ are expressible by $T1$ as follows:

$$T3 = \frac{Eat}{4b(1 + \mu)} - T1 \qquad (8.10.15)$$

$$T5 = T1 - \frac{Et[(1 - \mu)a^2 + 2b^2]}{4ab(1 - \mu^2)} \qquad (8.10.16)$$

$$T7 = \frac{Ebt}{2a(1 - \mu^2)} - T1 \qquad (8.10.17)$$

and $T4$, $T6$, and $T8$ are expressible by $T2$ as follows:

$$T4 = \frac{Ebt}{4a(1 + \mu)} - T2 \qquad (8.10.18)$$

$$T6 = T2 - \frac{Et[(1 - \mu)b^2 + 2a^2]}{4ab(1 - \mu^2)} \qquad (8.10.19)$$

$$T8 = \frac{Eat}{2b(1 - \mu^2)} - T2 \qquad (8.10.20)$$

That the expressions 8.10.13 to 8.10.20 are obtainable from the 12 equations 8.10.1 to 8.10.12 may be accounted by the following steps:

(a) adding Eq. 8.10.8 and Eq. 8.10.10,

$$T11 = T12 \qquad (8.10.21)$$

(b) subtracting Eq. 8.10.10 from Eq. 8.10.8,

$$T9 = T10 \qquad (8.10.22)$$

(c) adding μ/σ_1 times Eq. 8.10.1 to $1/\sigma_2$ times Eq. 8.10.3,

$$\frac{\mu t}{2} = \frac{2(1 - \mu^2)}{E}(T9 + T11) \qquad (8.10.23)$$

(d) adding $1/\sigma_1$ times Eq. 8.10.1 to μ/σ_2 times Eq. 8.10.3,

$$\frac{bt}{2} = \frac{a(1 - \mu^2)}{E}(T1 - T3 - T5 + T7) \qquad (8.10.24)$$

(e) adding μ/σ_1 times Eq. 8.10.2 to $1/\sigma_2$ times Eq. 8.10.4,

$$\frac{at}{2} = \frac{b(1 - \mu^2)}{E}(T2 + T8 - T6 - T4) \qquad (8.10.25)$$

(f) adding $1/\sigma_1$ times Eq. 8.10.2 to μ/σ_2 times Eq. 8.10.4,

$$\frac{\mu t}{2} = \frac{2(1 - \mu^2)}{E}(T9 + T11) \qquad (8.10.26)$$

(At this point it is seen that Eqs. 8.10.23 and 8.10.26 are identical, which means that at least one of the original 12 equations 8.10.1 to 8.10.12 is redundant.)

(g) combining Eqs. 8.10.5, 8.10.7, and 8.10.9 so that only $(T1 + T3)$ appears,

$$T1 + T3 = \frac{Eat}{4b(1 + \mu)} = (T11 - T9)\frac{a}{b} = -(T5 + T7) \qquad (8.10.27)$$

(It is interesting to note that, in the process, the constant k which has been used in the third principal stress mode cancels out.)

(h) combining Eqs. 8.10.6, 8.10.10, and 8.10.12 so that only $(T2 + T4)$ appears,

$$T2 + T4 = \frac{Ebt}{4a(1 + \mu)} = (T11 - T9)\frac{b}{a} = -(T6 + T8) \qquad (8.10.28)$$

(i) solving Eq. 8.10.23 (or Eq. 8.10.26) and Eq. 8.10.27 (or Eq. 8.10.28),

$$T9 = T10 = \frac{Et(3\mu - 1)}{8(1 - \mu^2)}$$

$$T11 = T12 = \frac{Et}{8(1 - \mu)}$$

(j) solving $T3$ in terms of $T1$ and $T4$ in terms of $T2$ from Eqs. 8.10.27 and 8.10.28, respectively,

(k) solving Eqs. 8.10.24 and 8.10.27 simultaneously for $T5$ and $T7$, and

(l) solving Eqs. 8.10.25 and 8.10.28 simultaneously for $T6$ and $T8$.

8.11. Nodal Forces in the Fixed Condition

Often the external forces are applied directly at the nodal points and as such can be entered directly into the input matrix. If, however, distributed forces are present at the boundary of the finite element, equivalent joint forces should be obtained and then used in the analysis. In order to do this, a set of locking forces, here called the *nodal forces in the fixed condition,* is determined to fix all nodal displacements at zero value when the finite element is subjected to the distributed forces. Then the reverses of the locking forces are applied as external forces in the displacement method.

The nodal forces in the fixed condition can be obtained by applying the reciprocal energy theorem between the real fixed condition and each of the fictitious Q-Y basic modes. Consider the real fixed condition of a rectangular finite element in plane stress analysis shown in Fig. 8.11.1. The right-hand boundary is subjected to a distributed tensile stress varying from σ_{01} at the lower edge to σ_{02} at the upper edge. It is required to obtain the locking nodal forces P_{01} to P_{08}.

For the finite-element model of linear edge displacement derived in Sec. 8.5, the horizontal displacement u at the right edge is, from substituting $x = +a/2$ in Eq. 8.5.1a,

$$u\,(x = +a/2) = \frac{a}{2}\,\alpha_1 + \frac{a}{2}\,y\,\alpha_2 + y\,\alpha_3 + \alpha_4 \qquad (8.11.1)$$

But α_1 to α_4 in each of the 8 Q-Y basic modes are, from Eq. 8.5.3,

α \ Y	1	2	3	4	5	6	7	8
1	$+\dfrac{1}{2a}$		$-\dfrac{1}{2a}$		$-\dfrac{1}{2a}$		$+\dfrac{1}{2a}$	
2	$+\dfrac{1}{ab}$		$-\dfrac{1}{ab}$		$+\dfrac{1}{ab}$		$-\dfrac{1}{ab}$	
3	$+\dfrac{1}{2b}$		$+\dfrac{1}{2b}$		$-\dfrac{1}{2b}$		$-\dfrac{1}{2b}$	
4	$+\dfrac{1}{4}$		$+\dfrac{1}{4}$		$+\dfrac{1}{4}$		$+\dfrac{1}{4}$	

$$(8.11.2)$$

Combining Eqs. 8.11.1 and 8.11.2, the horizontal displacements u at the right

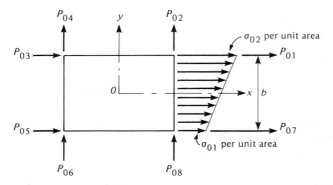

Figure 8.11.1. *Fixed-condition forces on a rectangular finite element.*

edge in each of the 8 Q-Y basic modes are:

$$\{u \text{ at } x = +a/2\} = \begin{Bmatrix} \left(+\dfrac{1}{2}+\dfrac{y}{b}\right) \\ 0 \\ 0 \\ 0 \\ 0 \\ 0 \\ \left(+\dfrac{1}{2}-\dfrac{y}{b}\right) \\ 0 \end{Bmatrix} \tag{8.11.3}$$

Applying the reciprocal energy theorem between the real fixed condition of Fig. 8.11.1 and the ith Q-Y mode,

$$P_{0i} * Y_i + \int_{-b/2}^{+b/2} \left(\frac{\sigma_1 + \sigma_2}{2} + \frac{\sigma_2 - \sigma_1}{b} y\right) (u_i * Y_i) t \, dy = 0$$

Note that the work done by the Q_i system in going through the displacements in the real fixed condition is equal to zero. In general,

$$\{P_0\} = -\int_{-b/2}^{+b/2} \left(\frac{\sigma_1 + \sigma_2}{2} + \frac{\sigma_2 + \sigma_1}{b}y \right) \left\{ \begin{array}{c} \text{Column} \\ \text{matrix} \\ \text{of} \\ \text{Eq. 8.11.3} \end{array} \right\} t\, dy = \left\{ \begin{array}{c} -\dfrac{1}{6}\sigma_1 bt - \dfrac{1}{3}\sigma_2 bt \\[2mm] 0 \\ 0 \\ 0 \\ 0 \\ 0 \\ -\dfrac{1}{3}\sigma_1 bt - \dfrac{1}{6}\sigma_2 bt \\[2mm] 0 \end{array} \right\}$$

$$(8.11.4)$$

For the finite-element model of linear edge stress derived in Sec. 8.6, the horizontal displacement u at the right edge is, from substituting $x = +a/2$ in Eq. 8.6.11,

$$u\,(x = +a/2) = \frac{1}{E}\left[\frac{a}{2}\alpha_1 + \frac{a}{2}y\alpha_2 - \frac{\mu a}{2}\alpha_3 - \left(\frac{\mu a^2}{8} + \frac{y^2}{2} \right)\alpha_4 + y\alpha_6 + \alpha_7 \right] \quad (8.11.5)$$

Substituting into the above equation the expressions of α available in Eq. 8.6.14, the horizontal displacements u at the right edge in each of the 8 Q-Y basic modes are:

$$\{u \text{ at } x = +a/2\} = \left\{ \begin{array}{c} +\dfrac{1}{2} + \dfrac{y}{b} \\[3mm] +\dfrac{b^2 - 4y^2}{8ab} \\[3mm] 0 \\[3mm] -\dfrac{b^2 - 4y^2}{8ab} \\[3mm] 0 \\[3mm] +\dfrac{b^2 - 4y^2}{8ab} \\[3mm] +\dfrac{1}{2} - \dfrac{y}{b} \\[3mm] -\dfrac{b^2 - 4y^2}{8ab} \end{array} \right\} \qquad (8.11.6)$$

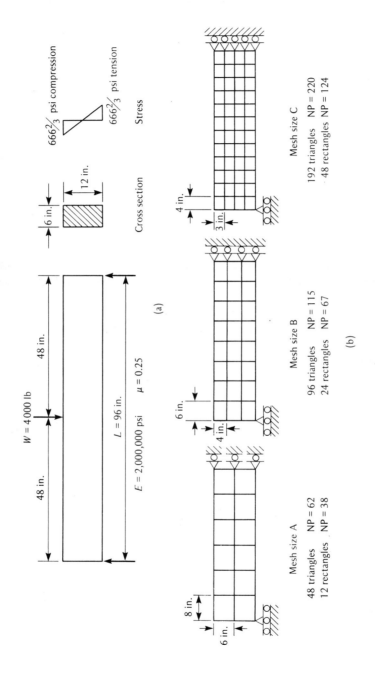

$W = 4\,000$ lb

48 in.

48 in.

$L = 96$ in.

$E = 2{,}000{,}000$ psi $\mu = 0.25$

(a)

$666\frac{2}{3}$ psi compression

$666\frac{2}{3}$ psi tension

Stress

12 in.

6 in.

Cross section

Mesh size A   NP = 62
48 triangles   NP = 38
12 rectangles

8 in.

6 in.

Mesh size B   NP = 115
96 triangles   NP = 67
24 rectangles

6 in.

4 in.

(b)

Mesh size C   NP = 220
192 triangles   NP = 124
48 rectangles

4 in.

3 in.

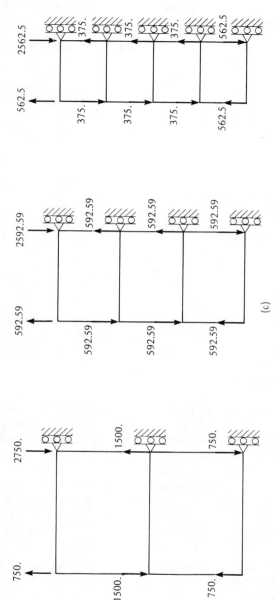

Figure 8.12.1. *Plane stress analysis of a simple beam. (a) A simple beam; (b) mesh sizes A, B, and C; (c) joint forces in the linear-edge-stress rectangular model.*

(c)

223

Applying the reciprocal energy theorem between the real fixed condition of Fig. 8.11.1 and the 8 *Q-Y* basic modes,

$$\{P_0\} = -\int_{-b/2}^{+b/2} \left(\frac{\sigma_1 + \sigma_2}{2} + \frac{\sigma_2 - \sigma_1}{b}y\right) \left\{\begin{array}{c} \text{Column} \\ \text{matrix} \\ \text{of} \\ (\text{Eq. 8.11.6}) \end{array}\right\} t\,dy = \left\{\begin{array}{c} -\dfrac{1}{6}\sigma_1 bt - \dfrac{1}{3}\sigma_2 bt \\[2mm] -\dfrac{1}{24}(\sigma_1 + \sigma_2)\dfrac{b^2 t}{a} \\[2mm] 0 \\[2mm] +\dfrac{1}{24}(\sigma_1 + \sigma_2)\dfrac{b^2 t}{a} \\[2mm] 0 \\[2mm] -\dfrac{1}{24}(\sigma_1 + \sigma_2)\dfrac{b^2 t}{a} \\[2mm] -\dfrac{1}{3}\sigma_1 bt - \dfrac{1}{6}\sigma_2 bt \\[2mm] +\dfrac{1}{24}(\sigma_1 + \sigma_2)\dfrac{b^2 t}{a} \end{array}\right\}$$

$$(8.11.7)$$

8.12. Numerical Example

In this section a numerical example will be described to show the results obtained from the computer programs in plane stress analysis. For convenience in reference, the three models developed in Secs. 8.4, 8.5, and 8.6 will be called (1) the constant-strain triangular model, (2) the linear-edge-displacement rectangular model, and (3) the linear-edge-stress rectangular model.

Three mesh sizes *A*, *B*, and *C*, as shown in Fig. 8.12.1b, are used to analyze the simple beam of Fig. 8.12.1a. A special application is made of the triangular model to the case where a group of four triangles forms a rectangle without external forces applied at the interior node. A condensed 8 × 8 stiffness matrix relating to the four corners of the rectangle may be derived from the 10 × 10 matrix compounded from the four triangles within the rectangle. The details of this modified rectangular model based on four triangles will not be shown, because the same output would have been obtained had the triangles been used as such at the expense of a larger global stiffness matrix.

The deflection at the concentrated load as computed by the conventional beam theory is

$$\Delta = \frac{WL^3}{48EI} = \frac{4000\,(96)^3}{48\,(2 \times 10^6)(864)} = 0.04267 \text{ in.}$$

This deflection as obtained from the finite-element method is tabulated in the adjacent table.

Mesh Size	Constant-Strain Triangular Model	Linear-Edge-Displacement Rectangular Model	Linear-Edge-Stress Rectangular Model
A	0.03479 in.	0.03738 in.	0.04438 in.
B	0.03833 in.	0.04004 in.	0.04430 in.
C	0.04131 in.	0.04225 in.	0.04423 in.

It is seen that in each model as the mesh size is decreased the deflection gets closer to that computed by the conventional beam theory. Since both displacement compatibility and stress incompatibility exist at the boundaries of the rectangle as well as along the diagonals inside the rectangle in the triangular model, the resulting deflection in this model is logically the smallest of all the three models. In the linear-edge-stress rectangular model it seems that the tendency of causing larger deflection by displacement incompatibility is more pronounced than that of causing smaller deflection by stress incompatibility.

Of the external forces, the 2000-lb concentrated force is applied directly at the node, but the stress shown in Fig. 8.12.1a as computed by the conventional flexure formula is a distributed force along the right edge of the half-beam model. The fixed-condition nodal forces are computed by the formulas in Sec. 8.11 and their reverses are then applied at the nodes. The actual nodal forces for the linear-edge-stress rectangular model are shown in Fig. 8.12.1c.

8.13. The Computer Program

In Appendix G is shown a typical computer program for plane stress analysis using rectangular elements with linear edge displacement as described in Sec. 8.5. The output would show first the nodal displacements along the global degrees of freedom, and then for each element the equations for σ_x (or σ_1), σ_y (or σ_2), τ_{xy} (or σ_3), u, and v in terms of the coordinates x and y referred to the center of the element as origin.

As a simple illustration, the input and output are shown for the numerical example in Sec. 8.12 using only 2 rectangular finite elements in one-half of the simple beam. The input data shown in Table 8.13.1 is in accord with the global degree-of-freedom and element numbers shown in Fig. 8.13.1. To test the program, the two loading conditions are made identical; i.e., a 2000-lb load opposite to the 8th degree of freedom.

The output information delivered by the computer program includes:

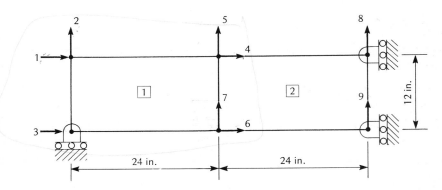

Figure 8.13.1. *Two finite-element solution for one-half of the simple beam in Figure 8.12.1.*

TABLE 8.13.1

Input for Plate Structure in Plane Stress Shown in Fig. 8.13.1

Card No.	Elements	Format	Remarks
1	1	I5	Data set No. 1
2	9 2 2 2000000. .25 6.	3I5, 3F10.4	NP, NELMT, NLC, E, μ, t
3	1 4 5 1 2 3 10 6 7 24. 12.	9I5, 2F10.4	Elem No., NP1 . . . NP8, a, b
4	2 10 8 4 5 6 7 10 9 24. 12.	9I5, 2F10.4	Elem No., NP1 . . . NP8, a, b
5	0	I5	No more rectangular element
6	8 1 −2000.	2I5, F10.4	Nonzero element in P-matrix
7	8 2 −2000.	2I5, F10.4	Nonzero element in P-matrix
8	0	I5	No more nonzero element in [P]
9 10 11	Repeat cards 3 to 5 for 1st loading condition		
12 13 14	Repeat cards 3 to 5 for 2nd loading condition		
15	0	I5	No more data set

(1) The nodal displacements along the global degrees of freedom are

$$X(1) = +.29583398E - 02 \qquad X(2) = -.14881078E - 03$$
$$X(3) = -.30416754E - 02 \qquad X(4) = +.22291761E - 02$$
$$X(5) = -.11375032E - 01 \qquad X(6) = -.22708446E - 02$$
$$X(7) = -.11440512E - 01 \qquad X(8) = -.16815553E - 01$$
$$X(9) = -.16666734E - 01$$

(2) For Element No. 1,

$$\sigma_x = (+.1244189E - 03) + (+.3968365E + 00)x + (-.1111107E + 02)y$$
$$\sigma_y = (-.6944061E + 01) + (+.1587346E + 01)x + (-.2777767E + 01)y$$
$$\tau_{xy} = (-.2777775E + 02) + (-.4166650E + 01)x + (+.5952548E + 00)y$$
$$u = (+.8680702E - 06)x + (-.5208314E - 05)xy + (+.4375015E - 03)y$$
$$\quad + (-.3125123E - 04)$$
$$v = (-.4722237E - 03)x + (+.7440686E - 06)xy + (-.3472048E - 05)y$$
$$\quad + (-.5741090E - 02)$$

(3) For Element No. 2,

$$\sigma_x = (+.6233071E - 04) + (-.3968536E + 00)x + (-.3333347E + 02)y$$
$$\sigma_y = (-.6944543E + 01) + (-.1587415E + 01)x + (-.8333369E + 01)y$$
$$\tau_{xy} = (-.2777836E + 02) + (-.1250006E + 02)x + (-.5952806E + 00)y$$
$$u = (+.8680993E - 06)x + (-.1562507E - 04)xy + (+.1875009E - 03)y$$
$$\quad + (-.1041719E - 04)$$
$$v = (-.2222238E - 03)x + (-.7441007E - 06)xy + (-.3472280E - 05)y$$
$$\quad + (-.1407446E - 01)$$

CHAPTER 9

■

Stiffness Matrix of Rectangular Element in Bending

9.1. Flat Plates in Bending

Analysis of flat plates in bending, next to plane stress analysis, is another common topic in Theory of Elasticity. In this case, vertically downward loads are applied to a horizontal flat plate, assumed to cause bending only without in-plane stretching. Supports may be provided at or within the edges, either continuous or concentrated. Generally, rigorous solutions are more readily obtainable in cases where only the edges are simply supported or fixed.

The stress condition at any point (x,y) of a flat plate may be described by three generalized internal forces M_x, M_y, and M_{xy}, as shown in Fig. 9.1.1. M_x and M_y are the bending moments per unit length; they are positive if they cause concave curvature at the top surface. M_{xy} is the twisting moment per unit length; it is positive if its vectors in the x-direction point away from each other.

The strain energy in an infinitesimal element $dydx$ due to M_x alone, as shown

229

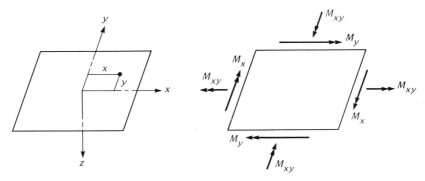

Figure 9.1.1. *Generalized internal forces in a flat plate under bending.*

in Fig. 9.1.2a, is

$$dU \text{ due to } M_x \text{ alone} = \frac{1}{2} (M_x \, dy)(\phi_1) - \frac{1}{2} (M_x \, dy)(\phi_2)$$

$$= \frac{1}{2} (M_x \, dy) \frac{\partial z}{\partial x} - \frac{1}{2} (M_x \, dy) \left(\frac{\partial z}{\partial x} + \frac{\partial^2 z}{\partial x^2} dx \right)$$

$$= \frac{1}{2} M_x \left(-\frac{\partial^2 z}{\partial x^2} \right) dy \, dx \qquad (9.1.1)$$

Similarly, the strain energy in *dydx* due to M_y alone is

$$dU \text{ due to } M_y \text{ alone} = \frac{1}{2} M_y \left(-\frac{\partial^2 z}{\partial y^2} \right) dy \, dx \qquad (9.1.2)$$

The strain energy in *dydx* due to M_{xy} alone, as shown in Fig. 9.1.2b, is

$$dU \text{ due to } M_{xy} \text{ alone} = -\frac{1}{2} M_{xy} \, dy \, (\phi_1) - \frac{1}{2} M_{xy} \, dx \, (\phi_2)$$

$$= -\frac{1}{2} M_{xy} \, dy \, \frac{\partial^2 z}{\partial x \partial y} dx - \frac{1}{2} M_{xy} \, dx \, \frac{\partial^2 z}{\partial x \partial y} dy$$

$$= \frac{1}{2} M_{xy} \left(-2 \frac{\partial^2 z}{\partial x \partial y} \right) dy \, dx \qquad (9.1.3)$$

Because the strain energy is equal to one-half of the product of an internal force and its associated deformation, the three generalized internal deformations can

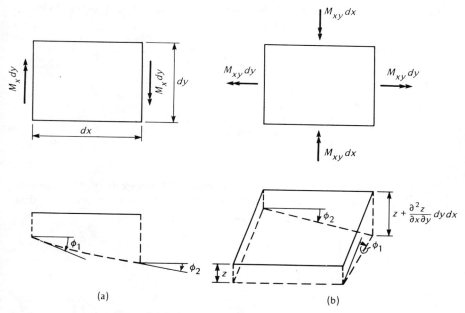

Figure 9.1.2. *Strain energy in a flat plate element.*

be observed from Eqs. 9.1.1 to 9.1.3 to be:

$$\phi_x = -\frac{\partial^2 z}{\partial x^2} \qquad \phi_y = -\frac{\partial^2 z}{\partial y^2} \qquad \phi_{xy} = -2\frac{\partial^2 z}{\partial x \, \partial y} \qquad (9.1.4)$$

9.2. Relationships between Internal Forces and Internal Deformations

The relationships between the three generalized internal forces $M_x - M_y - M_{xy}$ and their corresponding internal deformations $\phi_x - \phi_y - \phi_{xy}$ may be expressed by either the particle-flexibility matrix $[D]$ or the particle-stiffness matrix $[S]$.

By the definition of the Poisson's ratio μ and on the basis of simple bending theory, the curvatures ϕ_x and ϕ_y are equal to

$$\phi_x = -\frac{\partial^2 z}{\partial x^2} = \frac{M_x}{EI} - \frac{\mu M_y}{EI} \qquad (9.2.1)$$

$$\phi_y = -\frac{\partial^2 z}{\partial y^2} = \frac{M_y}{EI} - \frac{\mu M_x}{EI} \qquad (9.2.2)$$

in which E is the modulus of elasticity and $I = t^3/12$.

The flexibility relationship between the twist angle ϕ_{xy} and the twisting moment M_{xy} may be expressed by

$$\phi_{xy} = -2\frac{\partial^2 z}{\partial x \partial y} = CM_{xy} \tag{9.2.3a}$$

The quantity C may be shown to be

$$C = \frac{2(1+\mu)}{EI} \tag{9.2.3b}$$

Let M_x' and M_{xy}' in Fig. 9.2.1b be the bending and twisting moment vectors on a plane at angle α for the stress condition of Fig. 9.2.1a. From the resolution

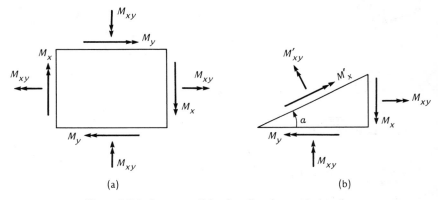

(a)　　　　　　　　　　　(b)

Figure 9.2.1. *Stress condition in a flat element in bending.*

equations of equilibrium along the vector directions of M_x' and M_{xy}'

$$M_x' = M_x \sin^2 \alpha + M_y \cos^2 \alpha - 2M_{xy} \sin \alpha \cos \alpha \tag{9.2.4}$$

and

$$M_{xy}' = (M_x - M_y) \sin \alpha \cos \alpha + M_{xy} (\sin^2 \alpha - \cos^2 \alpha) \tag{9.2.5}$$

By means of Eqs. 9.2.4 and 9.2.5 it may be verified that the stress conditions:

(1) at $\alpha = 0$, $\quad M_x = +M$, $\quad M_y = -M$, $\quad M_{xy} = 0$
(2) at $\alpha = 45°$, $\quad M_x' = 0$, $\quad M_y' = 0$, $\quad M_{xy}' = +M$

are identical. In the first case, the strain energy U_1 per unit volume is

$$U_1 = \frac{1}{2} M_x \phi_x + \frac{1}{2} M_y \phi_y = \frac{1}{2} (+M) \left(\frac{M}{EI} + \frac{\mu M}{EI} \right) + \frac{1}{2} (-M) \left(-\frac{M}{EI} - \frac{\mu M}{EI} \right)$$

$$= \frac{1 + \mu}{EI} M^2 \tag{9.2.6}$$

In the second case, the strain energy U_2 per unit volume is

$$U_2 = \frac{1}{2} M'_{xy} \phi'_{xy} = \frac{1}{2} M (CM) = \frac{1}{2} CM^2 \tag{9.2.7}$$

Since $U_1 = U_2$,

$$C = \frac{2(1 + \mu)}{EI}$$

The particle-flexibility matrix $[D]$ for the flat plate in bending is therefore,

$$[D] =$$

e \ F	M_x	M_y	M_{xy}
ϕ_x	$+\dfrac{1}{EI}$	$-\dfrac{\mu}{EI}$	0
ϕ_y	$-\dfrac{\mu}{EI}$	$+\dfrac{1}{EI}$	0
ϕ_{xy}	0	0	$+\dfrac{2(1+\mu)}{EI}$

$$\tag{9.2.8}$$

The particle-stiffness matrix $[S]$ may be obtained by inverting Eq. (9.2.8); thus:

$$[S] =$$

F \ e	ϕ_x	ϕ_y	ϕ_{xy}
M_x	$+\dfrac{EI}{1-\mu^2}$	$+\dfrac{\mu EI}{1-\mu^2}$	0
M_y	$+\dfrac{\mu EI}{1-\mu^2}$	$+\dfrac{EI}{1-\mu^2}$	0
M_{xy}	0	0	$+\dfrac{EI}{2(1+\mu)}$

$$\tag{9.2.9}$$

9.3. The Exact Differential Equation for Plate Bending

The exact differential equation for plate bending should involve the downward vertical deflection z and the applied load intensity q per unit area on a differential element $dydx$. Consider the three equations of equilibrium for the

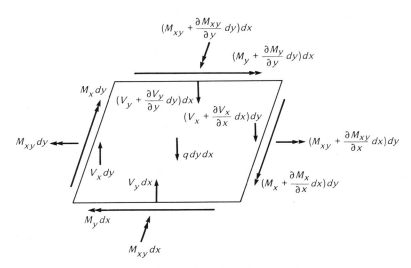

Figure 9.3.1. *Equilibrium of a differential element.*

differential element shown in Fig. 9.3.1. From the vertical resolution equation,

$$\frac{\partial V_x}{\partial x} + \frac{\partial V_y}{\partial y} + q = 0 \tag{9.3.1}$$

From the moment equation about the y-axis,

$$\frac{\partial M_x}{\partial x} + \frac{\partial M_{xy}}{\partial y} - V_x = 0 \tag{9.3.2}$$

From the moment equation about the x-axis,

$$\frac{\partial M_y}{\partial y} + \frac{\partial M_{xy}}{\partial x} - V_y = 0 \tag{9.3.3}$$

Substituting Eqs. 9.3.2 and 9.3.3 in Eq. 9.3.1,

$$\frac{\partial^2 M_x}{\partial x^2} + 2\frac{\partial^2 M_{xy}}{\partial x \partial y} + \frac{\partial^2 M_y}{\partial y^2} + q = 0 \tag{9.3.4}$$

From the particle-stiffness matrix,

$$M_x = \frac{EI}{1-\mu^2}(\phi_x + \mu\phi_y) = -\frac{EI}{1-\mu^2}\left(\frac{\partial^2 z}{\partial x^2} + \mu\frac{\partial^2 z}{\partial y^2}\right) \tag{9.3.5}$$

$$M_y = \frac{EI}{1-\mu^2}(\mu\phi_x + \phi_y) = -\frac{EI}{1-\mu^2}\left(\mu\frac{\partial^2 z}{\partial x^2} + \frac{\partial^2 z}{\partial y^2}\right) \tag{9.3.6}$$

$$M_{xy} = \frac{EI}{2(1+\mu)}\phi_{xy} = -\frac{EI}{(1+\mu)}\frac{\partial^2 z}{\partial x \partial y} = -\frac{EI}{1-\mu^2}\left[(1-\mu)\frac{\partial^2 z}{\partial x \partial y}\right] \tag{9.3.7}$$

Substituting Eqs. 9.3.5 to 9.3.7 in Eq. 9.3.4,

$$\frac{\partial^4 z}{\partial x^4} + \mu\frac{\partial^4 z}{\partial x^2 \partial y^2} + 2(1-\mu)\frac{\partial^4 z}{\partial x^2 \partial y^2} + \mu\frac{\partial^4 z}{\partial x^2 \partial y^2} + \frac{\partial^4 z}{\partial y^4} = \frac{q(1-\mu^2)}{EI}$$

or

$$\frac{\partial^4 z}{\partial x^4} + 2\frac{\partial^4 z}{\partial x^2 \partial y^2} + \frac{\partial^4 z}{\partial y^4} = \frac{q(1-\mu^2)}{EI} \tag{9.3.8}$$

Equation 9.3.8 is the exact differential equation for plate bending.

9.4. The Approximate Displacement Equation

When a rectangular finite element in bending is considered to joint with the adjacent elements at its four corners only, there are three degrees of freedom per node. The 12 local degrees of freedom are numbered as shown in Fig. 9.4.1, starting with the corner in the first quadrant and ending at the corner in the fourth quadrant.

The approximate displacement equation

$$\begin{aligned}
z = \alpha_1 &+ \alpha_2 x + \alpha_3 y + \alpha_4 x^2 + \alpha_5 xy + \alpha_6 y^2 \\
&+ \alpha_7 x^3 + \alpha_8 x^2 y + \alpha_9 xy^2 + \alpha_{10} y^3 \\
&+ \alpha_{11} x^3 y + \alpha_{12} xy^3
\end{aligned} \tag{9.4.1}$$

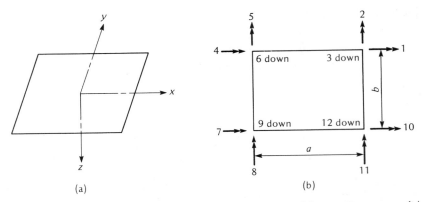

Figure 9.4.1. *Rectangular finite element in bending. (a) Coordinate axes, (b) P-X numbers.*

satisfies the requirement that it contains the same number of arbitrary constants as the number of local degrees of freedom per element. It also satisfies the exact differential equation 9.3.8 at all points within the element so long as external forces are applied at the nodes only. In addition, the equation is cubic in x when y is constant and cubic in y when x is constant. Since the cubic equation in one variable along any common edge between two adjacent elements should have only four coefficients and must at the same time yield common deflections and slopes at the two boundary nodes, there is in fact continuity in deflections at all points around the finite element. The only remaining discontinuity is in the slope across the boundary.

The stiffness matrix of a rectangular finite element in bending will be derived on the basis of the approximate displacement equation 9.4.1.

9.5. The Deformation Matrix $[B]$

The deformation matrix $[B]$ expresses the internal deformations at a point (x, y) in terms of the nodal displacements. In a rectangular finite plate element in bending, the internal deformations are, from Eq. 9.1.4,

$$\{e\} = \begin{Bmatrix} \phi_x \\ \phi_y \\ \phi_{xy} \end{Bmatrix} = \begin{Bmatrix} -\dfrac{\partial^2 z}{\partial x^2} \\ -\dfrac{\partial^2 z}{\partial y^2} \\ -2\dfrac{\partial^2 z}{\partial x \partial y} \end{Bmatrix} \tag{9.5.1}$$

Using the approximate equation 9.4.1 for z, the expression for $[G]$ in the equation

$$\{e\} = [G]\ \{\alpha\}$$

may be found to be

$$[G] =$$

e \ α	1	2	3	4	5	6	7	8	9	10	11	12
ϕ_x			-2				$-6x$	$-2y$			$-6xy$	
ϕ_y				-2					$-2x$	$-6y$		$-6xy$
ϕ_{xy}				-2				$-4x$	$-4y$		$-6x^2$	$-6y^2$

$$(9.5.2)$$

The matrix $[C]$ expresses the nodal displacements $\{X\}$ in terms of the arbitrary constants $\{\alpha\}$ in the approximate displacement equation. According to the P-X numbers and the positive x-y-z axes shown in Fig. 9.4.1,

$$X_1, X_4, X_7, X_{10} = \left(-\frac{\partial z}{\partial y}\right) \text{ at points } \left(+\frac{a}{2}, +\frac{b}{2}\right), \left(-\frac{a}{2}, +\frac{b}{2}\right), \left(-\frac{a}{2}, -\frac{b}{2}\right), \left(+\frac{a}{2}, -\frac{b}{2}\right)$$

$$X_2, X_5, X_8, X_{11} = \left(+\frac{\partial z}{\partial x}\right) \text{ at points } \left(+\frac{a}{2}, +\frac{b}{2}\right), \left(-\frac{a}{2}, +\frac{b}{2}\right), \left(-\frac{a}{2}, -\frac{b}{2}\right), \left(+\frac{a}{2}, -\frac{b}{2}\right)$$

$$X_3, X_6, X_9, X_{12} = (+z) \text{ at points } \left(+\frac{a}{2}, +\frac{b}{2}\right), \left(-\frac{a}{2}, +\frac{b}{2}\right), \left(-\frac{a}{2}, -\frac{b}{2}\right), \left(+\frac{a}{2}, -\frac{b}{2}\right)$$

Thus the expression for $[C]$ in the equation

$$\{X\} = [C]\ \{\alpha\}$$

may be found to be

$$[C] =$$

X \ α	1	2	3	4	5	6	7	8	9	10	11	12
1		-1			$-\dfrac{a}{2}$	$-b$		$-\dfrac{a^2}{4}$	$-\dfrac{ab}{2}$	$\dfrac{3b^2}{4}$	$-\dfrac{a^3}{8}$	$-\dfrac{3ab^2}{8}$
2		$+1$		$+a$	$+\dfrac{b}{2}$		$\dfrac{3a^2}{4}$	$+\dfrac{ab}{2}$	$+\dfrac{b^2}{4}$		$+\dfrac{3a^2b}{8}$	$+\dfrac{b^3}{8}$
3	$+1$	$+\dfrac{a}{2}$	$+\dfrac{b}{2}$	$+\dfrac{a^2}{4}$	$+\dfrac{ab}{4}$	$+\dfrac{b^2}{4}$	$\dfrac{a^3}{8}$	$+\dfrac{a^2b}{8}$	$+\dfrac{ab^2}{8}$	$+\dfrac{b^3}{8}$	$\dfrac{a^3b}{16}$	$+\dfrac{ab^3}{16}$
4		-1			$+\dfrac{a}{2}$	$-b$		$-\dfrac{a^2}{4}$	$+\dfrac{ab}{2}$	$-\dfrac{3b^2}{4}$	$+\dfrac{a^3}{8}$	$+\dfrac{3ab^2}{8}$
5		$+1$		$-a$	$+\dfrac{b}{2}$		$\dfrac{3a^2}{4}$	$-\dfrac{ab}{2}$	$+\dfrac{b^2}{4}$		$+\dfrac{3a^2b}{8}$	$+\dfrac{b^3}{8}$
6	$+1$	$-\dfrac{a}{2}$	$+\dfrac{b}{2}$	$+\dfrac{a^2}{4}$	$-\dfrac{ab}{4}$	$+\dfrac{b^2}{4}$	$-\dfrac{a^3}{8}$	$+\dfrac{a^2b}{8}$	$-\dfrac{ab^2}{8}$	$+\dfrac{b^3}{8}$	$\dfrac{a^3b}{16}$	$\dfrac{ab^3}{16}$
7		-1			$+\dfrac{a}{2}$	$+b$		$-\dfrac{a^2}{4}$	$-\dfrac{ab}{2}$	$\dfrac{3b^2}{4}$	$+\dfrac{a^3}{8}$	$+\dfrac{3ab^2}{8}$
8		$+1$		$-a$	$-\dfrac{b}{2}$		$+\dfrac{3a^2}{4}$	$+\dfrac{ab}{2}$	$+\dfrac{b^2}{4}$		$\dfrac{3a^2b}{8}$	$\dfrac{b^3}{8}$
9	$+1$	$-\dfrac{a}{2}$	$\dfrac{b}{2}$	$\dfrac{a^2}{4}$	$+\dfrac{ab}{4}$	$+\dfrac{b^2}{4}$	$-\dfrac{a^3}{8}$	$-\dfrac{a^2b}{8}$	$-\dfrac{ab^2}{8}$	$-\dfrac{b^3}{8}$	$+\dfrac{a^3b}{16}$	$+\dfrac{ab^3}{16}$
10		-1			$-\dfrac{a}{2}$	$+b$		$-\dfrac{a^2}{4}$	$+\dfrac{ab}{2}$	$-\dfrac{3b^2}{4}$	$-\dfrac{a^3}{8}$	$-\dfrac{3ab^2}{8}$
11		$+1$		$+a$	$-\dfrac{b}{2}$		$\dfrac{3a^2}{4}$	$-\dfrac{ab}{2}$	$+\dfrac{b^2}{4}$		$-\dfrac{3a^2b}{8}$	$\dfrac{b^3}{8}$
12	$+1$	$+\dfrac{a}{2}$	$-\dfrac{b}{2}$	$+\dfrac{a^2}{4}$	$-\dfrac{ab}{4}$	$+\dfrac{b^2}{4}$	$+\dfrac{a^3}{8}$	$-\dfrac{a^2b}{8}$	$+\dfrac{ab^2}{8}$	$+\dfrac{b^3}{8}$	$\dfrac{a^3b}{16}$	$-\dfrac{ab^3}{16}$

$$(9.5.3)$$

The $[C^{-1}]$ matrix is obtained by inverting the expression for the $[C]$ matrix in Eq. 9.5.3; thus,

$$\{\alpha\} = [C^{-1}]\ \{X\}$$

in which

$$[C^{-1}] =$$

α \ X	1	2	3	4	5	6	7	8	9	10	11	12
1	$+\dfrac{b}{16}$	$-\dfrac{a}{16}$	$+\dfrac{1}{4}$	$+\dfrac{b}{16}$	$+\dfrac{a}{16}$	$+\dfrac{1}{4}$	$-\dfrac{b}{16}$	$+\dfrac{a}{16}$	$+\dfrac{1}{4}$	$-\dfrac{b}{16}$	$-\dfrac{a}{16}$	$+\dfrac{1}{4}$
2	$+\dfrac{b}{8a}$	$-\dfrac{1}{8}$	$+\dfrac{3}{4a}$	$-\dfrac{b}{8a}$	$-\dfrac{1}{8}$	$-\dfrac{3}{4a}$	$+\dfrac{b}{8a}$	$-\dfrac{1}{8}$	$-\dfrac{3}{4a}$	$-\dfrac{b}{8a}$	$-\dfrac{1}{8}$	$+\dfrac{3}{4a}$
3	$+\dfrac{1}{8}$	$-\dfrac{a}{8b}$	$+\dfrac{3}{4b}$	$+\dfrac{1}{8}$	$+\dfrac{a}{8b}$	$+\dfrac{3}{4b}$	$+\dfrac{1}{8}$	$-\dfrac{a}{8b}$	$-\dfrac{3}{4b}$	$+\dfrac{1}{8}$	$+\dfrac{a}{8b}$	$-\dfrac{3}{4b}$
4		$+\dfrac{1}{4a}$			$-\dfrac{1}{4a}$			$+\dfrac{1}{4a}$			$+\dfrac{1}{4a}$	
5	$+\dfrac{1}{4a}$	$-\dfrac{1}{4b}$	$+\dfrac{2}{ab}$	$-\dfrac{1}{4a}$	$+\dfrac{1}{4b}$	$-\dfrac{2}{ab}$	$+\dfrac{1}{4a}$	$+\dfrac{1}{4b}$	$+\dfrac{2}{ab}$	$+\dfrac{1}{4a}$	$+\dfrac{1}{4b}$	$+\dfrac{2}{ab}$
6	$-\dfrac{1}{4b}$			$+\dfrac{1}{4b}$			$+\dfrac{1}{4b}$			$+\dfrac{1}{4b}$		
7		$+\dfrac{1}{2a^2}$	$-\dfrac{1}{a^3}$		$+\dfrac{1}{2a^2}$	$+\dfrac{1}{a^3}$		$+\dfrac{1}{2a^2}$	$+\dfrac{1}{a^3}$		$+\dfrac{1}{2a^2}$	$-\dfrac{1}{a^3}$
8		$+\dfrac{1}{2ab}$			$-\dfrac{1}{2ab}$			$+\dfrac{1}{2ab}$			$-\dfrac{1}{2ab}$	
9	$-\dfrac{1}{2ab}$			$+\dfrac{1}{2ab}$			$-\dfrac{1}{2ab}$			$+\dfrac{1}{2ab}$		
10	$-\dfrac{1}{2b^2}$		$-\dfrac{1}{b^3}$	$-\dfrac{1}{2b^2}$			$-\dfrac{1}{b^3}$	$-\dfrac{1}{2b^2}$	$+\dfrac{1}{b^3}$	$-\dfrac{1}{2b^2}$		$+\dfrac{1}{b^3}$
11		$+\dfrac{1}{a^2b}$	$-\dfrac{2}{a^3b}$		$+\dfrac{1}{a^2b}$	$+\dfrac{2}{a^3b}$		$-\dfrac{1}{a^2b}$	$+\dfrac{2}{a^3b}$		$+\dfrac{1}{a^2b}$	$+\dfrac{2}{a^3b}$
12	$-\dfrac{1}{ab^2}$		$-\dfrac{2}{ab^3}$	$+\dfrac{1}{ab^2}$		$+\dfrac{2}{ab^3}$	$+\dfrac{1}{ab^2}$		$+\dfrac{2}{ab^3}$	$-\dfrac{2}{ab^3}$	$-\dfrac{1}{ab^2}$	$+\dfrac{2}{ab^3}$

(9.5.4)

Finally the deformation matrix $[B]$ in the equation

$$\{e\} = [B]\ \{X\}$$

is obtained from

$$[B] = [G]\,[C^{-1}]$$

or,

$[B] =$ (9.5.5)

e \ X	1	2	3	4	5	6	7	8	9	10	11	12
ϕ_x		$-\dfrac{1}{2a}$			$+\dfrac{1}{2a}$			$+\dfrac{1}{2a}$			$-\dfrac{1}{2a}$	
		$-\dfrac{3x}{a^2}$	$+\dfrac{6x}{a^3}$		$-\dfrac{3x}{a^2}$	$-\dfrac{6x}{a^3}$		$\dfrac{3x}{a^2}$	$-\dfrac{6x}{a^3}$		$\dfrac{3x}{a^2}$	$+\dfrac{6x}{a^3}$
		$-\dfrac{y}{ab}$			$-\dfrac{y}{ab}$			$+\dfrac{y}{ab}$			$+\dfrac{y}{ab}$	
		$-\dfrac{6xy}{a^2b}$	$+\dfrac{12xy}{a^3b}$		$-\dfrac{6xy}{a^2b}$	$\dfrac{12xy}{a^3b}$		$+\dfrac{6xy}{a^2b}$	$\dfrac{12xy}{a^3b}$		$+\dfrac{6xy}{a^2b}$	$\dfrac{12xy}{a^3b}$
ϕ_y	$+\dfrac{1}{2b}$			$+\dfrac{1}{2b}$			$\dfrac{1}{2b}$			$\dfrac{1}{2b}$		
	$+\dfrac{x}{ab}$			$\dfrac{x}{ab}$			$+\dfrac{x}{ab}$			$\dfrac{x}{ab}$		
	$+\dfrac{3y}{b^2}$		$+\dfrac{6y}{b^3}$	$+\dfrac{3y}{b^2}$		$+\dfrac{6y}{b^3}$	$+\dfrac{3y}{b^2}$		$\dfrac{6y}{b^3}$	$+\dfrac{3y}{b^2}$		$\dfrac{6y}{b^3}$
	$+\dfrac{6xy}{ab^2}$		$+\dfrac{12xy}{ab^3}$	$+\dfrac{6xy}{ab^2}$		$-\dfrac{12xy}{ab^3}$	$-\dfrac{6xy}{ab^2}$		$+\dfrac{12xy}{ab^3}$	$+\dfrac{6xy}{ab^2}$		$\dfrac{12xy}{ab^3}$
ϕ_{xy}	$-\dfrac{1}{2a}$	$+\dfrac{1}{2b}$	$-\dfrac{4}{ab}$	$+\dfrac{1}{2a}$	$+\dfrac{1}{2b}$	$+\dfrac{4}{ab}$	$\dfrac{1}{2a}$	$-\dfrac{1}{2b}$	$-\dfrac{4}{ab}$	$\dfrac{1}{2a}$	$-\dfrac{1}{2b}$	$+\dfrac{4}{ab}$
		$-\dfrac{2x}{ab}$			$+\dfrac{2x}{ab}$			$-\dfrac{2x}{ab}$			$+\dfrac{2x}{ab}$	
	$+\dfrac{2y}{ab}$			$-\dfrac{2y}{ab}$			$+\dfrac{2y}{ab}$			$\dfrac{2y}{ab}$		
		$-\dfrac{6x^2}{a^2b}$	$+\dfrac{12x^2}{a^3b}$		$-\dfrac{6x^2}{a^2b}$	$\dfrac{12x^2}{a^3b}$		$\dfrac{6x^2}{a^2b}$	$-\dfrac{12x^2}{a^3b}$		$\dfrac{6x^2}{a^2b}$	$\dfrac{12x^2}{a^3b}$
	$+\dfrac{6y^2}{ab^2}$		$+\dfrac{12y^2}{ab^3}$	$\dfrac{6y^2}{ab^2}$		$-\dfrac{12y^2}{ab^3}$	$\dfrac{6y^2}{ab^2}$		$+\dfrac{12y^2}{ab^3}$	$\dfrac{6y^2}{ab^2}$		$\dfrac{12y^2}{ab^3}$

9.6. The Stiffness Matrix $[K]$

The stiffness matrix of a finite element in bending may be obtained by applying the equation

$$[K] = \int [B^T] \, [S] \, [B] \, dA \tag{9.6.1}$$

Multiplying the particle-stiffness matrix $[S]$ in Eq. 9.2.9 and the deformation matrix $[B]$ in Eq. 9.5.5 gives

$[SB] =$

F \ X	1	2	3	4	5	6	7	8	9	10	11	12
M_x	$SB(1,1)$	$SB(1,2)$	$SB(1,3)$	$SB(1,4)$	$SB(1,5)$	$SB(1,6)$	$SB(1,7)$	$SB(1,8)$	$SB(1,9)$	$SB(1,10)$	$SB(1,11)$	$SB(1,12)$
M_y	$SB(2,1)$	$SB(2,2)$	$SB(2,3)$	$SB(2,4)$	$SB(2,5)$	$SB(2,6)$	$SB(2,7)$	$SB(2,8)$	$SB(2,9)$	$SB(2,10)$	$SB(2,11)$	$SB(2,12)$
M_{xy}	$SB(3,1)$	$SB(3,2)$	$SB(3,3)$	$SB(3,4)$	$SB(3,5)$	$SB(3,6)$	$SB(3,7)$	$SB(3,8)$	$SB(3,9)$	$SB(3,10)$	$SB(3,11)$	$SB(3,12)$

$$(9.6.2)$$

in which

$$SB(1,1) = \frac{EI}{(1-\mu^2)} \left[+ \frac{\mu}{2b} + \frac{\mu x}{ab} + \frac{3\mu y}{b^2} + \frac{6\mu xy}{ab^2} \right]$$

$$SB(1,4) = \frac{EI}{(1-\mu^2)} \left[+ \frac{\mu}{2b} - \frac{\mu x}{ab} + \frac{3\mu y}{b^2} - \frac{6\mu xy}{ab^2} \right]$$

$$SB(1,7) = \frac{EI}{(1-\mu^2)} \left[- \frac{\mu}{2b} + \frac{\mu x}{ab} + \frac{3\mu y}{b^2} - \frac{6\mu xy}{ab^2} \right]$$

$$SB(1,10) = \frac{EI}{(1-\mu^2)} \left[- \frac{\mu}{2b} - \frac{\mu x}{ab} + \frac{3\mu y}{b^2} + \frac{6\mu xy}{ab^2} \right]$$

$$SB(1,2) = \frac{EI}{(1-\mu^2)} \left[- \frac{1}{2a} - \frac{3x}{a^2} - \frac{y}{ab} - \frac{6xy}{a^2 b} \right]$$

$$SB(1,5) = \frac{EI}{(1-\mu^2)} \left[+ \frac{1}{2a} - \frac{3x}{a^2} + \frac{y}{ab} - \frac{6xy}{a^2 b} \right]$$

$$SB(1,8) = \frac{EI}{(1-\mu^2)} \left[+ \frac{1}{2a} - \frac{3x}{a^2} - \frac{y}{ab} + \frac{6xy}{a^2 b} \right]$$

$$SB(1,11) = \frac{EI}{(1-\mu^2)} \left[- \frac{1}{2a} - \frac{3x}{a^2} + \frac{y}{ab} + \frac{6xy}{a^2 b} \right]$$

$$SB(1,3) = \frac{EI}{(1-\mu^2)} \left[+ \frac{6x}{a^3} + \frac{12xy}{a^3 b} + \frac{6\mu y}{b^3} + \frac{12\mu xy}{ab^3} \right]$$

$$SB(1,6) = \frac{EI}{(1-\mu^2)} \left[- \frac{6x}{a^3} - \frac{12xy}{a^3 b} + \frac{6\mu y}{b^3} - \frac{12\mu xy}{ab^3} \right]$$

$$SB(1,9) = \frac{EI}{(1-\mu^2)} \left[- \frac{6x}{a^3} + \frac{12xy}{a^3 b} - \frac{6\mu y}{b^3} + \frac{12\mu xy}{ab^3} \right]$$

$$SB(1,12) = \frac{EI}{(1-\mu^2)} \left[+ \frac{6x}{a^3} - \frac{12xy}{a^3 b} - \frac{6\mu y}{b^3} - \frac{12\mu xy}{ab^3} \right]$$

$$SB(2,1) = \frac{EI}{(1-\mu^2)} \left[+ \frac{1}{2b} + \frac{x}{ab} + \frac{3y}{b^2} + \frac{6xy}{ab^2} \right]$$

$$SB(2,4) = \frac{EI}{(1-\mu^2)} \left[+ \frac{1}{2b} - \frac{x}{ab} + \frac{3y}{b^2} - \frac{6xy}{ab^2} \right]$$

$$SB(2,7) = \frac{EI}{(1-\mu^2)} \left[- \frac{1}{2b} + \frac{x}{ab} + \frac{3y}{b^2} - \frac{6xy}{ab^2} \right]$$

$$SB\,(2,10) = \frac{EI}{(1-\mu^2)}\left[-\frac{1}{2b}-\frac{x}{ab}+\frac{3y}{b^2}+\frac{6xy}{ab^2}\right]$$

$$SB\,(2,2) = \frac{EI}{(1-\mu^2)}\left[-\frac{\mu}{2a}-\frac{3\mu x}{a^2}-\frac{\mu y}{ab}-\frac{6\mu xy}{a^2 b}\right]$$

$$SB\,(2,5) = \frac{EI}{(1-\mu^2)}\left[+\frac{\mu}{2a}-\frac{3\mu x}{a^2}+\frac{\mu y}{ab}-\frac{6\mu xy}{a^2 b}\right]$$

$$SB\,(2,8) = \frac{EI}{(1-\mu^2)}\left[+\frac{\mu}{2a}-\frac{3\mu x}{a^2}-\frac{\mu y}{ab}+\frac{6\mu xy}{a^2 b}\right]$$

$$SB\,(2,11) = \frac{EI}{(1-\mu^2)}\left[-\frac{\mu}{2a}-\frac{3\mu x}{a^2}+\frac{\mu y}{ab}+\frac{6\mu xy}{a^2 b}\right]$$

$$SB(2,3) = \frac{EI}{(1-\mu^2)}\left[+\frac{6\mu x}{a^3}+\frac{12\mu xy}{a^3 b}+\frac{6y}{b^3}+\frac{12xy}{ab^3}\right]$$

$$SB(2,6) = \frac{EI}{(1-\mu^2)}\left[-\frac{6\mu x}{a^3}-\frac{12\mu xy}{a^3 b}+\frac{6y}{b^3}-\frac{12xy}{ab^3}\right]$$

$$SB(2,9) = \frac{EI}{(1-\mu^2)}\left[-\frac{6\mu x}{a^3}+\frac{12\mu xy}{a^3 b}-\frac{6y}{b^3}+\frac{12xy}{ab^3}\right]$$

$$SB(2,12) = \frac{EI}{(1-\mu^2)}\left[+\frac{6\mu x}{a^3}-\frac{12\mu xy}{a^3 b}-\frac{6y}{b^3}-\frac{12xy}{ab^3}\right]$$

$$SB\,(3,1) = \frac{EI}{(1+\mu)}\left[-\frac{1}{4a}+\frac{y}{ab}+\frac{3y^2}{ab^2}\right]$$

$$SB\,(3,4) = \frac{EI}{(1+\mu)}\left[+\frac{1}{4a}-\frac{y}{ab}-\frac{3y^2}{ab^2}\right]$$

$$SB\,(3,7) = \frac{EI}{(1+\mu)}\left[+\frac{1}{4a}+\frac{y}{ab}-\frac{3y^2}{ab^2}\right]$$

$$SB\,(3,10) = \frac{EI}{(1+\mu)}\left[-\frac{1}{4a}-\frac{y}{ab}+\frac{3y^2}{ab^2}\right]$$

$$SB\,(3,2) = \frac{EI}{(1+\mu)}\left[+\frac{1}{4b}-\frac{x}{ab}-\frac{3x^2}{a^2 b}\right]$$

$$SB\,(3,5) = \frac{EI}{(1+\mu)}\left[+\frac{1}{4b}+\frac{x}{ab}-\frac{3x^2}{a^2 b}\right]$$

$$SB(3,8) = \frac{EI}{(1+\mu)} \left[-\frac{1}{4b} - \frac{x}{ab} + \frac{3x^2}{a^2 b} \right]$$

$$SB(3,11) = \frac{EI}{(1+\mu)} \left[-\frac{1}{4b} + \frac{x}{ab} + \frac{3x^2}{a^2 b} \right]$$

$$SB(3,3) = \frac{EI}{(1+\mu)} \left[-\frac{2}{ab} + \frac{6x^2}{a^3 b} + \frac{6y^2}{ab^3} \right]$$

$$SB(3,6) = \frac{EI}{(1+\mu)} \left[+\frac{2}{ab} - \frac{6x^2}{a^3 b} - \frac{6y^2}{ab^3} \right]$$

$$SB(3,9) = \frac{EI}{(1+\mu)} \left[-\frac{2}{ab} + \frac{6x^2}{a^3 b} + \frac{6y^2}{ab^3} \right]$$

$$SB(3,12) = \frac{EI}{(1+\mu)} \left[+\frac{2}{ab} - \frac{6x^2}{a^3 b} - \frac{6y^2}{ab^3} \right]$$

The stiffness matrix $[K]$ of a rectangular finite element in bending is obtained by applying Eq. 9.6.1 as

$[K] =$

P \ X	1	2	3	4	5	6	7	8	9	10	11	12
1	$T1$	$-T21$	$T9$	$T3$	$-T19$	$T11$	$T7$	$-T22$	$-T13$	$T5$	$T20$	$-T15$
2	$-T21$	$T2$	$-T10$	$T19$	$T6$	$T16$	$-T22$	$T8$	$T14$	$-T20$	$T4$	$-T12$
3	$T9$	$-T10$	$T23$	$T11$	$-T16$	$T17$	$T13$	$-T14$	$T24$	$T15$	$-T12$	$T18$
4	$T3$	$T19$	$T11$	$T1$	$T21$	$T9$	$T5$	$-T20$	$-T15$	$T7$	$T22$	$-T13$
5	$-T19$	$T6$	$-T16$	$T21$	$T2$	$T10$	$T20$	$T4$	$T12$	$T22$	$T8$	$-T14$
6	$T11$	$T16$	$T17$	$T9$	$T10$	$T23$	$T15$	$T12$	$T18$	$T13$	$T14$	$T24$
7	$T7$	$-T22$	$T13$	$T5$	$T20$	$T15$	$T1$	$-T21$	$-T9$	$T3$	$-T19$	$-T11$
8	$-T22$	$T8$	$-T14$	$-T20$	$T4$	$T12$	$-T21$	$T2$	$T10$	$T19$	$T6$	$-T16$
9	$-T13$	$T14$	$T24$	$-T15$	$T12$	$T18$	$-T9$	$T10$	$T23$	$-T11$	$T16$	$T17$
10	$T5$	$-T20$	$T15$	$T7$	$T22$	$T13$	$T3$	$T19$	$-T11$	$T1$	$T21$	$-T9$
11	$T20$	$T4$	$-T12$	$T22$	$T8$	$T14$	$-T19$	$T6$	$T16$	$T21$	$T2$	$-T10$
12	$-T15$	$-T12$	$T18$	$-T13$	$-T14$	$T24$	$-T11$	$-T16$	$T17$	$-T9$	$-T10$	$T23$

(9.6.3)

in which

$$T1 = \frac{Et^3}{(1-\mu^2)} \left[+\frac{a}{9b} + \frac{b(1-\mu)}{45a} \right]$$

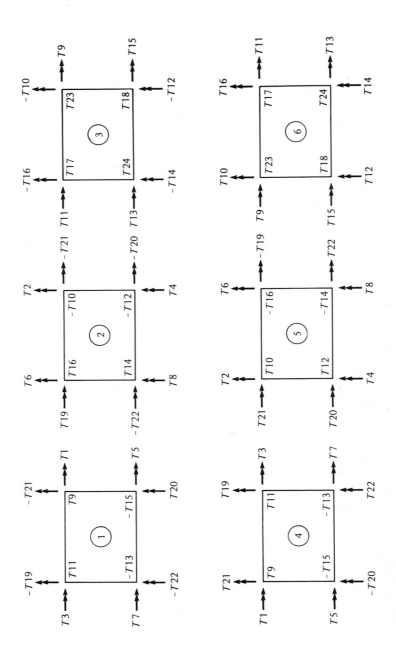

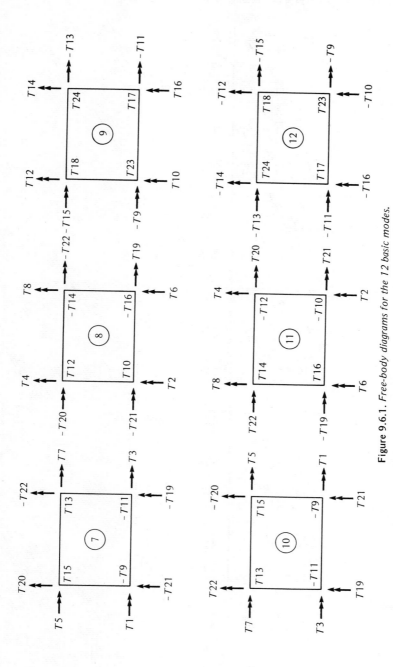

Figure 9.6.1. *Free-body diagrams for the 12 basic modes.*

$$T2 = \frac{Et^3}{(1 - \mu^2)} \left[+ \frac{b}{9a} + \frac{a(1 - \mu)}{45b} \right]$$

$$T3 = \frac{Et^3}{(1 - \mu^2)} \left[+ \frac{a}{18b} - \frac{b(1 - \mu)}{45a} \right]$$

$$T4 = \frac{Et^3}{(1 - \mu^2)} \left[+ \frac{b}{18a} - \frac{a(1 - \mu)}{45b} \right]$$

$$T5 = \frac{Et^3}{(1 - \mu^2)} \left[+ \frac{a}{18b} - \frac{b(1 - \mu)}{180a} \right]$$

$$T6 = \frac{Et^3}{(1 - \mu^2)} \left[+ \frac{b}{18a} - \frac{a(1 - \mu)}{180b} \right]$$

$$T7 = \frac{Et^3}{(1 - \mu^2)} \left[+ \frac{a}{36b} + \frac{b(1 - \mu)}{180a} \right]$$

$$T8 = \frac{Et^3}{(1 - \mu^2)} \left[+ \frac{b}{36a} + \frac{a(1 - \mu)}{180b} \right]$$

$$T9 = \frac{Et^3}{(1 - \mu^2)} \left[+ \frac{a}{6b^2} + \frac{(1 + 4\mu)}{60a} \right]$$

$$T10 = \frac{Et^3}{(1 - \mu^2)} \left[+ \frac{b}{6a^2} + \frac{(1 + 4\mu)}{60b} \right]$$

$$T11 = \frac{Et^3}{(1 - \mu^2)} \left[+ \frac{a}{12b^2} - \frac{(1 + 4\mu)}{60a} \right]$$

$$T12 = \frac{Et^3}{(1 - \mu^2)} \left[+ \frac{b}{12a^2} - \frac{(1 + 4\mu)}{60b} \right]$$

$$T13 = \frac{Et^3}{(1 - \mu^2)} \left[+ \frac{a}{12b^2} - \frac{(1 - \mu)}{60a} \right]$$

$$T14 = \frac{Et^3}{(1 - \mu^2)} \left[+ \frac{b}{12a^2} - \frac{(1 - \mu)}{60b} \right]$$

$$T15 = \frac{Et^3}{(1 - \mu^2)} \left[+ \frac{a}{6b^2} + \frac{(1 - \mu)}{60a} \right]$$

$$T16 = \frac{Et^3}{(1 - \mu^2)} \left[+ \frac{b}{6a^2} + \frac{(1 - \mu)}{60b} \right]$$

$$T17 = \frac{Et^3}{(1 - \mu^2)} \left[- \frac{b}{3a^3} + \frac{a}{6b^3} - \frac{(14 - 4\mu)}{60ab} \right]$$

$$T18 = \frac{Et^3}{(1-\mu^2)}\left[-\frac{a}{3b^3}+\frac{b}{6a^3}-\frac{(14-4\mu)}{60ab}\right]$$

$$T19 = 0.$$

$$T20 = 0.$$

$$T21 = \frac{Et^3}{(1-\mu^2)}\left[+\frac{\mu}{12}\right]$$

$$T22 = 0.$$

$$T23 = \frac{Et^3}{(1-\mu^2)}\left[+\frac{b}{3a^3}+\frac{a}{3b^3}+\frac{(14-4\mu)}{60ab}\right]$$

$$T24 = \frac{Et^3}{(1-\mu^2)}\left[-\frac{b}{6a^3}-\frac{a}{6b^3}+\frac{(14-4\mu)}{60ab}\right]$$

It is instructive to check the three equations of equilibrium for each of the 12 free-body diagrams of the 12 basic modes shown in Fig. 9.6.1. Note that modes 1-4-7-10 are substantially identical, and so are modes 2-5-8-11 and modes 3-6-9-12.

9.7. Principal Stress Modes

The three principal stress modes for a finite plate element in bending are (1) $M_x \neq 0$, $M_y = 0$, $M_{xy} = 0$; (2) $M_x = 0$, $M_y \neq 0$, $M_{xy} = 0$; and (3) $M_x = 0$, $M_y = 0$, $M_{xy} \neq 0$. The equivalent nodal forces and displacements corresponding to each of the principal stress modes may be observed from Fig. 9.7.1 and summarized in Table 9.7.1.

Each of the equivalent nodal forces in Fig. 9.7.1ab is clearly one-half of the total moment acting on one edge of the rectangle. However, in the twisting-moment case of Fig. 9.7.1c, the total twisting moment acting on any one edge of the rectangle may be replaced either by two nodal moment vectors or by two nodal forces in the z-direction. The fractional constant k is used for the former and consequently $(1 - k)$ is used for the latter.

In regard to the strain geometry of the first two principal stress modes, there are a constant concave curvature of

$$\phi_x = \frac{M_x}{EI} = \frac{12M_x}{Et^3} \qquad \phi_y = \frac{M_y}{EI} = \frac{12M_y}{Et^3} \tag{9.7.1}$$

in the direction of active bending and a constant convex curvature of

$$\phi_y = \frac{\mu M_x}{EI} = \frac{12\mu M_x}{Et^3} \qquad \phi_x = \frac{\mu M_y}{EI} = \frac{12\mu M_y}{Et^3} \tag{9.7.2}$$

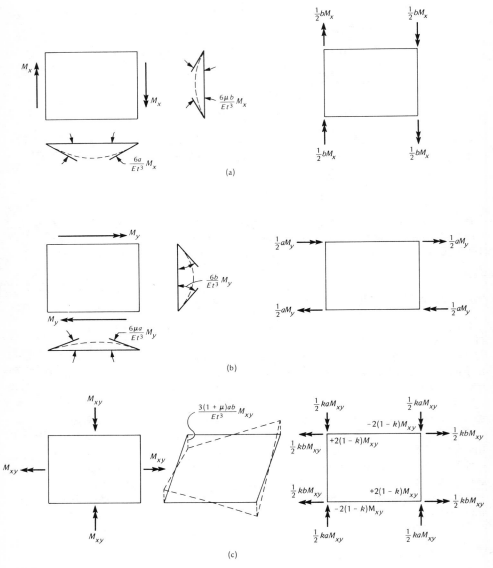

Figure 9.7.1. *Principal stress modes.* (a) $M_x \neq 0$, $M_y = 0$, $M_{xy} = 0$; (b) $M_x = 0$, $M_y \neq 0$, $M_{xy} = 0$, (c) $M_x = 0$, $M_y = 0$, $M_{xy} \neq 0$.

TABLE 9.7.1

Nodal Forces and Displacements in Principal Stress Modes

	Mode 1		Mode 2		Mode 3	
	P	X	P	X	P	X
1		$-\dfrac{6\mu b}{Et^3}M_x$	$+\dfrac{1}{2}a M_y$	$+\dfrac{6b}{Et^3}M_y$	$+\dfrac{kb}{2}M_{xy}$	$+\dfrac{6(1+\mu)a}{Et^3}M_{xy}$
2	$-\dfrac{1}{2}b M_x$	$-\dfrac{6a}{Et^3}M_x$		$+\dfrac{6\mu a}{Et^3}M_y$	$-\dfrac{ka}{2}M_{xy}$	$-\dfrac{6(1+\mu)b}{Et^3}M_{xy}$
3					$-2(1-k)M_{xy}$	$-\dfrac{3(1+\mu)ab}{Et^3}M_{xy}$
4		$-\dfrac{6\mu b}{Et^3}M_x$	$+\dfrac{1}{2}a M_y$	$+\dfrac{6b}{Et^3}M_y$	$-\dfrac{kb}{2}M_{xy}$	$-\dfrac{6(1+\mu)a}{Et^3}M_{xy}$
5	$+\dfrac{1}{2}b M_x$	$+\dfrac{6a}{Et^3}M_x$		$-\dfrac{6\mu a}{Et^3}M_y$	$-\dfrac{ka}{2}M_{xy}$	$-\dfrac{6(1+\mu)b}{Et^3}M_{xy}$
6					$+2(1-k)M_{xy}$	$+\dfrac{3(1+\mu)ab}{Et^3}M_{xy}$
7		$+\dfrac{6\mu b}{Et^3}M_x$	$-\dfrac{1}{2}a M_y$	$-\dfrac{6b}{Et^3}M_y$	$-\dfrac{kb}{2}M_{xy}$	$-\dfrac{6(1+\mu)a}{Et^3}M_{xy}$
8	$+\dfrac{1}{2}b M_x$	$+\dfrac{6a}{Et^3}M_x$		$-\dfrac{6\mu a}{Et^3}M_y$	$+\dfrac{ka}{2}M_{xy}$	$+\dfrac{6(1+\mu)b}{Et^3}M_{xy}$
9					$-2(1-k)M_{xy}$	$-\dfrac{3(1+\mu)ab}{Et^3}M_{xy}$
10		$+\dfrac{6\mu b}{Et^3}M_x$	$-\dfrac{1}{2}a M_y$	$-\dfrac{6b}{Et^3}M_y$	$+\dfrac{kb}{2}M_{xy}$	$+\dfrac{6(1+\mu)a}{Et^3}M_{xy}$
11	$-\dfrac{1}{2}b M_x$	$-\dfrac{6a}{Et^3}M_x$		$+\dfrac{6\mu a}{Et^3}M_y$	$+\dfrac{ka}{2}M_{xy}$	$+\dfrac{6(1+\mu)b}{Et^3}M_{xy}$
12					$+2(1-k)M_{xy}$	$+\dfrac{3(1+\mu)ab}{Et^3}M_{xy}$

in the direction of passive bending due to the Poisson effect. The slopes at the edges shown in Fig. 9.7.1ab are equal to the product of the curvatures in Eqs. 9.7.1 and 9.7.2 and one-half of the length of the appropriate side of the rectangle. The displacement in the z-direction at the corners of the rectangle in the principal twisting mode, as shown in Fig. 9.7.1c, is equal to

$$\frac{\partial^2 z}{\partial x \partial y}\left(\frac{a}{2}\right)\left(\frac{b}{2}\right) = \frac{(1+\mu)}{EI}M_{xy}\frac{ab}{4} = \frac{3(1+\mu)ab}{Et^3}M_{xy} \qquad (9.7.3)$$

On substitution of the three sets of X-values in the three principal modes into the stiffness matrix $[K]$ of Sec. 9.6, it is found that the three sets of P-values as shown in Fig. 9.7.1 or Table 9.7.1 are exactly identified except that the fractional constant k is zero so far as this finite element model is concerned.

9.8. Effect of Symmetrical Finite Element

It can be observed that the stiffness matrix $[K]$ of a rectangular finite element in bending can have only 24 different elements within the 12 by 12 panel, by

TABLE 9.8.1

Locations of Independent Element Values

Element Values	Element Locations			
$T1$	1- 1	4-4	7- 7	10-10
$T2$	2- 2	5-5	8- 8	11-11
$T3$	1- 4	4-1	7-10	10- 7
$T4$	2-11	11-2	5- 8	8- 5
$T5$	1-10	10-1	4- 7	7- 4
$T6$	2- 5	5-2	8-11	11- 8
$T7$	1- 7	7-1	4-10	10- 4
$T8$	2- 8	8-2	5-11	11- 5
$T9$	1- 3	3-1	4- 6	6- 4
$-T9$	7- 9	9-7	10-12	12-10
$T10$	5- 6	6-5	8- 9	9- 8
$-T10$	2- 3	3-2	11-12	12-11
$T11$	1- 6	6-1	3- 4	4- 3
$-T11$	9-10	10-9	7-12	12- 7
$T12$	5- 9	9-5	6- 8	8- 6
$-T12$	2-12	12-2	3-11	11- 3
$T13$	3- 7	7-3	6-10	10- 6
$-T13$	1- 9	9-1	4-12	12- 4
$T14$	2- 9	9-2	6-11	11- 6
$-T14$	3- 8	8-3	5-12	12- 5
$T15$	3-10	10-3	6- 7	7- 6
$-T15$	1-12	12-1	4- 9	9- 4
$T16$	2- 6	6-2	9-11	11- 9
$-T16$	3- 5	5-3	8-12	12- 8
$T17$	3- 6	6-3	9-12	12- 9
$T18$	3-12	12-3	6- 9	9- 6
$T19$	2- 4	4-2	8-10	10- 8
$-T19$	1- 5	5-1	7-11	11- 7
$T20$	1-11	11-1	5- 7	7- 5
$-T20$	2-10	10-2	4- 8	8- 4
$T21$	4- 5	5-4	10-11	11-10
$-T21$	1- 2	2-1	7- 8	8- 7
$T22$	4-11	11-4	5-10	10- 5
$-T22$	1- 8	8-1	2- 7	7- 2
$T23$	3- 3	6-6	9- 9	12-12
$T24$	3- 9	9-3	6-12	12- 6

virtue of the four equal quadrants into which the rectangle may be divided. The first 20 of these quantities occur in pairs; that is, the odd and even-numbered quantities are analogous except the symbols a and b should be interchanged. The locations of elements which should have the common values have already been indicated in Sec. 9.6, but they are listed in order of the independent values in Table 9.8.1.

9.9. Independent Elements in the Stiffness Matrix

Although the 144 elements in the stiffness matrix of a rectangular finite element in bending have been expressed in terms of 24 different quantities $T1$ to $T24$ by reason of symmetry, it can be shown that these 24 quantities can again be expressed in terms of 9 independent quantities, in order to satisfy the equilibrium equations for the basic modes (Fig. 9.6.1) and to fulfill the P-X requirements of the three principal modes (Table 9.7.1).

There are 3 equations of equilibrium for Modes 1-4-7-10, 2-5-8-11, and 3-6-9-12, respectively, making a total of 9 equations as shown.
Modes 1-4-7-10 (Fig. 9.6.1),

$$T9 + T11 - T13 - T15 = 0 \tag{9.9.1}$$
$$T1 + T3 + T5 + T7 - b(T9 + T11) = 0 \tag{9.9.2}$$
$$T19 - T20 + T21 + T22 + a(T11 - T13) = 0 \tag{9.9.3}$$

Modes 2-5-8-11 (Fig. 9.6.1),

$$-T10 - T12 + T14 + T16 = 0 \tag{9.9.4}$$
$$T2 + T4 + T6 + T8 - a(T10 + T12) = 0 \tag{9.9.5}$$
$$-T19 + T20 + T21 + T22 + b(T12 - T14) = 0 \tag{9.9.6}$$

Modes 3-6-9-12 (Fig. 9.6.1),

$$T17 + T18 + T23 + T24 = 0 \tag{9.9.7}$$
$$T9 + T11 + T13 + T15 - b(T17 + T23) = 0 \tag{9.9.8}$$
$$T10 + T12 + T14 + T16 + a(T17 + T24) = 0 \tag{9.9.9}$$

The three nodal forces at any one corner (say the corner in the first quadrant) in each of the three principal stress modes may be expressed by the following 9 equations.

Principal stress mode 1 (Table 9.7.1),

$$P_1 = 0 = \frac{6\mu b}{Et^3} M_x \ (-T1 - T3 + T7 + T5) + \frac{6a}{Et^3} M_x \ (T21 - T19 - T22 - T20)$$

$$(9.9.10)$$

$$P_2 = -\frac{b}{2} M_x = \frac{6\mu b}{Et^3} M_x \ (T21 - T19 - T22 - T20)$$

$$+ \frac{6a}{Et^3} M_x \ (-T2 + T6 + T8 - T4) \tag{9.9.11}$$

$$P_3 = 0 = \frac{6\mu b}{Et^3} M_x \ (-T9 - T11 + T13 + T15)$$

$$+ \frac{6a}{Et^3} M_x \ (T10 - T16 - T14 + T12) \tag{9.9.12}$$

Principal stress mode 2 (Table 9.7.1),

$$P_1 = +\frac{a}{2} M_y = \frac{6b}{Et^3} M_y \ (T1 + T3 - T7 - T5)$$

$$+ \frac{6\mu a}{Et^3} M_y \ (-T21 + T19 + T22 + T20) \tag{9.9.13}$$

$$P_2 = 0 = \frac{6b}{Et^3} M_y \ (-T21 + T19 + T22 + T20) + \frac{6\mu a}{Et^3} M_y \ (T2 - T6 - T8 + T4)$$

$$(9.9.14)$$

$$P_3 = 0 = \frac{6b}{Et^3} M_y \ (T9 + T11 - T13 - T15)$$

$$+ \frac{6\mu a}{Et^3} M_y \ (-T10 + T16 + T14 - T12) \tag{9.9.15}$$

Principal stress mode 3 (Table 9.7.1),

$$P_1 = +\frac{kb}{2} M_{xy} = \frac{6(1+\mu)a}{Et^3} M_{xy} \ (T1 - T3 - T7 + T5)$$

$$+ \frac{6(1+\mu)b}{Et^3} M_{xy} \ (T21 + T19 - T22 + T20)$$

$$+ \frac{3(1 + \mu) ab}{Et^3} M_{xy} (-T9 + T11 + T13 - T15) \qquad (9.9.16)$$

$$P_2 = -\frac{ka}{2} M_{xy} = \frac{6(1 + \mu) a}{Et^3} M_{xy} (-T21 - T19 + T22 - T20)$$

$$+ \frac{6(1 + \mu) b}{Et^3} M_{xy} (-T2 - T6 + T8 + T4)$$

$$+ \frac{3(1 + \mu) ab}{Et^3} M_{xy} (T10 + T16 - T14 - T12) \qquad (9.9.17)$$

$$P_3 = -2(1 - k) M_{xy} = \frac{6(1 + \mu) a}{Et^3} M_{xy} (T9 - T11 - T13 + T15)$$

$$+ \frac{6(1 + \mu) b}{Et^3} M_{xy} (T10 + T16 - T14 - T12)$$

$$+ \frac{3(1 + \mu) ab}{Et^3} M_{xy} (-T23 + T17 - T24 + T18) \qquad (9.9.18)$$

Three dependency relationships exist within the 18 conditions expressed by Eqs. 9.9.1 to 9.9.18. Each of Eqs. 9.9.12 and 9.9.15 is a combination of Eqs. 9.9.1 and 9.9.4. Furthermore, the same equation would be obtained if the expression $(-T21 + T19 + T22 + T20)$ is eliminated between Eqs. 9.9.11 and 9.9.13 or between Eqs. 9.9.10 and 9.9.14. Consequently, there are remaining 15 independent conditions from which to solve the 24 quantities $T1$ to $T24$. The constant k which appears in the third principal stress mode is assumed to be a preset value in the finite-element model.

After many hours of algebraic manipulations, the 9 independent elements are chosen to be $T1$, $T2$, $T5$, $T6$, $T9$, $T10$, $T11$, $T12$, and one of $T13$-$T14$. Perhaps in an experimental model, these independent quantities should be tackled first. The relationships between the pair $T13$-$T14$ is:

$$T13 = \frac{b}{a} T14 + \frac{2b}{a^2} (T2 + T6) - \frac{2}{b} (T1 + T5) - \frac{b}{a} (2T10 + T12)$$

$$+ (2T9 + T11) \qquad (9.9.19a)$$

$$T14 = \frac{a}{b} T13 + \frac{2a}{b^2} (T1 + T5) - \frac{2}{a} (T2 + T6) - \frac{a}{b} (2T9 + T11) + (2T10 + T12)$$

$$(9.9.19b)$$

The formulas for the remaining 14 quantities are

$$T3 = -T1 + \frac{b}{2}(T9 + T11) + \frac{Et^3}{(1 - \mu^2)} \frac{a}{24b} \tag{9.9.20}$$

$$T4 = -T2 + \frac{a}{2}(T10 + T12) + \frac{Et^3}{(1 - \mu^2)} \frac{b}{24a} \tag{9.9.21}$$

$$T7 = -T5 + \frac{b}{2}(T9 + T11) - \frac{Et^3}{(1 - \mu^2)} \frac{a}{24b} \tag{9.9.22}$$

$$T8 = -T6 + \frac{a}{2}(T10 + T12) - \frac{Et^3}{(1 - \mu^2)} \frac{b}{24a} \tag{9.9.23}$$

$$T15 = T9 + T11 - T13 \tag{9.9.24}$$

$$T16 = T10 + T12 - T14 \tag{9.9.25}$$

$$T17 = \frac{1}{b}(T11 + T13) - \frac{1}{a}(2T10 + T12 - T14)$$
$$- \frac{Et^3}{(1 - \mu^2)} \frac{(1 - k)(1 - \mu)}{6ab} \tag{9.9.26}$$

$$T18 = -\frac{1}{b}(2T9 + T11 - T13) + \frac{1}{a}(T12 + T14)$$
$$- \frac{Et^3}{(1 - \mu^2)} \frac{(1 - k)(1 - \mu)}{6ab} \tag{9.9.27}$$

$$T19 = -\frac{a}{2b}(T1 + T5) + \frac{a}{2}T9 + \frac{b}{4}(T12 - T14)$$
$$+ \frac{Et^3}{(1 - \mu^2)} \left[\frac{k(1 - \mu)}{48} - \frac{\mu}{48} \right] \tag{9.9.28}$$

$$T20 = -\frac{a}{2b}(T1 + T5) + \frac{a}{2}(T9 + T11 - T13) - \frac{b}{4}(T12 - T14)$$
$$+ \frac{Et^3}{(1 - \mu^2)} \left[\frac{k(1 - \mu)}{48} - \frac{\mu}{48} \right] \tag{9.9.29}$$

$$T21 = -\frac{a}{2b}(T1 + T5) + \frac{a}{2}T9 - \frac{b}{4}(T12 - T14)$$

$$+ \frac{Et^3}{(1 - \mu^2)} \left[\frac{k(1 - \mu)}{48} + \frac{\mu}{48} \right] \tag{9.9.30}$$

$$T22 = \frac{a}{2b} (T1 + T5) - \frac{a}{2} (T9 + T11 - T13) + \frac{b}{4} (T12 - T14)$$

$$- \frac{Et^3}{(1 - \mu^2)} \left[\frac{k(1 - \mu)}{48} + \frac{\mu}{48} \right] \tag{9.9.31}$$

$$T23 = \frac{1}{b} (2T9 + T11 - T13) + \frac{1}{a} (2T10 + T12 - T14)$$

$$+ \frac{Et^3}{(1 - \mu^2)} \frac{(1 - k)(1 - \mu)}{6ab} \tag{9.9.32}$$

$$T24 = -\frac{1}{b} (T11 + T13) - \frac{1}{a} (T12 + T14) + \frac{Et^3}{(1 - \mu^2)} \frac{(1 - k)(1 - \mu)}{6ab} \tag{9.9.33}$$

9.10. Fixed-Condition Nodal Forces for Uniform Load

When a finite rectangular element is subjected to a uniform load of q per unit area, there should be a set of nodal forces F_{01} to F_{012} to keep the 12 nodal displacements at zero. The magnitude of a particular nodal force F_{0i} may be obtained by applying the reciprocal energy theorem between the real fixed condition of Fig. 9.10.1a and the ith fictitious Q-Y basic mode of Fig. 9.10.1b. The

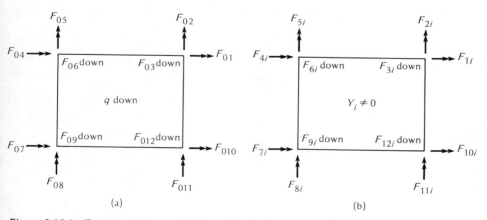

Figure 9.10.1. *Fixed-condition nodal forces for uniform load. (a) Real system (all X's = 0); (b) fictitious system (only $Y_i \neq 0$).*

work done by the nodal forces in the fictitious system in going through the nodal displacements of the real system is zero, which is equated to the work done by the nodal forces in the real system in going through the nodal displacements of the fictitious system. Thus,

$$F_{0i}Y_i + \int_{-a/2}^{+a/2} \int_{-b/2}^{+b/2} q\,(z_i Y_i)\,dy\,dx = 0 \qquad (9.10.1)$$

But z_i is the displacement equation in the ith $Q\text{-}Y$ mode, or

$$\begin{aligned}
z_i = {}& \alpha_{1i} + \alpha_{2i}x + \alpha_{3i}y + \alpha_{4i}x^2 + \alpha_{5i}xy + \alpha_{6i}y^2 \\
&+ \alpha_{7i}x^3 + \alpha_{8i}x^2 y + \alpha_{9i}xy^2 + \alpha_{10i}y^3 \\
&+ \alpha_{11i}x^3 y + \alpha_{12i}xy^3
\end{aligned} \qquad (9.10.2)$$

in which the α-values for the ith mode are given by the ith column in Eq. 9.5.4. Substituting Eq. 9.10.2 in Eq. 9.10.1, cancelling Y_i from each term, and performing the integration,

$$F_{0i} = -q\left[ab\alpha_{1i} + \frac{1}{12}a^3 b\alpha_{4i} + \frac{1}{12}ab^3\alpha_{6i}\right] \qquad (9.10.3)$$

The values of α_{1i}, α_{4i}, and α_{6i} are taken from Eq. 9.5.4 and shown below:

i	α_{1i}	α_{4i}	α_{6i}
1	$+\dfrac{b}{16}$	0	$-\dfrac{1}{4b}$
4	$+\dfrac{b}{16}$	0	$-\dfrac{1}{4b}$
7	$-\dfrac{b}{16}$	0	$+\dfrac{1}{4b}$
10	$-\dfrac{b}{16}$	0	$+\dfrac{1}{4b}$
2	$-\dfrac{a}{16}$	$+\dfrac{1}{4a}$	0
5	$+\dfrac{a}{16}$	$-\dfrac{1}{4a}$	0
8	$+\dfrac{a}{16}$	$-\dfrac{1}{4a}$	0
11	$-\dfrac{a}{16}$	$+\dfrac{1}{4a}$	0

3	$+\dfrac{1}{4}$	0	0
6	$+\dfrac{1}{4}$	0	0
9	$+\dfrac{1}{4}$	0	0
12	$+\dfrac{1}{4}$	0	0

On substitution of the above α-values in Eq. 9.10.3 the fixed-condition forces F_{01} to F_{012} for a rectangular finite element under uniform load are found to be

$$F_{01} = -\frac{1}{24}qab^2 \quad F_{04} = -\frac{1}{24}qab^2 \quad F_{07} = +\frac{1}{24}qab^2 \quad F_{010} = +\frac{1}{24}qab^2$$

$$F_{02} = +\frac{1}{24}qba^2 \quad F_{05} = -\frac{1}{24}qba^2 \quad F_{08} = -\frac{1}{24}qba^2 \quad F_{011} = +\frac{1}{24}qba^2$$

$$F_{03} = -\frac{1}{4}qab \quad F_{06} = -\frac{1}{4}qab \quad F_{09} = -\frac{1}{4}qab \quad F_{012} = -\frac{1}{4}qab$$

Of course, the reverses of these locking forces should be applied as external forces in the displacement method.

TABLE 9.11.1

Input for Plate Bending Problem Shown in Fig. 9.11.1

Card No.	Elements	Format	Remarks
1	5 3 2 400000000. .25 .5	3I5, 3F10.4	NP, NELMT, NLC, E, μ, t
2	6 6 6 6 6 6 6 4 6 2 3 1 6. 9.	12I4, 2F10.4	NP1 ... NP12, a, b
3	2 3 1 ° 6 4 6 6 6 6 5 6 6 6. 3.	12I4, 2F10.4	NP1 ... NP12, a, b
4	6 6 6 2 3 1 5 6 6 6 6 6 12. 3.	12I4, 2F10.4	NP1 ... NP12, a, b
5	1 1 10000.	2I5, F10.4	Nonzero element in [P]
6	1 2 10000.	2I5, F10.4	Nonzero element in [P]
7	0	I5	No more nonzero element in [P]
8	0	I5	No more data set

9.11. The Computer Program

Provided in Appendix H is a computer program using the element stiffness matrix developed in Sec. 9.6. For purpose of simple illustration, the *L*-shaped plate shown in Fig. 9.11.1 is divided into 3 rectangular finite elements. A con-

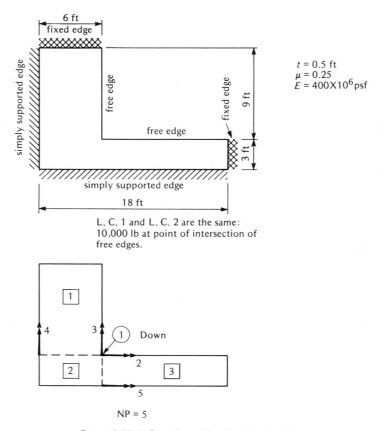

Figure 9.11.1. *Sample problem in plate bending.*

centrated load of 10,000 lb is placed at the intersection of the two free edges. As shown by the input data in Table 9.11.1, the two loading conditions are made identical, just to test the loops in the computer program.

The output information delivered by the computer program includes:

(1) The nodal displacements along the global degrees of freedom,

$$X(1) = +.47624189E - 02$$
$$X(2) = -.12540290E - 02$$
$$X(3) = +.56446806E - 03$$
$$X(4) = +.87971188E - 03$$
$$X(5) = -.17495913E - 02$$

(2) For Element No. 1,

$$
\begin{aligned}
z = &(+.20142125E - 02) + (+.64991030E - 03)x + (-.57989213E - 03)y \\
&+ (-.13135158E - 04)x^2 + (-.18852093E - 03)xy \\
&+ (-.34834140E - 04)y^2 + (-.19901781E - 05)x^3 \\
&+ (+.29189244E - 05)x^2y + (-.16611377E - 04)xy^2 \\
&+ (+.14273728E - 04)y^3 + (+.44226272E - 06)x^3y \\
&+ (+.47579097E - 05)xy^3
\end{aligned}
$$

$$
\begin{aligned}
M_x = &(+.19416618E + 03) + (+.78874492E + 02)x + (-.12110415E + 03)y \\
&+ (-.43513068E + 02)xy
\end{aligned}
$$

$$
\begin{aligned}
M_y = &(+.33882611E + 03) + (+.11648011E + 03)x + (-.38711919E + 03)y \\
&+ (-.12982597E + 03)xy
\end{aligned}
$$

$$
\begin{aligned}
M_{xy} = &(+.62840318E + 03) + (-.19459488E + 02)x + (+.77409184E + 02)y \\
&+ (-.44226258E + 01)x^2 + (-.47579081E + 02)y^2
\end{aligned}
$$

(3) For Element No. 2,

$$
\begin{aligned}
z = &(+.14017390E - 02) + (+.44575252E - 03)x + (+.89396304E - 03)y \\
&+ (-.13135158E - 04)x^2 + (+.28365850E - 03)xy \\
&+ (-.41296858E - 04)y^2 + (-.19901781E - 05)x^3 \\
&+ (-.87567729E - 05)x^2y + (-.13765618E - 04)xy^2 \\
&+ (-.95180294E - 05)y^3 + (-.13267872E - 05)x^3y \\
&+ (-.31726886E - 05)xy^3
\end{aligned}
$$

$$
\begin{aligned}
M_x = &(+.20852776E + 03) + (+.83661669E + 02)x + (+.14129148E + 03)y \\
&+ (+.56532245E + 02)xy
\end{aligned}
$$

$$
\begin{aligned}
M_y = &(+.39627241E + 03) + (+.13562893E + 03)x + (+.27327362E + 03)y \\
&+ (+.93450272E + 02)xy
\end{aligned}
$$

$$
\begin{aligned}
M_{xy} = &(-.94552813E + 03) + (+.58378482E + 02)x + (+.91770783E + 02)y \\
&+ (+.13267873E + 02)x^2 + (+.31726887E + 02)y^2
\end{aligned}
$$

(4) For Element No. 3,

$$z = (+.17068735E - 02) + (-.38369599E - 03)x + (+.10973860E - 02)y$$
$$+ (-.11759747E - 04)x^2 + (-.24904235E - 03)xy$$
$$+ (-.41296858E - 04)y^2 + (.47159870E - 05)x^3$$
$$+ (-.78398325E - 05)x^2y + (+.68828100E - 05)xy^2$$
$$+ (-.95180294E - 05)y^3 + (+.31439911E - 05)x^3y$$
$$+ (.15863443E - 05)xy^3$$

$$M_x = (+.19630186E + 03) + (-.14105477E + 03)x + (+.13314095E + 03)y$$
$$+ (-.94415371E + 02)xy$$

$$M_y = (+.39321599E + 03) + (-.92620410E + 02)x (+.27123600E + 03)y$$
$$+ (-.63262448E + 02)xy$$

$$M_{xy} = (+.83014121E + 03) + (+.52265551E + 02)x + (-.45885384E + 02)y$$
$$+ (-.31439907E + 02)x^2 + (-.15863441E + 02)y^2$$

Because of the fact that the output yields the equations for M_x, M_y, and M_{xy} in the form

$$M_x = A_{11} + A_{12}x + A_{13}y + A_{14}xy \qquad (9.11.1)$$

$$M_y = A_{21} + A_{22}x + A_{23}y + A_{24}xy \qquad (9.11.2)$$

$$M_{xy} = A_{31} + A_{32}x + A_{33}y + A_{34}x^2 + A_{35}y^2 \qquad (9.11.3)$$

it is possible to test the computing accuracy by (1) first computing the local $\{P\}$ matrix of each element from the constants in Eqs. 9.11.1 to 9.11.3, (2) then obtaining the composite global $\{P\}$ matrix, and (3) finally comparing the result of Step No. 2 with the original $\{P\}$ matrix.

The formulas for the local $\{P\}$ matrix in terms of the constants in the equations for the stress resultants M_x, M_y, and M_{xy} are:

$$P_1 = \left[+\frac{a}{2}A_{21} + \frac{a^2}{12}A_{22} + \frac{ab}{4}A_{23} + \frac{a^2b}{24}A_{24} \right] + \left[+\frac{b^2}{6}A_{33} + \frac{b^3}{30}A_{35} \right] \qquad (9.11.4)$$

$$P_4 = \left[+\frac{a}{2}A_{21} - \frac{a^2}{12}A_{22} + \frac{ab}{4}A_{23} - \frac{a^2b}{24}A_{24} \right] + \left[-\frac{b^2}{6}A_{33} - \frac{b^3}{30}A_{35} \right] \qquad (9.11.5)$$

$$P_7 = \left[-\frac{a}{2}A_{21} + \frac{a^2}{12}A_{22} + \frac{ab}{4}A_{23} - \frac{a^2b}{24}A_{24} \right] + \left[+\frac{b^2}{6}A_{33} - \frac{b^3}{30}A_{35} \right] \qquad (9.11.6)$$

$$P_{10} = \left[-\frac{a}{2}A_{21} - \frac{a^2}{12}A_{22} + \frac{ab}{4}A_{23} + \frac{a^2 b}{24}A_{24} \right] + \left[-\frac{b^2}{6}A_{33} + \frac{b^3}{30}A_{35} \right] \qquad (9.11.7)$$

$$P_2 = \left[-\frac{b}{2}A_{11} - \frac{ab}{4}A_{12} - \frac{b^2}{12}A_{13} - \frac{ab^2}{24}A_{14} \right] + \left[-\frac{a^2}{6}A_{32} - \frac{a^3}{30}A_{34} \right] \qquad (9.11.8)$$

$$P_5 = \left[+\frac{b}{2}A_{11} - \frac{ab}{4}A_{12} + \frac{b^2}{12}A_{13} - \frac{ab^2}{24}A_{14} \right] + \left[+\frac{a^2}{6}A_{32} - \frac{a^3}{30}A_{34} \right] \qquad (9.11.9)$$

$$P_8 = \left[+\frac{b}{2}A_{11} - \frac{ab}{4}A_{12} - \frac{b^2}{12}A_{13} + \frac{ab^2}{24}A_{14} \right] + \left[-\frac{a^2}{6}A_{32} + \frac{a^3}{30}A_{34} \right] \qquad (9.11.10)$$

$$P_{11} = \left[-\frac{b}{2}A_{11} - \frac{ab}{4}A_{12} + \frac{b^2}{12}A_{13} + \frac{ab^2}{24}A_{14} \right] + \left[+\frac{a^2}{6}A_{32} + \frac{a^3}{30}A_{34} \right] \qquad (9.11.11)$$

$$P_3 = \left[+\frac{b}{2}A_{12} + \frac{b^2}{12}A_{14} \right] + \left[+\frac{a}{2}A_{23} + \frac{a^2}{12}A_{24} \right] + \left[-2A_{31} - \frac{a^2}{10}A_{34} - \frac{b^2}{10}A_{35} \right]$$
$$(9.11.12)$$

$$P_6 = \left[-\frac{b}{2}A_{12} - \frac{b^2}{12}A_{14} \right] + \left[+\frac{a}{2}A_{23} - \frac{a^2}{12}A_{24} \right] + \left[+2A_{31} + \frac{a^2}{10}A_{34} + \frac{b^2}{10}A_{35} \right]$$
$$(9.11.13)$$

$$P_9 = \left[-\frac{b}{2}A_{12} + \frac{b^2}{12}A_{14} \right] + \left[-\frac{a}{2}A_{23} + \frac{a^2}{12}A_{24} \right] + \left[-2A_{31} - \frac{a^2}{10}A_{34} - \frac{b^3}{10}A_{35} \right]$$
$$(9.11.14)$$

$$P_{12} = \left[+\frac{b}{2}A_{12} - \frac{b^2}{12}A_{14} \right] + \left[-\frac{a}{2}A_{23} - \frac{a^2}{12}A_{24} \right] + \left[+2A_{31} + \frac{a^2}{10}A_{34} + \frac{b^2}{10}A_{35} \right]$$
$$(9.11.15)$$

The above expressions may be derived by applying the reciprocal energy theorem; thus

$$\text{Real } P_i * Y_i \text{ (in the Q-mode)}$$
$$= \int [Se_{Qi}]^T \{\text{Real } e\} \, dA = \int [e_{Qi}^T] [S] \{\text{Real } e\} \, dA$$
$$= \int [B_{1i} \, B_{2i} \, B_{3i}] \, Y_i \{\text{Real } \sigma\} \, dA$$

$$= \int [B_{1i}\ B_{2i}\ B_{3i}]\ Y_i \begin{Bmatrix} M_x \\ M_y \\ M_{xy} \end{Bmatrix} dA$$

For example,

$$P_3 = \int_{-a/2}^{+a/2} \int_{-b/2}^{+b/2} \left[\frac{6x}{a^3} + \frac{12xy}{a^3 b} \;\middle|\; \frac{6y}{b^3} + \frac{12xy}{ab^3} \;\middle|\; -\frac{4}{ab} + \frac{12x^2}{a^3 b} + \frac{12y^2}{ab^3} \right]$$

$$* \left[\begin{array}{l} A_{11} + A_{12}x + A_{13}y + A_{14}xy \\ A_{21} + A_{22}x + A_{23}y + A_{24}xy \\ A_{31} + A_{32}x + A_{33}y + A_{34}x^2 + A_{35}y^2 \end{array} \right] dy\,dx$$

$$= \left[+\frac{b}{2}A_{12} + \frac{b^2}{12}A_{14} \right] + \left[+\frac{a}{2}A_{23} + \frac{a^2}{12}A_{24} \right] + \left[-2A_{31} - \frac{a^2}{10}A_{34} - \frac{b^2}{10}A_{35} \right]$$

For the present example, the composite global $\{P\}$ matrix computed from Eqs. 9.11.4 to 9.11.15 is

$$P(1) = +10000.0087$$
$$P(2) = -0.0075$$
$$P(3) = +0.0012$$
$$P(4) = -0.0027$$
$$P(5) = +0.0079$$

These values compare well with those in the original $\{P\}$ matrix.

CHAPTER 10

■

Introduction to Linear Programming

10.1. General Remarks

Linear programming is indeed a large subject and any introductory treatment in a limited way would be most difficult. An attempt is made here to show one of its applications in minimization by the simplex method. In spite of the rudimentary nature of the discussions made in this chapter, it is hoped that the reader having no prior knowledge of this subject can gain enough to prompt himself toward further study.

10.2. A Minimization Problem in Two Dimensions

Consider the simple algebra problem: "Find the minimum value of z defined by

$$z = 2x_1 + 7x_2$$

subjected to the constraints

$$x_1 - 2x_2 \geqslant -14$$
$$5x_1 + 2x_2 \leqslant +50$$

$$x_1 + 2x_2 \geqslant +18$$

and the requirement that x_1 and x_2 must be positive."

In this problem the function z is called the *merit function,* because it measures merit by virtue of its being the minimum. The variables x_1 and x_2 are called the *design variables,* because the choice of their values directly influences the merit.

When the number of design variables is two, it is possible to solve the minimization problem by a semigraphical procedure. Changing the three constraints from inequalities to equations, one obtains

$$x_1 - 2x_2 = -14$$
$$5x_1 + 2x_2 = -50$$
$$x_1 + 2x_2 = -18$$

These equations are plotted as straight lines in Fig. 10.2.1. A little reflection

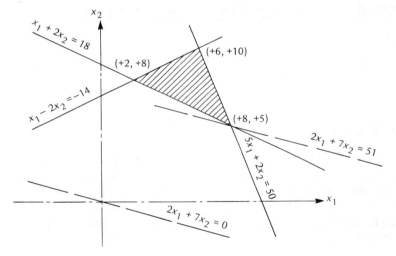

Figure 10.2.1. *A minimization problem in two dimensions.*

will show that all points within the shaded triangle satisfy the three constraints in their original inequality form. To do this it is only necessary to test the point $(0,0)$. When $(0,0)$ is substituted into the first constraint,

$$(0) - 2(0) \geqslant -14$$

which is correct. Therefore, the straight line representing the equation

$$x_1 - 2x_2 = -14$$

divides the two-dimensional space into two regions; the one containing the origin satisfies the inequality and the other does not.

The merit function $z = 2x_1 + 7x_2$ represents parallel lines, of which the one passing through the origin is as shown in Fig. 10.2.1. Raising this line just enough to pass through a point in the shaded triangle yields the solution

$$x_1 = +8; \quad x_2 = +5$$

and

$$z = 2x_1 + 7x_2 = 2(+8) + 7(+5) = +51$$

Although a successful solution happens to be obtainable in this particular case, on other occasions a minimization problem may be trivial, indeterminate, or infeasible.

10.3. Solution Trivial

Consider the minimization problem: "Find the minimum value of z defined by

$$z = 2x_1 + 7x_2$$

subjected to the constraints

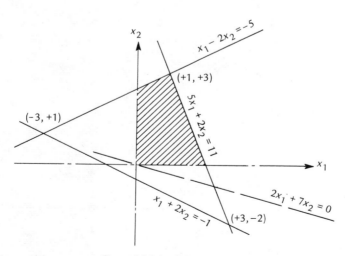

Figure 10.3.1. *Solution trivial.*

$$x_1 - 2x_2 \geqslant -5$$
$$5x_1 + 2x_2 \leqslant +11$$
$$x_1 + 2x_2 \geqslant -1$$

and the requirement that x_1 and x_2 must be positive."

By a semigraphical procedure the feasible region is found to be an area in the first quadrant bounded by the two reference axes (Fig. 10.3.1). An infinite number of straight lines parallel to the line $2x_1 + 7x_2 = 0$ may be drawn through this region, each containing many feasible solutions with the same merit function, which is higher than the one through the origin. The solution in this case is said to be *trivial*.

10.4. Solution Indeterminate

Consider the minimization problem: "Find the minimum value of z defined by

$$z = x_1 + 2x_2$$

subjected to the constraints

$$x_1 - 2x_2 \geqslant -14$$
$$5x_1 + 2x_2 \leqslant +50$$
$$x_1 + 2x_2 \geqslant +18$$

and the requirement that x_1 and x_2 must be positive."

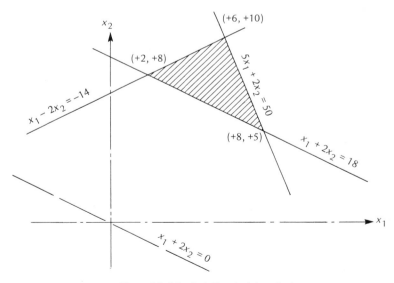

Figure 10.4.1. *Solution indeterminate.*

By a semigraphical procedure the feasible region is found to be an area in the first quadrant with the lowest boundary parallel to the straight line representing the merit function (Fig. 10.4.1). There is definitely an optimum value of z, although the values of the design variables are somewhat indeterminate so long as they satisfy one of the constraints in its equation form. The solution in this case is said to be *indeterminate*.

10.5. Solution Infeasible

Consider the minimization problem: "Find the minimum value of z defined by

$$z = 2x_1 + 7x_2$$

subjected to the constraints

$$x_1 - 2x_2 \geqslant +8$$
$$5x_1 + 2x_2 \leqslant +28$$
$$x_1 + 2x_2 \geqslant -4$$

and the requirement that x_1 and x_2 must be positive."

By a semigraphical procedure the region satisfying the constraints is found to lie entirely in the fourth quadrant (Fig. 10.5.1) so that the requirement that all design variables must be positive cannot be satisfied. Thus there is no feasible solution at all for this problem.

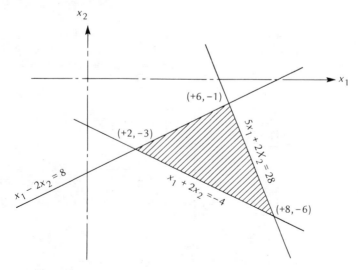

Figure 10.5.1. *Solution infeasible.*

10.6. General Formulation for More than Two Design Variables

It has been shown that the semigraphical procedure may be used to solve a minimization problem in two dimensions, although the solution may prove to be successful, trivial, indeterminate, or infeasible. When the number of design variables is more than two, a general algebraic formulation is needed.

Consider the minimization problem: "Find the minimum value of z defined by

$$z = c_1 x_1 + c_2 x_2$$

subjected to the constraints

$$a_{11} x_1 + a_{12} x_2 \leqslant b_1$$
$$a_{21} x_1 + a_{22} x_2 \leqslant b_2$$
$$a_{31} x_1 + a_{32} x_2 \leqslant b_3$$

and the requirement that x_1 and x_2 must be positive."

The three constraints in the inequality form may be replaced by three equations

$$a_{11} x_1 + a_{12} x_2 + 1.0 x_3 \qquad\qquad = b_1$$
$$a_{21} x_1 + a_{22} x_2 \qquad +1.0 x_4 \qquad = b_2$$
$$a_{31} x_1 + a_{32} x_2 \qquad\qquad +1.0 x_5 = b_3$$

in which x_3, x_4, and x_5 are defined to be the *slack variables* which must be positive.

The first-hand information for this problem may be displayed in the *first matrix form* of 4 rows and 6 columns, in which 4 is one more than the number of slack variables and 6 is one more than the sum of design and slack variables, as follows:

i \ j	1	2	3	4	5	6
1	a_{11}	a_{12}	+1.	0.	0.	b_1
2	a_{21}	a_{22}	0.	+1.	0.	b_2
3	a_{31}	a_{32}	0.	0.	+1.	b_3
4	c_1	c_2	0.	0.	0.	z†

†In the computer, a zero quantity is stored in place of the symbol z.

In fact, the solution to this first matrix form is

$$\{x\} = \begin{Bmatrix} x_1 \\ x_2 \\ x_3 \\ x_4 \\ x_5 \end{Bmatrix} = \begin{Bmatrix} 0. \\ 0. \\ b_1 \\ b_2 \\ b_3 \end{Bmatrix} \quad \text{and} \quad z = 0$$

Had b_1, b_2, and b_3 been all positive, the trivial solution $x_1 = 0$, $x_2 = 0$, and $z = 0$ is obtained and the solution to the minimization problem falls into the "trivial" category.

10.7. The Intermediate Matrix Form

In order to develop the algorithm of arriving at a solution (successful, indeterminate, or infeasible) of a minimization problem involving N design variables and M slack variables, observations will be made of an *intermediate matrix form* which has supposedly been obtained from the first matrix form after a number of *Gauss-Jordan substitutions*. For $N = 2$ and $M = 3$, this intermediate matrix form may appear as

$\diagdown$ j i	1	2	3	4	5	6
1	0.	$A(1,2)$	$A(1,3)$	+1.	0.	$A(1,6)$
2	0.	$A(2,2)$	$A(2,3)$	0.	+1.	$A(2,6)$
3	+1.	$A(3,2)$	$A(3,3)$	0.	0.	$A(3,6)$
4	0.	$A(4,2)$	$A(4,3)$	0.	0.	$z + A(4,6)$

The solution at this point (which may or may not be acceptable) is

$$\{x\} = \begin{Bmatrix} x_1 \\ x_2 \\ x_3 \\ x_4 \\ x_5 \end{Bmatrix} = \begin{Bmatrix} A(3,6) \\ 0. \\ 0. \\ A(1,6) \\ A(2,6) \end{Bmatrix} \quad \text{and} \quad z = -A(4,6)$$

This solution would have been acceptable if all nonzero values of x were positive.

In the computer, an NIN (the x-numbers which are in) array of M elements is used to keep record of the subscripts of x, whose values appear in the last column of the matrix form. Thus, in the present case,

$$NIN(1) = 4$$
$$NIN(2) = 5$$
$$NIN(3) = 1$$

An INDEX array of $(N + M)$ elements is used to indicate whether the value at the last row of each column is zero or not. Thus in the present case,

$$INDEX(1) = 0$$
$$INDEX(2) = 1$$
$$INDEX(3) = 1$$
$$INDEX(4) = 0$$
$$INDEX(5) = 0$$

It may be noted that x_2 and x_3 are equal to zero at this point making INDEX(2) and INDEX(3) nonzero.

10.8. The Gauss-Jordan Substitution

When the solution at any intermediate matrix form is not acceptable, an attempt may be made to improve this solution by choosing a pivot and applying a Gauss-Jordan substitution. This pivot should occur only in the first M rows of those N columns whose "INDEX" is nonzero. For instance, in the intermediate matrix, form described in the preceding section, the pivot may be any one of the 6 elements in the first three rows of the 2nd or 3rd column.

Before developing rules for determining the best of all eligible pivots, it is desirable to see what a Gauss-Jordan substitution will do if some element at (IROW, ICOL) is used as the pivot. Using $A(2,3)$ as the pivot (IROW = 2, ICOL = 3) and applying Gauss-Jordan substitution, the intermediate matrix form in the preceding section becomes

i \ j	1	2	3	4	5	6
1	0.	$A(1,2) - \dfrac{A(1,3)*A(2,2)}{\text{pivot}}$	0.	+1.	$-\dfrac{A(1,3)}{\text{pivot}}$	$A(1,6) - \dfrac{A(1,3)*A(2,6)}{\text{pivot}}$
2	0.	$+\dfrac{A(2,2)}{\text{pivot}}$	+1.	0.	$+\dfrac{1}{\text{pivot}}$	$+\dfrac{A(2,6)}{\text{pivot}}$
3	+1.	$A(3,2) - \dfrac{A(3,3)*A(2,2)}{\text{pivot}}$	0.	0.	$-\dfrac{A(3,3)}{\text{pivot}}$	$A(3,6) - \dfrac{A(3,3)*A(2,6)}{\text{pivot}}$
4	0.	$A(4,2) - \dfrac{A(4,3)*A(2,2)}{\text{pivot}}$	0.	0.	$-\dfrac{A(4,3)}{\text{pivot}}$	$A(4,6) - \dfrac{A(4,3)*A(2,6)}{\text{pivot}}$

in which

$$NIN(1) = 4 \qquad INDEX(1) = 0$$
$$NIN(2) = 3 \qquad INDEX(2) = 1$$
$$NIN(3) = 1 \qquad INDEX(3) = 0$$
$$INDEX(4) = 0$$
$$INDEX(5) = 1$$

and

$$x(1) = A(3,6) - \frac{A(3,3)*A(2,6)}{\text{pivot}}$$

$$x(2) = 0$$

$$x(3) = +\frac{A(2,6)}{\text{pivot}} \qquad\qquad z = -A(4,6) + \frac{A(4,3)*A(2,6)}{\text{pivot}}$$

$$x(4) = A(1,6) - \frac{A(1,3)*A(2,6)}{\text{pivot}}$$

$$x(5) = 0$$

The effects of this reduction may be tabulated in general and specific terms as follows:

Item	General	Specific
1	NTEMP = NIN(IROW)	NTEMP = NIN(2) = 5
2	x(NTEMP) = 0.	$x(5)$ = 0.
3	INDEX (NTEMP) = 1	INDEX(5) = 1
4	NIN (IROW) = ICOL	NIN(2) = 3
5	$x(\text{ICOL}) = +\dfrac{A(\text{IROW},N + M + 1)}{\text{Pivot}}$	$x(3) = +\dfrac{A(2,6)}{\text{pivot}}$
6	INDEX (ICOL) = 0	INDEX(3) = 0
7	z increases by $\dfrac{A(M + 1,\text{ICOL}) * A(\text{IROW},N + M + 1)}{\text{pivot}}$	z increases by $\dfrac{A(4,3) * A(2,6)}{\text{pivot}}$

The first three items show that x(NTEMP) now becomes zero, and the next three items show that x(ICOL) changes from zero to nonzero.

Since the purpose of the Gauss-Jordan substitution is to drive out a negative A(IROW,N + M + 1), to obtain a positive X(ICOL) = A(IROW,N + M + 1)/pivot, and to raise by the least amount of

$$\frac{A(M + 1,\text{ICOL}) * A(\text{IROW},N + M + 1)}{\text{pivot}}$$

the selection of the pivot should follow the following criteria:
1. The pivot must be negative.
2. The last column of the pivotal row must be negative.
3. The last row of the pivotal column must be positive.
4. The best† pivot is the one giving the least value of

$$\frac{A(M + 1,\text{ICOL}) * A(\text{IROW},N + M + 1)}{\text{pivot}}$$

The method of using successive Gauss-Jordan substitutions to arrive at a conclusion of successful, trivial, indeterminate or infeasible solution is called the *simplex method* in linear programming.

10.9. Simplex Method: Solution Successful

If after one or more Gauss-Jordan substitutions all the x-values which appear in the first M rows of the last column are nonnegative, the solution is successful.

---

†This criterion may be modified as in the third version of the computer program shown in Appendix I.

Example 10.9.1. Find the minimum value of z defined by

$$z = 2x_1 + 7x_2$$

subjected to the constraints

$$x_1 - 2x_2 \geqslant -14$$
$$5x_1 + 2x_2 \leqslant +50$$
$$x_1 + 2x_2 \geqslant +18$$

and the requirement that x_1 and x_2 must be positive.

Solution: The three constraints are changed into the three equations

$$-x_1 + 2x_2 + x_3 \qquad\qquad = +14$$
$$+5x_1 + 2x_2 \qquad +x_4 \qquad = +50$$
$$-x_1 - 2x_2 \qquad\qquad +x_5 = -18$$

The first matrix form is

i \ j	1	2	3	4	5	6
1	-1	+2	+1	0	0	+14
2	+5	+2	0	+1	0	+50
3	-1	-2	0	0	+1	-18
4	+2	+7	0	0	0	$z + 0$

in which

$$\begin{array}{lll}
\text{NIN}(1) = 3 & \text{INDEX}(1) = 1 & x(1) = 0 \\
\text{NIN}(2) = 4 & \text{INDEX}(2) = 1 & x(2) = 0 \\
\text{NIN}(3) = 5 & \text{INDEX}(3) = 0 & x(3) = +14 \qquad z = 0 \\
& \text{INDEX}(4) = 0 & x(4) = +50 \\
& \text{INDEX}(5) = 0 & x(5) = -18
\end{array}$$

Of the 6 elements in the first three rows of the 1st or 2nd column, the elements at (3,1) and (3,2) are eligible to be pivots. If the element at (3,1) is used as pivot, z is increased by $(+2)(-18)/(-1) = 36$; if the element at (3,2) is used as pivot, z is increased by $(+7)(-18)/(-2) = 63$. Using the element at (3,1) as pivot,

(IROW = 3, ICOL = 1), the matrix form becomes

j / *i*	1	2	3	4	5	6
1	0	+4	+1	0	-1	+32
2	0	-8	0	+1	+5	-40
3	+1	+2	0	0	-1	+18
4	0	+3	0	0	+2	z - 36

in which

$$
\begin{array}{lll}
NIN(1) = 3 & INDEX(1) = 0 & x(1) = +18 \\
NIN(2) = 4 & INDEX(2) = 1 & x(2) = \;\;\;0 \\
NIN(3) = 1 & INDEX(3) = 0 & x(3) = +32 \quad z = 36 \\
 & INDEX(4) = 0 & x(4) = -\;40 \\
 & INDEX(5) = 1 & x(5) = \;\;\;0
\end{array}
$$

Of the 6 elements in the first three rows of the 2nd or 5th column, only the element at (2,2) is eligible to be the pivot. Using this element as the pivot (IROW = 2, ICOL = 2), the matrix form becomes

j / *i*	1	2	3	4	5	6
1	0	0	+1	+0.5	+1.5	+12
2	0	+1	0	-0.125	-0.625	+5
3	+1	0	0	+0.25	+0.25	+8
4	0	0	0	+0.375	+3.875	z - 51

in which

$$
\begin{array}{lll}
NIN(1) = 3 & INDEX(1) = 0 & x(1) = +8 \\
NIN(2) = 2 & INDEX(2) = 0 & x(2) = +5 \\
NIN(3) = 1 & INDEX(3) = 0 & x(3) = +12 \quad z = 51 \\
 & INDEX(4) = 1 & x(4) = \;\;\;0 \\
 & INDEX(5) = 1 & x(5) = \;\;\;0
\end{array}
$$

Because the three *x*-values which are in are now all positive, the solution is successful.

10.10. Simplex Method: Solution Trivial

If the elements in the first M rows of the last column of the first matrix form are all positive at the outset, then all slack variables are positive, all design variables are zero, and the merit function is zero. In such case the solution is trivial.

Example 10.10.1. Find the minimum value of z defined by

$$z = 2x_1 + 7x_2$$

subjected to the constraints

$$x_1 - 2x_2 \geqslant -5$$
$$5x_1 + 2x_2 \leqslant +11$$
$$x_1 + 2x_2 \geqslant -1$$

and the requirement that x_1 and x_2 must be positive.

Solution: The three constraints are changed into the three equations

$$-x_1 + 2x_2 + x_3 \qquad\qquad = +5$$
$$+5x_1 + 2x_2 \qquad +x_4 \qquad = +11$$
$$-x_1 - 2x_2 \qquad\qquad +x_5 = +1$$

The first matrix form is

i \ j	1	2	3	4	5	6
1	-1	+2	+1	0	0	+5
2	+5	+2	0	+1	0	+11
3	-1	-2	0	0	+1	+1
4	+2	+7	0	0	0	$z + 0$

in which

$$
\begin{array}{lll}
\text{NIN}(1) = 3 & \text{INDEX}(1) = 1 & x(1) = 0 \\
\text{NIN}(2) = 4 & \text{INDEX}(2) = 1 & x(2) = 0 \\
\text{NIN}(3) = 5 & \text{INDEX}(3) = 0 & x(3) = +5 \qquad z = 0 \\
& \text{INDEX}(4) = 0 & x(4) = +11 \\
& \text{INDEX}(5) = 0 & x(5) = +1
\end{array}
$$

Since the slack variables are already all positive at the beginning, the problem is trivial.

10.11. Simplex Method: Solution Indeterminate

Before a solution is declared successful, a determination should be made whether the element at $(M + 1, K)$ turns out to be zero although it is not supposed to be. If this happens, $x(K)$ could assume any value without affecting the merit function. Since the solution needs not to lie on the constraint of which $x(K)$ is the slack variable, it is indeterminate.

Example 10.11.1. Find the minimum value of z defined by

$$z = x_1 + 2x_2$$

subjected to the constraints

$$x_1 - 2x_2 \geqslant -14$$
$$5x_1 + 2x_2 \leqslant +50$$
$$x_1 + 2x_2 \geqslant +18$$

and the requirement that x_1 and x_2 must be positive.

Solution: The three constraints are changed into the three equations

$$-x_1 + 2x_2 + x_3 \qquad\qquad = +14$$
$$+5x_1 + 2x_2 \qquad +x_4 \qquad = +50$$
$$-x_1 - 2x_2 \qquad\qquad +x_5 = -18$$

The first matrix form is

i \ j	1	2	3	4	5	6
1	-1	+2	+1	0	0	+14
2	+5	+2	0	+1	0	+50
3	-1	-2	0	0	+1	-18
4	+1	+2	0	0	0	$z + 0$

in which

$$NIN(1) = 3 \quad INDEX(1) = 1 \quad x(1) = 0$$
$$NIN(2) = 4 \quad INDEX(2) = 1 \quad x(2) = 0$$
$$NIN(3) = 5 \quad INDEX(3) = 0 \quad x(3) = +14 \quad z = 0$$
$$INDEX(4) = 0 \quad x(4) = +50$$
$$INDEX(5) = 0 \quad x(5) = -18$$

Of the 6 elements in the first three rows of the 1st or 2nd column, the elements at (3,1) and (3,2) are eligible to be pivots. If the element at (3,1) is used as pivot, z is increased by $(+1)(-18)/(-1) = 18$; if the element at (3,2) is used as pivot, z is increased by $(+2)(-18)/(-2) = 18$. Using the element at (3,1) as pivot (IROW = 3, ICOL = 1), the matrix form becomes

i \ j	1	2	3	4	5	6
1	0	+4	+1	0	-1	+32
2	0	-8	0	+1	+5	-40
3	+1	+2	0	0	-1	+18
4	0	0	0	0	+1	$z-18$

in which

$$NIN(1) = 3 \quad INDEX(1) = 0 \quad x(1) = +18$$
$$NIN(2) = 4 \quad INDEX(2) = 1 \quad x(2) = 0$$
$$NIN(3) = 1 \quad INDEX(3) = 0 \quad x(3) = +32 \quad z = 18$$
$$INDEX(4) = 0 \quad x(4) = -40$$
$$INDEX(5) = 1 \quad x(5) = 0$$

Of the six elements in the first three rows of the 2nd or 5th column, only the element at (2,2) is eligible to be the pivot. Using this element as the pivot (IROW = 2, ICOL = 2), the matrix form becomes

i \ j	1	2	3	4	5	6
1	0	0	+1	+0.5	+1.5	+12
2	0	+1	0	-0.125	-0.625	+5
3	+1	0	0	+0.25	+0.25	+8
4	0	0	0	0	+1	$z-18$

in which

$$
\begin{array}{llll}
\text{NIN}(1) = 3 & \text{INDEX}(1) = 0 & x(1) = +8 & \\
\text{NIN}(2) = 2 & \text{INDEX}(2) = 0 & x(2) = +5 & \\
\text{NIN}(3) = 1 & \text{INDEX}(3) = 0 & x(3) = +12 & z = 18 \\
& \text{INDEX}(4) = 1 & x(4) = 0 & \\
& \text{INDEX}(5) = 1 & x(5) = 0 &
\end{array}
$$

Here INDEX(4) = 1, but the element at (4,4) is unexpectedly zero; so the problem is indeterminate. Since $x(4)$ is the slack variable in the second constraint equation, points other than (+8, +5), away from the equation $5x_1 + 2x_2 = 50$ (see Fig. 10.4.1) would have given the same value for the merit function.

10.12. Simplex Method: Solution Infeasible

Whenever there are still negative values remaining in the solution vector (or in the first M rows of the last column in the matrix form) and yet no eligible pivot can be found for another Gauss-Jordan substitution, there is no feasible solution.

Example 10.12.1. Find the minimum value of z defined by

$$z = 2x_1 + 7x_2$$

subjected to the constraints

$$
\begin{aligned}
x_1 - 2x_2 &\geqslant +8 \\
5x_1 + 2x_2 &\leqslant +28 \\
x_1 + 2x_2 &\geqslant -4
\end{aligned}
$$

and the requirement that x_1 and x_2 must be positive.

Solution: The three constraints are changed into the three equations

$$
\begin{aligned}
-x_1 + 2x_2 + x_3 &= -8 \\
+5x_1 + 2x_2 + x_4 &= +28 \\
-x_1 - 2x_2 + x_5 &= +4
\end{aligned}
$$

The first matrix form is

j\i	1	2	3	4	5	6
1	-1	+2	+1	0	0	-8
2	+5	+2	0	+1	0	+28
3	-1	-2	0	0	+1	+4
4	+2	+7	0	0	0	z + 0

in which

$$NIN(1) = 3 \qquad INDEX(1) = 1 \qquad x(1) = 0$$
$$NIN(2) = 4 \qquad INDEX(2) = 1 \qquad x(2) = 0$$
$$NIN(3) = 5 \qquad INDEX(3) = 0 \qquad x(3) = -8 \qquad z = 0$$
$$INDEX(4) = 0 \qquad x(4) = +28$$
$$INDEX(5) = 0 \qquad x(5) = +4$$

Of the 6 elements in the first three rows of the 1st or 2nd column, the only eligible pivot is at (1,1). Using IROW = 1 and ICOL = 1 and applying a Gauss-Jordan substitution, the matrix form becomes

i \ j	1	2	3	4	5	6
1	+1	-2	-1	0	0	+8
2	0	+12	+5	+1	0	-12
3	0	-4	-1	0	+1	+12
4	0	+11	+2	0	0	$z - 16$

in which

$$NIN(1) = 1 \qquad INDEX(1) = 0 \qquad x(1) = +8$$
$$NIN(2) = 4 \qquad INDEX(2) = 1 \qquad x(2) = 0$$
$$NIN(3) = 5 \qquad INDEX(3) = 1 \qquad x(3) = 0 \qquad z = 16$$
$$INDEX(4) = 0 \qquad x(4) = -12$$
$$INDEX(5) = 0 \qquad x(5) = +12$$

Now of the 6 elements in the first three rows of the 2nd or 3rd column, no eligible pivot exists. There is no feasible solution.

10.13. Flow Chart for Computer Program

In Appendix I are shown three different versions of a similarly constructed computer program for minimizing a linear function by the simplex method using the algorithm described in this chapter. As later explained in Appendix I, the difference between Version 3 and Versions 1 and 2 lies in the way of choosing the best pivot, whereas in Versions 2 and 3 the columns with only 1's and 0's in them are not stored in memory. A brief flow chart for this program is shown in Fig. 10.13.1.

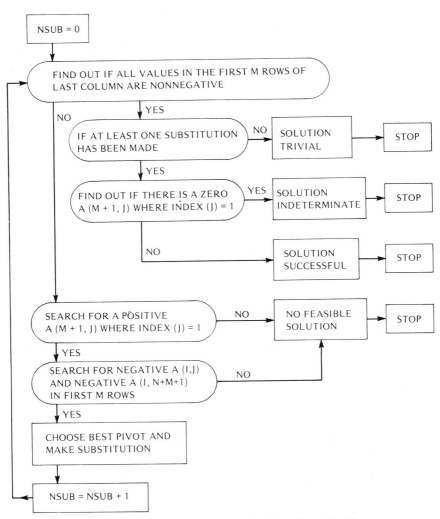

Figure 10.13.1. *Flow chart for minimizing a linear function.*

CHAPTER 11

■

Minimum-Weight Design of Trusses

11.1. General Description

In this chapter a definite procedure for arriving at the minimum-weight design of trusses will be described. Because it is a simple type of structure, the truss is chosen as the vehicle for conveying a general concept.

The merit function is the weight or volume of the truss, which is the summation of the products of the bar areas and their respective lengths. The constraints are taken to be a permissible unit tensile stress and a permissible unit compressive stress. At the beginning of the iteration, an initial design is made so that one of the two permissible stresses is reached within at least one bar in at least one of the loading conditions.

The number of design variables is equal to the number of bars, each taken as the ratio of the unknown "new" bar area to the known "old" bar area in the initial design.

If by some means the changes in the bar forces due to a change in each bar area may be found in the immediate vicinity of the initial design, linear inequalities may be set up to limit the "new" actual stresses to the permissible values.

Linear programming methods are then used to obtain a "new" set of bar areas, all of which may need to be scaled upward slightly because the partial derivatives of the bar forces with respect to the changes in bar areas used in building the constraints are only approximately accurate, as will be shown.

This first improved design may then be taken as the initial design, and a second improved design obtained in the same manner. The procedure is repeated until the improvement becomes insignificant.

11.2. Initial Design

The bar forces in statically determinate trusses are independent of the bar areas, but those in indeterminate trusses are. In the former case, no matter what bar areas are used in the displacement method of analysis, the same bar forces are obtained. The reason is that the statics matrix $[A]$ of any statically determinate truss is square, and the bar forces $\{F\}$ are simply equal to $\{A^{-1}P\}$. When the displacement method is used for a statically determinate truss, the expression $\{F\} = [SA^T] \{X\}$ may be shown to become $\{F\} = [A^{-1}] \{P\}$; thus

$$F = SA^T X = SA^T [ASA^T]^{-1} P = SA^T [A^T]^{-1} [AS]^{-1} P$$
$$= S[AS]^{-1} P = SS^{-1}A^{-1}P = A^{-1}P$$

Nevertheless, the bar forces in statically indeterminate trusses depend only on the relative bar areas, but not on their absolute sizes. This fact may be proved by inserting a factor α in front of the member stiffness matrix $[S]$; thus

$$F = [\alpha S] A^T [A \alpha S A^T]^{-1} P = SA^T [ASA^T]^{-1} P$$

In making an initial design, any set of trial bar areas A_0 may be chosen. A set of actual stresses σ_0 are found by dividing the actual bar forces F, computed by the displacement method of analysis, by the areas A_0. Then the stress factors f are computed by dividing the actual stresses σ_0 by the appropriate permissible stresses σ_p. The actual bar areas A in the initial design are equal to the trial bar areas A_0, multiplied by the largest value of f. In this way, one of the permissible stresses σ_p is reached in at least one bar.

It may be noted that the number of F, σ_0, or f is equal to the number of loading conditions times the number of bars. Also, in computing the stress factor $f = \sigma_0/\sigma_p$, either the permissible tensile or compressive stress should be used depending on whether σ_0 is positive or negative. The stress factors f themselves are quantities without signs.

Example 11.2.1. Make an initial design of the 4-bar structure in Fig. 11.2.1

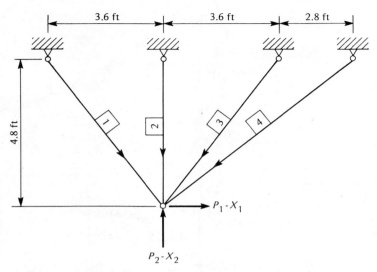

Figure 11.2.1. *Minimum-weight design of a truss.*

using the trial bar areas

$$\{A_0\} \text{ in sq in.} = \begin{Bmatrix} 1.44 \\ 2.00 \\ 1.80 \\ 2.00 \end{Bmatrix}$$

The two loading conditions are

$$[P] \text{ in kips} = \begin{bmatrix} 0 & +5 \\ -10 & -6 \end{bmatrix}$$

Allowable σ_P is +20 ksi in tension and −15 ksi in compression. Use $E =$ 30,000 ksi.

Solution: The input matrices for the displacement method of analysis are:

$$[A] = \begin{bmatrix} +0.6 & 0. & -0.6 & -0.8 \\ -0.8 & -1.0 & -0.8 & -0.6 \end{bmatrix} \quad \begin{matrix} x & \text{eq—th—} \\ y & \end{matrix}$$

$$[S] \text{ in kips per ft} = \begin{bmatrix} 7200 & & & \\ & 12500 & & \\ & & 9000 & \\ & & & 7500 \end{bmatrix}$$

$$[P] \text{ in kips} = \begin{bmatrix} 0 & +5 \\ -10 & -6 \end{bmatrix}$$

The output matrices are

$$[X] \text{ in } 10^{-3} \text{ ft} = \begin{bmatrix} +0.1772 & +0.6138 \\ -0.4221 & -0.3418 \end{bmatrix}$$

$$[F] \text{ in kips} = \begin{bmatrix} +3.197 & +4.621 \\ +5.276 & +4.273 \\ +2.082 & -0.853 \\ +0.836 & -2.145 \end{bmatrix}$$

The actual stresses σ_0 based on the trial bar areas are

$$[\sigma_0] = \begin{bmatrix} +3.197/1.44 & +4.621/1.44 \\ +5.276/2.00 & +4.273/2.00 \\ +2.082/1.80 & -0.853/1.80 \\ +0.836/2.00 & -2.145/2.00 \end{bmatrix} = \begin{bmatrix} +2.220 & +3.209 \\ +2.638 & +2.136 \\ +1.157 & -0.474 \\ +0.418 & -1.072 \end{bmatrix}$$

The stress factors $f = \sigma_0/\sigma_P$ are

$$[f] = \begin{bmatrix} +2.220/+20 & +3.209/+20 \\ +2.638/+20 & +2.136/+20 \\ +1.157/+20 & -0.474/-15 \\ +0.418/+20 & -1.072/-15 \end{bmatrix} = \begin{bmatrix} 0.1110 & 0.1604 \\ 0.1319 & 0.1068 \\ 0.0578 & 0.0316 \\ 0.0209 & 0.0715 \end{bmatrix}$$

in which the largest value is 0.1604. The actual bar areas which should be used are

$$\{A\} \text{ in sq in.} = \begin{Bmatrix} 0.1604(1.44) \\ 0.1604(2.00) \\ 0.1604(1.80) \\ 0.1604(2.00) \end{Bmatrix} = \begin{Bmatrix} 0.2310 \\ 0.3209 \\ 0.2888 \\ 0.3209 \end{Bmatrix}$$

The volume function in the initial design in units of ft-in.^{2} is

$$\begin{aligned} z &= \Sigma LA \\ &= 6(0.2310) + 4.8(0.3209) + 6(0.2888) + 8(0.3209) \\ &= 7.226 \text{ ft-in.}^2 \end{aligned}$$

11.3. Changes in Bar Forces per Changes in Bar Areas

The key values required in the linear programming formulation to minimize
the volume of a truss are the changes in bar forces per changes in bar areas, at
the immediate vicinity of the initial design. Required are the changes in bar-
forces $\Delta F(i,j,k)$ in the ith bar, for the jth loading condition, and due to a small
increase in the area of the kth bar.

Since the inverse of the $[ASA^T]$ matrix at the initial design is available in the
computer memory, the effort is directed toward making use of it, even though
the values of ΔF thus obtained might be only approximate. Let $[\Delta S_k]$ be the
increase in the member stiffness matrix due to a small increase in the area of the
kth bar equal to $(u_k - 1)A_k$, in which A_k is the bar area in the initial design and
$u_k A_k$ is the unknown new bar area; then

$$[\Delta S_k] = $$

F \ e	1	2	k	NF
1	0			
2		0		
k			$E(u_k - 1)A_k/L$	
NF				0

(11.3.1)

An approximate formula for $\Delta F(\text{NFXNLC})$ due to a small $\Delta S(\text{NFXNF})$ can
be derived as follows:

Given: X, $[K]^{-1} = [ASA^T]^{-1}$, $\Delta K = A(\Delta S)A^T$, and P

To find: ΔF for constant P

Solution: (1) Subtracting $P = KX$ from $P = (K + \Delta K)(X + \Delta X)$,

$$0 = (\Delta K)X + K(\Delta X) + (\Delta K)(\Delta X)$$

from which

$$(\Delta X) = -(K + \Delta K)^{-1}(\Delta K)X \tag{11.3.2}$$

(2) Subtracting $F = SA^T X$ from $F + \Delta F = (S + \Delta S)A^T(X + \Delta X)$,

$$\Delta F = (\Delta S)A^T X + (S + \Delta S)A^T(\Delta X) \tag{11.3.3}$$

(3) Substituting Eq. 11.3.2 in Eq. 11.3.3,

$$\Delta F = (\Delta S)A^T X - (S + \Delta S)A^T(K + \Delta K)^{-1}(\Delta K)X \tag{11.3.4}$$

(4) Approximating $(S + \Delta S)$ and $(K + \Delta K)^{-1}$ in the above equation by S and $[K]^{-1}$, respectively,

$$\Delta F = (\Delta S)A^T X - SA^T K^{-1} A(\Delta S)A^T X \tag{11.3.5}$$

Two interesting observations may be made from the approximate formula 11.3.5. The first is that if $[\Delta S]$ is equal to a constant α times $[S]$, the changes in the bar forces are zero. Of course ΔF has to be zero when $\alpha[S]$ is substituted for $[\Delta S]$ in the exact formula 11.3.4 because it has been proved before that the bar forces depend only on the relative bar areas. The other observation is that if (ΔS_k) in Eq. 11.3.1 is substituted in Eq. 11.3.5, all elements in the $[\Delta F]$ matrix are $(u_k - 1)$ times those in the $[\Delta F]$ matrix for doubling the area of the kth bar. Equation 11.3.5 can then be used to find the $\Delta F(\text{NFXNLC})$ matrix, due to change in each bar area taken one at a time.

It is possible to interpret Eq. 11.3.5 in a physical way. The first term $(\Delta S)A^T X$ represents the incremental forces in the bars owing to the increased bar stiffness. The second term represents the incremental forces in the bars owing to the application of a set of joint forces, $[-A(\Delta S)A^T X]$, to maintain the constant $[P]$ matrix.

Example 11.3.1. Given for the 4-bar structure shown in Fig. 11.2.1, at one initial design:

$$\{A_0\} \text{ in sq in.} = \begin{Bmatrix} 1.44 \\ 2.00 \\ 1.80 \\ 2.00 \end{Bmatrix} \quad [S] \text{ in k/ft} = \begin{bmatrix} 7200 & & & \\ & 12500 & & \\ & & 9000 & \\ & & & 7500 \end{bmatrix}$$

$$[A] = \begin{bmatrix} +0.6 & 0. & -0.6 & -0.8 \\ -0.8 & -1.0 & -0.8 & -0.6 \end{bmatrix}$$

$$[K^{-1}] \text{ in } 10^{-3} \text{ ft/k} = \begin{bmatrix} +0.10150 & -0.01772 \\ -0.01772 & +0.04220 \end{bmatrix}$$

$$[X] \text{ in } 10^{-3} \text{ ft} = \begin{bmatrix} +0.1772 & +0.6138 \\ -0.4221 & -0.3418 \end{bmatrix}$$

find the changes in the bar forces owing to the doubling of each bar area, taken one at a time.

Solution: Since the expression $[SA^TK^{-1}]$ in

$$\Delta F = [(\Delta S_k)A^T - SA^TK^{-1}A(\Delta S_k)A^T]X$$

is common for all values of k, it is computed first.

$[SA^TK^{-1}] =$

$$\begin{bmatrix} 7200 & & & \\ & 12500 & & \\ & & 9000 & \\ & & & 7500 \end{bmatrix} \begin{bmatrix} +0.6 & -0.8 \\ 0. & -1.0 \\ -0.6 & -0.8 \\ -0.8 & -0.6 \end{bmatrix} \begin{bmatrix} +0.10150 & -0.01772 \\ -0.01772 & +0.04220 \end{bmatrix} \times 10^{-3}$$

$$= \begin{bmatrix} +0.5405 & -0.3196 \\ +0.2215 & -0.5276 \\ -0.4205 & -0.2082 \\ -0.5292 & -0.0836 \end{bmatrix}$$

(1) Doubling the area of Bar No. 1.

$\Delta F =$

$$
\left[\begin{bmatrix} 7200 & & & \\ & 0 & & \\ & & 0 & \\ & & & 0 \end{bmatrix} \begin{bmatrix} +0.6 & -0.8 \\ 0 & -1.0 \\ -0.6 & -0.8 \\ -0.8 & -0.6 \end{bmatrix} - [SA^T K^{-1}][A] \begin{bmatrix} 7200 & & & \\ & 0 & & \\ & & 0 & \\ & & & 0 \end{bmatrix} [A^T] \right] [X]
$$

$$
= \left[\begin{bmatrix} +4320 & -5760 \\ 0 & 0 \\ 0 & 0 \\ 0 & 0 \end{bmatrix} - \begin{bmatrix} +0.5405 & -0.3196 \\ +0.2215 & -0.5276 \\ -0.4205 & -0.2082 \\ -0.5292 & -0.0836 \end{bmatrix} \begin{bmatrix} +2592 & -3456 \\ -3456 & +4608 \end{bmatrix} \right] [X]
$$

$$
= \begin{bmatrix} +1814 & -2419 \\ -2397 & +3196 \\ +370 & -494 \\ +1083 & -1444 \end{bmatrix} \begin{bmatrix} +0.1772 & +0.6138 \\ -0.4221 & -0.3418 \end{bmatrix} \times 10^{-3}
$$

$$
= \begin{bmatrix} +1.342 & +1.940 \\ -1.774 & -2.564 \\ +0.274 & +0.396 \\ +0.801 & +1.158 \end{bmatrix}
$$

(2) Doubling the area of Bar No. 2,

$$
\Delta F = \left[\begin{bmatrix} 0 & & & \\ & 12{,}500 & & \\ & & 0 & \\ & & & 0 \end{bmatrix} [A^T] - [SA^T K^{-1}][A] \begin{bmatrix} 0 & & & \\ & 12{,}500 & & \\ & & 0 & \\ & & & 0 \end{bmatrix} [A^T] \right] [X]
$$

$$
= \begin{bmatrix} -1.686 & -1.366 \\ +2.492 & +2.019 \\ -1.098 & -0.890 \\ -0.441 & -0.357 \end{bmatrix}
$$

(3) Doubling the area of Bar No. 3,

$$\Delta F = \begin{bmatrix} 0 & & & \\ & 0 & & \\ & & 9000 & \\ & & & 0 \end{bmatrix} [A^T] - [SA^T K^{-1}] [A] \begin{bmatrix} 0 & & & \\ & 0 & & \\ & & 9000 & \\ & & & 0 \end{bmatrix} [A^T] \; [X]$$

$$= \begin{bmatrix} +0.143 & -0.058 \\ -0.602 & +0.247 \\ +1.210 & -0.496 \\ -0.800 & +0.328 \end{bmatrix}$$

(4) Doubling the area of Bar No. 4,

$$\Delta F = \begin{bmatrix} 0 & & & \\ & 0 & & \\ & & 0 & \\ & & & 7500 \end{bmatrix} [A^T] - [SA^T K^{-1}] [A] \begin{bmatrix} 0 & & & \\ & 0 & & \\ & & 0 & \\ & & & 7500 \end{bmatrix} [A^T] \; [X]$$

$$= \begin{bmatrix} +0.201 & -0.516 \\ -0.116 & +0.299 \\ -0.386 & +0.989 \\ +0.440 & -1.129 \end{bmatrix}$$

11.4. Building the Constraints

In the linear programming formulation of minimizing the volume function of a truss, the design variables are $u_1, u_2, \ldots, u_{NF}$ where the "new" bar areas are $u_1 A_1, u_2 A_2, \ldots, u_{NF} A_{NF}$, the "old" bar areas are $A_1, A_2, \ldots, A_{NF}$, and NF is the total number of bars. In this way, $u_1, u_2, \ldots, u_{NF}$ are always positive.

The merit function is the "new" volume, which is

$$z = L_1 A_1 u_1 + L_2 A_2 u_2 + \cdots + L_{NF} A_{NF} u_{NF} \tag{11.4.1}$$

in which L_i and A_i are the length and "old" area of the ith bar.

The number of constraints is equal to the number of bars times the number of loading conditions. The constraint is that the "new" actual stress must be less than the permissible stress. Using the symbol $\Delta F (i,j,k)$ to mean the change of force in the ith bar in the jth loading condition due to 100 percent increase of the kth bar area, the "new" actual stress $\sigma(i,j)$ due to all the changes in bar areas is

$$\sigma(i,j) = \frac{F_0(i,j) + \displaystyle\sum_{k=1}^{k=NF} \Delta F(i,j,k) * (u_k - 1)}{u_i A_i}$$

$$= \frac{F_0(i,j) + \displaystyle\sum_{k=1}^{k=NF} \Delta F(i,j,k) * u_k - \overset{\to 0}{\displaystyle\sum_{k=1}^{k=NF} \Delta F(i,j,k)}}{u_i A_i}$$

$$= \frac{F_0(i,j) + \displaystyle\sum_{k=1}^{k=NF} \Delta F(i,j,k) * u_k}{u_i A_i} \qquad (11.4.2)$$

in which $F_0(i,j)$ is the actual force in the initial design. Note that in the derivation of Eq. 11.4.2 the term $\displaystyle\sum_{k=1}^{k=NF} \Delta F(i,j,k)$ is zero because the change in the bar force due to 100% increase in all bar areas at the same time is zero.

If σ is tensile or positive, the constraint is

$$\sigma \leqslant \sigma p \qquad \text{(e.g., } +19 \leqslant +20) \qquad (11.4.3)$$

If σ is compressive or negative, the constraint is

$$\sigma \geqslant \sigma p \qquad \text{(e.g., } -14 \geqslant -15) \qquad (11.4.4)$$

When a bar is in tension, the constraint is obtained by substituting Eq. 11.4.2 in Eq. 11.4.3; thus

$$\frac{F_0(i,j) + \displaystyle\sum_{k=1}^{k=NF} \Delta F(i,j,k) * u_k}{u_i A_i} \leqslant \sigma_P$$

or, on simplification,

$$\left(\sum_{k=1}^{k=NF} \Delta F(i,j,k) * u_k\right) - \sigma_p A_j u_j \leqslant -F_0(i,j) \tag{11.4.5}$$

When a bar is in compression, the constraint is obtained by substituting Eq. 11.4.2 in Eq. 11.4.4; thus

$$\left(\sum_{k=1}^{k=NF} \Delta F(i,j,k) * u_k\right) - \sigma_p A_j u_j \geqslant -F_0(i,j)$$

or, on reversing all signs,

$$-\left(\sum_{k=1}^{k=NF} \Delta F(i,j,k) * u_k\right) + \sigma_p A_j u_j \leqslant +F_0(i,j) \tag{11.4.6}$$

The application of Eqs. 11.4.5 and 11.4.6 will be illustrated by the following example.

Example 11.4.1. For the 4-bar structure shown in Fig. 11.2.1, build the constraints required in the linear programming formulation on the basis of the following information on the initial design:

$$[F_0] = \begin{bmatrix} +3.197 & +4.621 \\ +5.276 & +4.273 \\ +2.082 & -0.853 \\ +0.836 & -2.145 \end{bmatrix} \qquad \{A\} = \begin{Bmatrix} 0.2310 \\ 0.3209 \\ 0.2888 \\ 0.3209 \end{Bmatrix}$$

$$\Delta F(i,j,1) = \begin{bmatrix} +1.342 & +1.940 \\ -1.774 & -2.564 \\ +0.274 & +0.396 \\ +0.801 & +1.158 \end{bmatrix} \qquad \Delta F(i,j,2) = \begin{bmatrix} -1.686 & -1.366 \\ +2.492 & +2.019 \\ -1.098 & -0.890 \\ -0.441 & -0.357 \end{bmatrix}$$

TABLE 11.4.1

Constraints for Example 11.4.1

Constraint No.	Bar No.	L.C. No.	T or C	u_1	u_2	u_3	u_4	$-F_0(i,j)$
1	1	1	T	$+1.342-0.2310(+20)$ $=-3.278$	-1.686	$+0.143$	$+0.201$	$\leqslant -3.197$
2	2	1	T	-1.774	$+2.492-0.3209(+20)$ $=-3.926$	-0.602	-0.116	$\leqslant -5.276$
3	3	1	T	$+0.274$	-1.098	$+1.210-0.2888(+20)$ $=-4.566$	-0.386	$\leqslant -2.082$
4	4	1	T	$+0.801$	-0.441	-0.800	$+0.440-0.3209(+20)$ $=-5.978$	$\leqslant -0.836$
5	1	2	T	$+1.940-0.2310(+20)$ $=-2.680$	-1.366	-0.058	-0.516	$\leqslant -4.621$
6	2	2	T	-2.564	$+2.019-0.3209(+20)$ $=-4.399$	$+0.247$	$+0.299$	$\leqslant -4.273$
7	3	2	C	-0.396	$+0.890$	$+0.496+0.2888(-15)$ $=-3.836$	-0.989	$\leqslant -0.853$
8	4	2	C	-1.158	$+0.357$	-0.328	$+1.129+0.3209(-15)$ $=-3.684$	$\leqslant -2.145$

$$\Delta F(i,j,3) = \begin{bmatrix} +0.143 & -0.058 \\ -0.602 & +0.247 \\ +1.210 & -0.496 \\ -0.800 & +0.328 \end{bmatrix} \qquad \Delta F(i,j,4) = \begin{bmatrix} +0.201 & -0.516 \\ -0.116 & +0.299 \\ -0.386 & +0.989 \\ +0.440 & -1.129 \end{bmatrix}$$

Use a permissible tensile stress of $\sigma_P = +20$ ksi and a permissible compressive stress of $\sigma_P = -15$ ksi.

Solution: The eight constraints are tabulated in Table 11.4.1. Note that Eq. 11.4.5 is used for constraints Nos. 1 to 6, but Eq. 11.4.6 is used for constraints Nos. 7 and 8.

11.5. Optimization by Linear Programming

After the formulation of the merit function and the constraints for minimizing the volume of a truss, the next step is to obtain the values of the design variables $u_1, u_2, \ldots, u_{NF}$ by the simplex method in linear programming. The "new" trial bar areas are then equal to $u_1 A_1, u_2 A_2, \ldots, u_{NF} A_{NF}$ where $A_1, A_2, \ldots, A_{NF}$ are the "old" actual bar areas in the initial design.

The "new" trial bar areas may need to be scaled upward by a constant ratio because the partial derivatives of the bar forces with respect to the changes in bar areas used in building the constraints are only approximations at the initial design point. Thus it is necessary to reanalyze the truss by the displacement method using these newly obtained trial bar areas. The "new" actual bar areas in the improved design are equal to the "new" trial bar areas, multiplied by the largest value of the (NFXNLC) stress factors f, which is the ratio of the actual stress σ_0 to the permissible stress σ_P.

The volume of the truss in the improved design can finally be computed using the "new" actual bar areas.

Example 11.5.1. For the 4-bar structure shown in Fig. 11.2.1, perform the linear programming for the merit function

$$z = \Sigma LAu$$

where

$$\{L\} \text{ in ft} = \begin{Bmatrix} 6.0 \\ 4.8 \\ 6.0 \\ 8.0 \end{Bmatrix} \qquad \{A\} \text{ in sq. in.} = \begin{Bmatrix} 0.2310 \\ 0.3209 \\ 0.2888 \\ 0.3209 \end{Bmatrix}$$

and the constraints shown in Table 11.4.1.

Solution: The merit function is

$$z = 6(0.2310)u_1 + 4.8(0.3209)u_2 + 6(0.2888)u_3 + 8(0.3209)u_4$$
$$= 1.386u_1 + 1.540u_2 + 1.733u_3 + 2.567u_4$$

The first matrix form is shown in Table 11.5.1. The first column shows the row numbers from 1 to 9 and the first row shows the column numbers from 1 to 5. The numbers 1-2-3-4 at the bottom show that $u(1) = u(2) = u(3) = u(4) = 0$. The numbers 5-6-7-8-9-10-11-12 at the right-hand edge show that the values of $u(5)$ to $u(12)$ are equal to those in Column 5. Thus at this point all the 4 design variables are equal to zero and all the 8 slack variables are negative.

Of the first matrix form, there are 6 eligible pivots in each of the first four columns, but the best pivot is at (4,4) which gives z the smallest rise of $(+2.567)$ $(-0.836)/(-5.978) = 0.359$.

The second matrix form is shown in Table 11.5.2. Note that the number 8 at the right-hand edge of the pivotal (4th) row in Table 11.5.1 now goes to the bottom of the pivotal (4th) column in Table 11.5.2; and the number 4 at the bottom of the pivotal (4th) column in Table 11.5.1 goes to the right-hand edge of the pivotal (4th) row in Table 11.5.2. Thus the design variable $u(4)$ takes a positive value of 0.140 and in the meantime drives the slack variable $u(8)$ out.

The rows in the second matrix form are obtained from the rows in the first matrix form by (1) replacing the pivot by +1.0 and dividing the entire pivotal row by the pivot, (2) replacing the element at (1,4) by zero and subtract +0.201 times the "new" pivotal row from the "old" first row thus modified, and (3) repeating the second step for rows Nos. 2-3-5-6-7-8-9. Note, however, the eight columns with only 1's and 0's in them are not shown in Tables 11.5.1 to 11.5.4.

The twelfth matrix form and the final (13th) matrix form are shown in Tables 11.5.3 and 11.5.4. The reader may review the algorithm described in Chapter 10

TABLE 11.5.1

The First Matrix Form

	1	2	3	4	5	
1	−3.278	−1.686	+0.143	+0.201	−3.197	5
2	−1.774	−3.926	−0.602	−0.116	−5.276	6
3	+0.274	−1.098	−4.566	−0.386	−2.082	7
4	+0.801	−0.441	−0.800	−5.978 (pivot)	−0.836	8
5	−2.680	−1.366	−0.058	−0.516	−4.621	9
6	−2.564	−4.399	+0.247	+0.299	−4.273	10
7	−0.396	+0.890	−3.836	−0.989	−0.853	11
8	−1.158	+0.357	−0.328	−3.684	−2.145	12
9	+1.386	+1.540	+1.733	+2.567	z	
	1	2	3	4		

TABLE 11.5.2

The Second Matrix Form

	1	2	3	4	5	
1	−3.251	−1.701	+0.116	+0.034	−3.225	5
2	−1.790	−3.916	−0.586	−0.020	−5.259	6
3	+0.222	−1.070	−4.514	−0.064	−2.028	7
4	−0.134	+0.074	+0.134	−0.167	+0.140	4
5	−2.749	−1.328	+0.011	−0.086	−4.548	9
6	−2.524	−4.421	+0.207	+0.050	−4.315	10
7	−0.529	+0.963	−3.703	−0.166	−0.715	11
8	−1.652	+0.629	+0.165	−0.616	−1.629	12
9	+1.730	+1.351	+1.389	+0.429	$z - 0.359$	
	1	2	3	8		

TABLE 11.5.3

The Twelfth Matrix Form

	1	2	3	4	5	
1	−0.456	+0.148	−0.025	+0.040	+1.309	1
2	−0.329	−0.966	+0.208	+0.063	+2.115	10
3	+0.823	−0.819	−1.087 (pivot)	+0.060	−0.686	7
4	−0.090	+0.056	+0.027	−0.165	+0.237	4
5	−0.892	+0.456	−0.030	−0.543	+0.052	12
6	+0.191	−0.308	+0.049	−0.019	+0.716	2
7	+0.115	−0.101	−0.254	+0.034	+0.192	3
8	−1.169	−0.030	+0.033	+0.130	+2.228	5
9	+0.371	+0.300	+0.329	+0.337	$z - 3.858$	
	9	6	11	8		

TABLE 11.5.4

The Final (13th) Matrix Form

	1	2	3	4	5	
1	−0.474	+0.167	−0.023	+0.039	+1.325	1
2	−0.172	−1.123	+0.191	+0.074	+1.984	10
3	−0.758	+0.754	−0.920	−0.055	+0.631	11
4	−0.070	+0.036	+0.025	−0.164	+0.220	4
5	−0.914	+0.478	−0.028	−0.545	+0.071	12
6	+0.228	−0.345	+0.045	−0.016	+0.685	2
7	−0.078	+0.090	−0.233	+0.020	+0.352	3
8	−1.145	−0.054	+0.030	+0.132	+2.208	5
9	+0.620	+0.052	+0.302	+0.355	$z - 4.066$	
	9	6	7	8		

by actually going over the arithmetic of obtaining the second matrix form from the first matrix form, and the final (13th) matrix form from the twelfth matrix form.

The successful solution gives

$$\begin{Bmatrix} u_1 \\ u_2 \\ u_3 \\ u_4 \end{Bmatrix} = \begin{Bmatrix} +1.325 \\ +0.685 \\ +0.352 \\ +0.220 \end{Bmatrix} \quad \{A\} = \begin{Bmatrix} 1.325(0.2310) \\ 0.685(0.3209) \\ 0.352(0.2888) \\ 0.220(0.3209) \end{Bmatrix} = \begin{Bmatrix} 0.3061 \\ 0.2197 \\ 0.1017 \\ 0.0705 \end{Bmatrix}$$

and

$$z = 4.066 \text{ ft-in.}^2$$

The zero slack variables $u(6)$-$u(7)$-$u(8)$-$u(9)$ show that constraint Nos. 2-3-4-5 are critical. Had the partial derivatives used to build the constraints been exact at this new design point (they cannot be), the actual tensile stresses in bar Nos. 2-3-4 in loading condition No. 1 and in bar No. 1 in loading condition No. 2 would all have reached no higher than $\sigma_p = +20$ ksi.

Example 11.5.2. For the 4-bar structure shown in Fig. 11.2.1, make a re-analysis by the displacement method using the trial bar areas of

$$\{A_0\} \text{ in sq in.} = \begin{Bmatrix} 0.3061 \\ 0.2197 \\ 0.1017 \\ 0.0705 \end{Bmatrix}$$

Solution: The input matrices are:

$$[A] = \begin{bmatrix} +0.6 & 0. & -0.6 & -0.8 \\ -0.8 & -1.0 & -0.8 & -0.6 \end{bmatrix}$$

$$[S] \text{ in k/ft} = \begin{bmatrix} 1530 & & & \\ & 1373 & & \\ & & 508 & \\ & & & 264 \end{bmatrix}$$

$$[P] \text{ in kips} = \begin{bmatrix} 0 & +5 \\ -10 & -6 \end{bmatrix}$$

The output matrix $[F]$ is

$$[F] \text{ in kips} = \begin{bmatrix} +3.254 & +6.380 \\ +5.227 & +2.084 \\ +2.016 & -0.885 \\ +0.928 & -0.801 \end{bmatrix}$$

The actual stresses σ_0 based on the trial bar areas are

$$[\sigma_0] = \begin{bmatrix} +3.254/0.3061 & +6.380/0.3061 \\ +5.227/0.2197 & +2.084/0.2197 \\ +2.016/0.1017 & -0.885/0.1017 \\ +0.928/0.0705 & -0.801/0.0705 \end{bmatrix} = \begin{bmatrix} +10.63 & +20.84 \\ +23.79 & +9.49 \\ +19.82 & -8.70 \\ +13.16 & -11.36 \end{bmatrix}$$

The stress factors $f = \sigma_0/\sigma_P$ are

$$[f] = \begin{bmatrix} +10.63/+20 & +20.84/+20 \\ +23.79/+20 & +9.49/+20 \\ +19.82/+20 & -8.70/-15 \\ +13.16/+20 & -11.36/-15 \end{bmatrix} = \begin{bmatrix} 0.531 & 1.042 \\ 1.190 & 0.474 \\ 0.991 & 0.580 \\ 0.658 & 0.757 \end{bmatrix}$$

in which the largest value is 1.190. The actual bar areas which should be used in the improved design are

$$\{A\} \text{ in sq in.} = \begin{Bmatrix} 1.190(0.3061) \\ 1.190(0.2197) \\ 1.190(0.1017) \\ 1.190(0.0705) \end{Bmatrix} = \begin{Bmatrix} 0.3642 \\ 0.2614 \\ 0.1210 \\ 0.0839 \end{Bmatrix}$$

The volume function in the improved design is

$$z = \Sigma LA = 6(0.3642) + 4.8(0.2614) + 6(0.1210) + 8(0.0839) = 4.837 \text{ ft-in.}^2$$

which is quite a reduction from 7.226 ft-in.^{2} in the initial design.

11.6. The Computer Program

A complete computer program for the minimum-weight design of a truss should take as input: (1) the configuration of the truss, (2) the applied loads in several loading conditions, (3) a set of trial bar areas, (4) the permissible tensile and compressive stresses, and (5) the tolerance between the weight (or volume) of the truss in the final design and in the one preceding it. The output would simply be the actual bar areas to be used in the final design.

To accomplish the objective outlined above, two subroutines are essential. One is the linear programming method of minimizing a function, which is provided in Appendix I. The other is the computation of changes in bar forces $\Delta F(i,j,k)$ in the ith bar of the jth loading condition due to the effect of doubling the kth bar area, as i varies from 1 to NF, j from 1 to NLC, and k from 1 to NF, where NF is the total number of bars and NLC is the number of loading conditions. This subroutine is provided in Appendix J.

APPENDIXES

■

FORTRAN Programs

The ten computer programs shown here have been developed along with the text material and actually tested on the several computers which were then available at the University of Wisconsin. The readers may study these programs as if they were flow charts. For production runs it is expected that the users will prepare their own card decks to suit the accessible computers. For easiness in reading, these programs are purposely set in tables at the end of each appendix and separated by spaces into parts in order to match the explanatory notes.

299

■

Free Vibrations of Rigid Frames with Lumped Masses

Problem Statement

Given the configuration of a rigid frame, the stiffness properties EI/L of the members, and the number, location, and amount of lumped masses, find the fundamental frequency of free vibration with its unitized mode vector, and also as many higher frequencies with unitized mode vectors as may be called; and, if all modes are called for, compute the null $[\delta_m M]_{n+1}$ matrix, where n is the number of lumped masses.

Analysis

In using this computer program, it is necessary to consider each location of the lumped masses as a joint and a degree of freedom is assigned to the linear displacement of each lumped mass. Furthermore, wherever any of the lumped masses, or combinations thereof, may be subjected to sidesway displacement, these lumped masses or combinations thereof will constitute additional degrees of freedom in free vibration. It is important that the degrees of freedom in free vibration be numbered *after* all other statical degrees of freedom of the structure, since the lower right-hand corner of the inverse $[ASA^T]$ matrix is to be taken as the $[\delta_m]$ matrix.

The configuration of the structure is described by the input matrix $[A]$, which is in the order of the total statical degree of freedom by twice the number of members, for a rigid frame without axial deformation. The $[ASA^T]$ matrix is then computed and inverted and the $[\delta_m]$ matrix is taken from it. Although this portion of the computer program is written for rigid frames with axial deformation neglected, it may be replaced by the direct element method of building the global $[ASA^T]$ matrix, for any other type of structures, such as trusses, rigid frames with axial deformation, plane grids, and space rigid frames.

The diagonal elements of the mass matrix $[M]$ are read in as a singly subscripted array, in the same sequence as the degrees of freedom in vibration.

The program is made flexible in that any number of modes between one and the degree of freedom in vibration may be called for. If all the modes are called, then the $[\delta_m M]$ matrix is reduced once more and printed out, so that it may be compared with the original $[\delta_m M]$ matrix as being close to a null matrix.

Also, in the computer program not only the unitized mode vector is printed out together with the frequency, but this unitized vector is used as amplitudes once again, in the original $\{A\} = [\delta_m M]\{A\}$ equation and a new unitized displacement vector computed and printed out. This new vector is called the "check nodal deflections" in the output.

FORTRAN Program

The FORTRAN program for free vibrations of structural frames with lumped masses is shown in Table A. Some explanations are presented below.

1. *Lines 1 to 3. Dimension Statements.* The $[CDM]$ matrix is used to store the original $[DM]$ matrix, which is being successively reduced for computing higher frequencies, the $\{CDMX\}$ vector is for the "check nodal deflections." The $\{X\}$ and $\{DMX\}$ vectors are for the assumed amplitudes and the resulting unitized nodal deflections, respectively. The statical and dynamic degrees of freedom may be as large as 45 and 25, respectively. The number of members may be as large as 30.

2. *Lines 4 to 6.* Program may be used for more than one data set.

3. *Lines 7 and 8.* Read total statical degree of freedom NP, number of members NM, number of vibrating lumped masses NPS, and number of modes required NMR.

4. *Lines 9 to 27.* Read and print the statics matrix $[A]$, the $S = EI/L$ values of the members, and the values of the lumped masses AMASS (NPS).

5. *Lines 28 to 35.* Build the $[ASA^T]$ matrix.

6. *Lines 36 to 60.* Invert the $[ASA^T]$ matrix.

7. *Lines 61 to 66.* Print the submatrix $D(NPS, NPS)$ at the lower right corner of the inverse $[ASA^T]$ matrix.

8. *Lines 67 and 68.* Print the number of modes required NMR.

9. *Lines 69 to 75.* Compute and print the $[DM]$ matrix.

10. *Lines 76 to 78.* Place the $[DM]$ matrix in $[CDM]$ matrix.

11. *Lines 79 and 80.* Initialize the mode number to be sought and the number of iterations.

12. *Lines 81 and 82.* Initialize all nodal displacements to be equal to unity.

13. *Line 83.* Keep account of the number of iterations required for this mode.

14. *Lines 84 and 85.* Take the unitized nodal displacements as the next amplitudes.

15. *Lines 86 to 89.* Compute the nodal displacements.

16. *Lines 90 to 97.* Unitize the just obtained nodal displacements.

17. *Lines 98 to 100.* If a tolerance of 0.000001 between any assumed amplitude and the corresponding element in the unitized nodal displacement vector is exceeded, proceed with the next iteration. Note that this tolerance may be changed, usually increased, to save computing time.

18. *Lines 101 to 110.* Print out the mode number, the number of iterations, the circular frequency, and the mode vector.

19. *Lines 111 to 120.* Compute and print the unitized displacement vector obtained by multiplying the original $[DM]$ matrix and the just obtained mode vector.

20. *Line 121.* If NMR = NPS, proceed to compute the reduced $[DM]$ matrix whether NM is already equal to NPS or not; if NMR < NPS, see whether NM is now equal to NMR.

21. *Line 122.* If NMR < NPS and NM is now equal to NMR, go to the next data set; if NMR < NPS and NM is not yet equal to NMR, proceed to compute the reduced $[DM]$ matrix.

22. *Lines 123 to 134.* Compute and print the reduced $[DM]$ matrix.

23. *Lines 135.* Proceed to solve for the next mode.

24. *Line 136.* Go to the next data set.

25. *Lines 137 and 138.* End of program.

TABLE A

Free Vibrations of Rigid Frames with Lumped Masses

Line No.	Stat. No.	Statement
1		DIMENSION A(45,60),S(30),ASAT(45,45),AMASS(25)
2		DIMENSION INDEX(45),DM(25,25),CDM(25,25),DMX(25),CDMX(25)
3		DIMENSION X(25)
4	1	READ 2, JJ
5	2	FORMAT (I5)
6		IF (JJ) 59,59,3
7	3	READ 5, NP,NM,NPS,NMR
8	5	FORMAT (4I5)
9		NMT2=2*NM
10		READ 6, ((A(I,J),J=1,NMT2),I=1,NP)
11	6	FORMAT (7F10.4)
12		READ 6, (S(I),I=1,NM)
13		READ 6, (AMASS(I),I=1,NPS)
14		PRINT 7
15	7	FORMAT (33H1FREE VIBRATIONS OF LUMPED MASSES//)
16		PRINT 8
17	8	FORMAT (13H0THE MATRIX A)
18		DO 9 I=1,NP
19	9	PRINT 10, I,(A(I,J),J=1,NMT2)
20	10	FORMAT (4H ROW,I3,1X,7E16.8/(8X,7E16.8))
21		PRINT 11
22	11	FORMAT (25H0THE STIFFNESS OF MEMBERS)
23		PRINT 12, (I,S(I),I=1,NM)
24	12	FORMAT (5(5X,I3,E16.8)/)
25		PRINT 13
26	13	FORMAT (18H0THE LUMPED MASSES)
27		PRINT 12, (I,AMASS(I),I=1,NPS)
28		DO 15 I=1,NP
29		DO 15 J=1,NP
30		ASAT(I,J)=0.
31		DO 15 K=1,NM
32		L=2*K-1
33		M=2*K
34		ASAT(I,J)=ASAT(I,J)+A(I,L)*(4.*S(K)*A(J,L)+2.*S(K)*A(J,M))
35	15	ASAT(I,J)=ASAT(I,J)+A(I,M)*(2.*S(K)*A(J,L)+4.*S(K)*A(J,M))
36		DO 16 I=1,NP
37	16	INDEX(I)=0
38	17	AMAX=-1.
39		DO 18 I=1,NP
40		IF (INDEX(I)) 18,19,18
41	19	TEMP=ABSF(ASAT(I,I))
42		IF (TEMP-AMAX) 18,18,20

TABLE A (cont.)

Line No.	Stat. No.	Statement
43	20	ICOL=I
44		AMAX=TEMP
45	18	CONTINUE
46		IF (AMAX) 21,52,22
47	22	INDEX(ICOL)=1
48		PIVOT=ASAT(ICOL,ICOL)
49		ASAT(ICOL,ICOL)=1.0
50		PIVOT=1./PIVOT
51		DO 23 J=1,NP
52	23	ASAT(ICOL,J)=ASAT(ICOL,J)*PIVOT
53		DO 24 I=1,NP
54		IF (I-ICOL) 25,24,25
55	25	TEMP=ASAT(I,ICOL)
56		ASAT(I,ICOL)=0.0
57		DO 26 J=1,NP
58	26	ASAT(I,J)=ASAT(I,J)-ASAT(ICOL,J)*TEMP
59	24	CONTINUE
60		GO TO 17
61	21	PRINT 123
62	123	FORMAT (13H0THE MATRIX D)
63		NPR=NP-NPS
64		DO 124 I=1,NPS
65		II=I+NPR
66	124	PRINT 10, II,(ASAT(I+NPR,J+NPR),J=1,NPS)
67		PRINT 125, NMR
68	125	FORMAT (27H0NUMBER OF MODES REQUIRED =,I5)
69		DO 29 I=1,NPS
70		DO 29 J=1,NPS
71	29	DM(I,J)=ASAT(I+NPR,J+NPR)*AMASS(J)
72		PRINT 30
73	30	FORMAT (14H0THE MATRIX DM)
74		DO 31 I=1,NPS
75	31	PRINT 10, I,(DM(I,J),J=1,NPS)
76		DO 152 I=1,NPS
77		DO 152 J=1,NPS
78	152	CDM(I,J)=DM(I,J)
79		NM=0
80	32	NITER=0
81		DO 33 I=1,NPS
82	33	DMX(I)=1.
83	34	NITER=NITER+1
84		DO 35 I=1,NPS

TABLE A (cont.)

Line No.	Stat. No.	Statement
85	35	X(I)=DMX(I)
86		DO 36 I=1,NPS
87		DMX(I)=0.
88		DO 36 K=1,NPS
89	36	DMX(I)=DMX(I)+DM(I,K)*X(K)
90		DMXMX=−1.
91		DO 37 I=1,NPS
92		IF (ABSF(DMX(I))−DMXMX) 37,37,38
93	38	K=I
94		DMXMX=ABSF(DMX(K))
95	37	CONTINUE
96		DO 39 I=1,NPS
97	39	DMX(I)=DMX(I)/DMX(K)
98		DO 40 I=1,NPS
99		IF (ABSF(X(I)−DMX(I))−0.000001) 40,40,34
100	40	CONTINUE
101		NM=NM+1
102		P=SQRTF(ABSF(X(K))/DMXMX)
103		PRINT 42, NITER,NM
104	42	FORMAT (7H0AFTER ,I3,21H ITERATIONS, MODE NO.,I3,12H IS OBTAINED)
105		PRINT 43, P
106	43	FORMAT (26H0THE CIRCULAR FREQUENCY IS, E16.8)
107		PRINT 47
108	47	FORMAT (26H0THE NODAL DEFLECTIONS ARE)
109		NPR1=NPR+1
110		PRINT 12, (I,DMX(I−NPR),I=NPR1,NP)
111		DO 101 I=1,NPS
112		CDMX(I)=0.
113		DO 101 L=1,NPS
114	101	CDMX(I)=CDMX(I)+CDM(I,L)*DMX(L)
115		TEMP=CDMX(K)
116		DO 102 I=1,NPS
117	102	CDMX(I)=CDMX(I)/TEMP
118		PRINT 103
119	103	FORMAT (32H0THE CHECK NODAL DEFLECTIONS ARE)
120		PRINT 12, (I,CDMX(I−NPR),I=NPR1,NP)
121		IF (NMR−NPS) 49,51,51
122	49	IF (NM−NMR) 51,52,52
123	51	XTMX=0.
124		DO 53 I=1,NPS
125	53	XTMX=XTMX+DMX(I)*AMASS(I)*DMX(I)

TABLE A (cont.)

Line No.	Stat. No.	Statement
126		FATR=1./(P*P*XTMX)
127		DO 54 I=1,NPS
128		DO 54 J=1,NPS
129	54	DM(I,J)=DM(I,J)−FATR*DMX(I)*AMASS(J)*DMX(J)
130		PRINT 57
131	57	FORMAT (18H0THE NEW DM MATRIX)
132		DO 60 I=1,NPS
133		II=NPR+I
134	60	PRINT 10, II,(DM(I,J),J=1,NPS)
135		IF (NM−NPS) 32,52,52
136	52	GO TO 1
137	59	STOP
138		END

APPENDIX   B

Free Vibrations of Rigid Frames with Distributed Masses

Problem Statement

Let NP be the degree of freedom, of which NPR is in rotation and NPS is in sidesway. Let NM be the number of members, of which NM1 members have no transverse displacement of their ends but each of the NM2 members does have such displacement at either or both of its ends. The number of internal forces is, then, NF = 2 $*$ NM1 + 4 $*$ NM2. Given the statics matrix A(NPXNF), the sidesway inertia-force matrix G(NPSXNPS), the member lengths $XL(1) \ldots XL(NM)$, the member moments of inertia $XI(1) \ldots XI(NM)$, the distributed mass per unit length $XM(1) \ldots XM(NM)$, the modulus of elasticity E, the standard member length XLC, and the standard moment of inertia XIC, and the standard mass per unit length XMC, obtain the standard fundamental frequency angle ϕ_c and the fundamental circular frequency in radians per second.

Analysis

In order that the determinant of the dynamic stiffness matrix $[ASA^T - G]$ may be computed for a number of trial values of ϕ_c, two subroutines BUASAT

309

and COMDET are separated from the main program. Subroutine BUASAT stands for "building the ASA^T minus G matrix"; and subroutine COMDET stands for "computing the determinant." The ϕ_c value begins at $\phi_c = 0.50$ and is increased by $\Delta\phi_c = 0.10$ each time until the determinant changes sign from positive to negative. Then the correct value of ϕ_c to the nearest 0.0001 is obtained by an iterative linear interpolation procedure. Finally the fundamental circular frequency is computed by the formula

$$p = \frac{\phi_c^2}{L_c^2} \sqrt{\frac{EI_c}{m_c}}$$

FORTRAN Program

The main program and the two subroutines are shown in Tables B.1 to B.3. Explanations for the main program and subroutine BUASAT are itemized below. For the main program,

1. *Lines 1 and 2. Dimension statements.* NP may be as large as 20; NPS, 5; NF, 50; NM, 25. The INDEX array is to keep record of the pivot selection in subroutine COMDET.

2. *Lines 3 to 5.* The program may be used to process any number of data sets at a time.

3. *Lines 6 and 7.* Read fixed point variables as defined. Note that NP = NPR + NPS, NF = 2 ∗ NM1 + 4 ∗ NM2, and NM = NM1 + NM2.

4. *Lines 8 to 10.* Zero out the $[A]$ matrix.

5. *Lines 11 to 15.* Read the nonzero elements in the $[A]$ matrix.

6. *Line 16.* If NPS is zero, there is no $[G]$ matrix to be read.

7. *Lines 17 to 19.* Zero out the $[G]$ matrix.

8. *Lines 20 to 23.* Read the nonzero elements in the $[G]$ matrix.

9. *Lines 24 to 29.* Read E, XLC, XIC, XMC, XL(1) ... XL(NM), XI(1) ... XI(NM), and XM(1) ... XM(NM).

10. *Lines 30 to 32.* Print title.

11. *Lines 33 to 37.* Print the $[A]$ matrix.

12. *Line 38.* If NPS is zero, there is no $[G]$ matrix to be printed.

13. *Lines 39 to 42.* Print the $[G]$ matrix.

14. *Lines 43 to 61.* Print E, XLC, XIC, XMC, XL(1) ... XL(NM), XI(1) ... XI(NM), and XM(1) ... XM(NM).

15. *Lines 62 and 63.* Compute the δ values of the members.

16. *Lines 64 to 67.* Compute the determinant for $\phi_c = 0.50$. It is presupposed that the determinant at $\phi_c = 0.50$ is positive. If, in any problem, this determinant happens to be negative, Line 64 must be changed to a lower value of ϕ_c.

17. *Lines 68 to 74.* If determinant is zero, the correct value of ϕ_c has been found. If determinant is positive, store ϕ_c value and determinant in PHICA and DETA, go up one increment, and go back to Line 65 or Statement 513. If determinant is negative, store ϕ_c value and determinant in PHICB and DETB.

18. *Lines 75 to 77.* Print the values PHICA and DETA at the left station where DETA is positive, and the values PHICB and DETB at the right station where DETB is negative.

19. *Lines 78 and 79.* Compute the first iterative value of ϕ_c by linear interpolation using the controlling values at the left and right stations. Store this value in TEMP so that it may be compared with the next iterative value of ϕ_c.

20. *Lines 80 to 84.* Compute the determinant for the latest value of ϕ_c.

21. *Lines 85 to 89.* If determinant is now zero, the correct value of ϕ_c has been found. If determinant is negative, compute the next iterative value of ϕ_c by interpolating between the present value of ϕ_c and the value of PHICA on the left and then compare the new value of ϕ_c with TEMP in which the old value of ϕ_c has been stored. If determinant is positive, compute the next iterative value of ϕ_c by interpolating between the present value of ϕ_c and the value of PHICB on the right and then compare the new value of ϕ_c with its old value in TEMP. If the comparison in either case is unfavorable, go back to Line 79 or Statement 560.

22. *Lines 90 and 91.* Print the final value of ϕ_c which is within a tolerance of 0.0001.

23. *Lines 92 to 97.* Compute and print the final dynamic stiffness matrix, of which the determinant should be very close to zero.

24. *Lines 98 to 100.* Compute and print the final value of the determinant.

25. *Lines 101 to 103.* Compute and print the final fundamental circular frequency.

26. *Line 104.* Go to Line 3 or Statement 701 and find out if there is another data set.

27. *Lines 105 and 106.* End of main program.

For subroutine BUASAT,

1. *Lines 1 and 2.* Name of subroutine and all variable names involved in this subroutine.

2. *Lines 3 and 4.* Dimension statement.

3. *Lines 5 to 7.* Zero out the $[ASA^T]$ matrix. This is necessary because the contributions to the $[ASA^T]$ matrix from the two types of members (without and with transverse displacement of ends) are to be considered in two separate DO-loops.

4. *Line 8.* If Type 1 members do not exist, go to Type 2 members. Note that the two end moments of Type 1 members should be counted before the two end moments and two end shears of Type 2 members, with the resulting NF = 2 * NM1 + 4 * NM2.

5. *Lines 9 to 19.* Accumulate the contributions to the NPR×NPR portion of the $[ASA^T]$ matrix, from the NM1 members without transverse end displacement. Note the stiffness $T1$ and $T2$ for the ith and jth ends respectively.

6. *Line 20.* If there are no Type 2 members, go to end of subroutine.

7. *Lines 21 to 42.* Accumulate the contributions to the entire $[ASA^T]$ matrix, from the NM2 members with transverse end displacement. Note that all 6 stiffness values $T1$ to $T6$ in the member stiffness matrix are needed

8. *Lines 43 to 48.* Subtract the sidesway inertia-force matrix $p^2[G]$ from the $[ASA^T]$ matrix now in memory.

9. *Lines 49 and 50.* End of subroutine.

TABLE B.1

Free Vibrations of Rigid Frames with Distributed Masses: Main Program

Line No.	Stat. No.	Statement
1		DIMENSION A(20,50),ASAT(20,20),INDEX(20),G(5,5)
2		DIMENSION XM(25),XL(25),XI(25),DELTA(25)
3	701	READ 101,NDATA
4	101	FORMAT (I5)
5		IF (NDATA) 801,801,102
6	102	READ 103, NP,NPR,NPS,NF,NM,NM1,NM2
7	103	FORMAT (7I5)
8		DO 104 I=1,NP
9		DO 104 J=1,NF
10	104	A(I,J)=0.
11	108	READ 105, I,J,AIJ
12	105	FORMAT (2I5,F15.4)
13		IF (I) 12,12,107
14	107	A(I,J)=AIJ
15		GO TO 108

TABLE B.1 (cont.)

Line No.	Stat. No.	Statement
16	12	IF (NPS) 106,112,106
17	106	DO 111 I=1,NPS
18		DO 111 J=1,NPS
19	111	G(I,J)=0.
20	114	READ 105, I,J,GIJ
21		IF (I) 112,112,113
22	113	G(I,J)=GIJ
23		GO TO 114
24	112	READ 115, E,XLC,XIC,XMC
25	115	FORMAT (4F10.4)
26		READ 116, (XL(I),I=1,NM)
27	116	FORMAT (5F10.4)
28		READ 116, (XI(I),I=1,NM)
29		READ 116, (XM(I),I=1,NM)
30		PRINT 201
31	201	FORMAT (56H1FREE VIBRATIONS OF RIGID FRAMES WITH DISTRIBUTED MASSES
32		1//)
33		PRINT 202
34	202	FORMAT (13H0THE A MATRIX)
35		DO 203 I=1,NP
36	203	PRINT 204, I,(A(I,J),J=1,NF)
37	204	FORMAT (4H ROW,I3,1X,5E16.8/(8X,5E16.8))
38		IF (NPS) 14,15,14
39	14	PRINT 901
40	901	FORMAT (13H0THE G MATRIX)
41		DO 205 I=1,NPS
42	205	PRINT 204, I,(G(I,J),J=1,NPS)
43	15	PRINT 206, E
44	206	FORMAT (33H0MODULUS OF ELASTICITY IN KSFT2 =,F11.4)
45		PRINT 207, XLC
46	207	FORMAT (26H0STANDARD LENGTH IN FEET =,F10.4)
47		PRINT 208, XIC
48	208	FORMAT (44H0STANDARD MOMENT OF INERTIA IN FOOT FOURTH =,F12.4)
49		PRINT 251, XMC
50	251	FORMAT (50H0STANDARD DISTRIBUTED MASS IN KIP SEC2 PER FOOT2 =,
51		1F10.4)
52		PRINT 209
53	209	FORMAT (18H0LENGTH OF MEMBERS)
54		PRINT 210, (I,XL(I),I=1,NM)

TABLE B.1 (cont.)

Line No.	Stat. No.	Statement
55	210	FORMAT (5(5X,I3,E16.8))
56		PRINT 211
57	211	FORMAT (30H0MOMENTS OF INERTIA OF MEMBERS)
58		PRINT 210, (I,XI(I),I=1,NM)
59		PRINT 212
60	212	FORMAT (39H0DISTRIBUTED MASS IN KIP SEC2 PER FOOT2)
61		PRINT 210, (I,XM(I),I=1,NM)
62		DO 301 I=1,NM
63	301	DELTA(I)=XL(I)/XLC*SQRT(SQRT(XM(I)*XIC/(XMC*XI(I))))
64		PHIC=0.5
65	513	CALL BUASAT(NP,NM1,DELTA,PHIC,E,XI,XL,A,NM2,XIC,XLC,NPS, NPR,G,
66		1XM,ASAT,XMC)
67		CALL COMDET(NP,ASAT,INDEX,DET,ICOL)
68		IF (DET) 511,601,512
69	512	PHICA=PHIC
70		DETA=DET
71		PHIC=PHIC+0.10
72		GO TO 513
73	511	PHICB=PHIC
74		DETB=DET
75		PRINT 514, PHICA,DETA,PHICB,DETB
76	514	FORMAT (10H0AT PHIC =,E16.8,10X,5HDET =,E16.8/10H AT PHIC =,
77		1E16.8,10X,5HDET =,E16.8)
78		PHIC=PHICA+DETA*(PHICB−PHICA)/(DETA−DETB)
79	560	TEMP=PHIC
80		CALL BUASAT(NP,NM1,DELTA,PHIC,E,XI,XL,A,NM2,XIC,XLC,NPS, NPR,G,
81		1XM,ASAT,XMC)
82		CALL COMDET(NP,ASAT,INDEX,DET,ICOL)
83		PRINT 531, PHIC,DET
84	531	FORMAT (10H0AT PHIC =,E16.8,10X,5HDET =,E16.8)
85		IF (DET) 551,601,552
86	551	PHIC=PHICA+DETA*(PHIC−PHICA)/(DETA−DET)
87		IF ((TEMP−PHIC)−0.0001) 601,601,560
88	552	PHIC=PHICB+DETB*(PHICB−PHIC)/(DET−DETB)
89		IF ((PHIC−TEMP)−0.0001) 601,601,560
90	601	PRINT 602, PHIC
91	602	FORMAT (13H0FINAL PHIC =,E16.8)
92		CALL BUASAT(NP,NM1,DELTA,PHIC,E,XI,XL,A,NM2,XIC,XLC,NPS, NPR,G,
93		1XM,ASAT,XMC)
94		PRINT 603

TABLE B.1 (cont.)

Line No.	Stat. No.	Statement
95	603	FORMAT (31H0FINAL DYNAMIC STIFFNESS MATRIX)
96		DO 604, I=1,NP
97	604	PRINT 204, I,(ASAT(I,J),J=1,NP)
98		CALL COMDET(NP,ASAT,INDEX,DET,ICOL)
99		PRINT 605, DET
100	605	FORMAT (29H0FINAL VALUE OF DETERMINANT =,E16.8)
101		P=SQRT(E*XIC/XMC)*PHIC*PHIC/(XLC*XLC)
102		PRINT 655, P
103	655	FORMAT (43H0FUNDAMENTAL FREQUENCY IN RADIANS PER SEC =,E16.8)
104		GO TO 701
105	801	STOP
106		END

TABLE B.2

Free Vibrations of Rigid Frames with Distributed Masses: Subroutine BUASAT

Line No.	Stat. No.	Statement
1		SUBROUTINE BUASAT(NP,NM1,DELTA,PHIC,E,XI,XL,A,NM2,XIC,XLC,NPS,
2		1NPR,G,XM,ASAT,XMC)
3		DIMENSION DELTA(25),XI(25),XL(25),A(20,50),G(5,5)XM(25),
4		1ASAT(20,20)
5		DO 301 I=1,NP
6		DO 301 J=1,NP
7	301	ASAT(I,J)=0.
8		IF (NM1) 1,2,1
9	1	DO 302 I=1,NPR
10		DO 302 J=1,NPR
11		DO 302 K=1,NM1
12		NFI=2*K-1
13		NFJ=2*K
14		PHI=DELTA(K)*PHIC
15		TEMP=PHI/(1.-COS(PHI)*COSH(PHI))*E*XI(K)/XL(K)
16		T1=(SIN(PHI)*COSH(PHI)-COS(PHI)*SINH(PHI))*TEMP
17		T2=(SINH(PHI)-SIN(PHI))*TEMP
18	302	ASAT(I,J)=ASAT(I,J)+A(I,NFI)*(T1*A(J,NFI)+T2*A(J,NFJ))+A(I,NFJ)
19		1*(T2*A(J,NFI)+T1*A(J,NFJ))
20		IF (NM2) 2,3,2

TABLE B.2 (cont)

Line No.	Stat. No.	Statement
21	2	DO 303 I=1,NP
22		DO 303 J=1,NP
23		DO 303 K=1,NM2
24		NF1=2*NM1+4*K-3
25		NF2=2*NM1+4*K-2
26		NF3=2*NM1+4*K-1
27		NF4=2*NM1+4*K
28		KK=NM1+K
29		PHI=DELTA(KK)*PHIC
30		TEMP=PHI*E*XI(K)/XL(K)/(1.-COS(PHI)*COSH(PHI))
31		T1=TEMP*(SIN(PHI)*COSH(PHI)-COS(PHI)*SINH(PHI))
32		T2=TEMP*(SINH(PHI)-SIN(PHI))
33		TEMP=-PHI*PHI*E*XI(K)/(XL(K)*XL(K))/(1.-COS(PHI)*COSH(PHI))
34		T3=TEMP*SIN(PHI)*SINH(PHI)
35		T4=TEMP*(COSH(PHI)-COS(PHI))
36		TEMP=PHI**3*E*XI(K)/XL(K)**3/(1.-COS(PHI)*COSH(PHI))
37		T5=TEMP*(SIN(PHI)*COSH(PHI)+COS(PHI)*SINH(PHI))
38		T6=TEMP*(SINH(PHI)+SIN(PHI))
39	303	ASAT(I,J)=ASAT(I,J)+A(I,NF1)*(T1*A(J,NF1)+T2*A(J,NF2)+T3*A(J,NF3)+
40		1T4*A(J,NF4))+A(I,NF2)*(T2*A(J,NF1)+T1*A(J,NF2)+T4*A(J,NF3)+T3*A(J,
41		1NF4))+A(I,NF3)*(T3*A(J,NF1)+T4*A(J,NF2)+T5*A(J,NF3)+T6*A(J,NF4))+A
42		1(I,NF4)*(T4*A(J,NF1)+T3*A(J,NF2)+T6*A(J,NF3)+T5*A(J,NF4))
43		TEMP=E*XIC/XMC*(PHIC/XLC)**4
44		DO 304 I=1,NPS
45		II=NPR+I
46		DO 304 J=1,NPS
47		JJ=NPR+J
48	304	ASAT(II,JJ)=ASAT(II,JJ)-TEMP*G(I,J)
49	3	RETURN
50		END

TABLE B.3

Free Vibrations of Rigid Frames with Distributed Masses: Subroutine COMDET

Line No.	Stat. No.	Statement
1		SUBROUTINE COMDET(NP,ASAT,INDEX,DET,ICOL)
2		DIMENSION ASAT(20,20),INDEX(20)
3		DET=1.0
4		DO 401 I=1,NP
5	401	INDEX(I)=0
6	410	AMAX=-1.
7		DO 402 I=1,NP
8		IF (INDEX(I)) 402,403,402
9	403	TEMP=ABS(ASAT(I,I))
10		IF (TEMP-AMAX) 402,402,404
11	404	ICOL=I
12		AMAX=TEMP
13	402	CONTINUE
14		IF (AMAX) 451,452,405
15	405	INDEX(ICOL)=1
16		PIVOT=ASAT(ICOL,ICOL)
17		ASAT(ICOL,ICOL)=1.0
18		DET=DET*PIVOT
19		PIVOT=1./PIVOT
20		DO 406 J=1,NP
21	406	ASAT(ICOL,J)=ASAT(ICOL,J)*PIVOT
22		DO 407 I=1,NP
23		IF (I-ICOL) 408,407,408
24	408	TEMP=ASAT(I,ICOL)
25		ASAT(I,ICOL)=0.
26		DO 409 J=1,NP
27	409	ASAT(I,J)=ASAT(I,J)-ASAT(ICOL,J)*TEMP
28	407	CONTINUE
29		GO TO 410
30	452	PRINT 453
31	453	FORMAT (24H0ZERO PIVOT IN INVERSION)
32	451	RETURN
33		END

APPENDIX C

■

Undamped Forced Motion of Rigid Frames with Lumped Masses

Problem Statement

Given (1) the static degree of freedom NP, (2) the number of prismatic members NM, (3) the degree of freedom in sidesway or the number of lumped masses NPS, (4) the statics matrix $[A\,(\text{NP}\times 2\text{NM})]$, (5) the $S = EI/L$ values $S(1)$ to $S(\text{NM})$, (6) the lumped masses AMASS(1) to AMASS(NM), (7) the values of $C(1)$ to $C(\text{NPS})$ in the force function $C - Dt$, (8) the values of $D(1)$ to $D(\text{NPS})$ in the force function $C - Dt$, and (9) the number of divisions NDIV by which the time limit C/D is to be divided, find, at each lumped mass, the general equations of displacement, velocity, and acceleration as functions of time t, and also their tabulated values from $t = 0$ to $t = C/D$ at intervals of $\Delta t = (C/D)/\text{NDIV}$. Note that this computer program applies only to the case in which the duration time of the force function is identical at each lumped mass.

Analysis

The natural frequencies and the associated unitized mode vectors, equal in number to the dynamic degree of freedom, are determined first by a trimmed version of the computer program described in Appendix A. The modifications are minor including the calling of all modes of free vibration and the omission of the printouts of the original and the reduced $[\delta_m M]$ matrices.

The transformation matrix $[a]$, which is named $[TA]$ in the computer program, is computed by placing the normalized mode vectors columnwise.

The $\{C'\}$ and $\{D'\}$ vectors, which are named $\{CP\}$ and $\{DP\}$ in the computer program, are computed from

$$\{CP\} = [TA]^T \{C\} \tag{C.1}$$

and

$$\{DP\} = [TA]^T \{D\} \tag{C.2}$$

For zero initial conditions and at lumped mass i,

$$X_{mi} = \sum_{j=1}^{j=NPS} a_{ij} X'_{mj} = \sum_{j=1}^{j=NPS} a_{ij} \left[\frac{D'_j}{p_j^3} \sin p_j t - \frac{C'_j}{p_j^2} \cos p_j t + \frac{C'_j}{p_j^2} - \frac{D'_j t}{p_j^2} \right] \tag{C.3}$$

Calling

$$\overline{AA}(j) = + a_{ij} \frac{D'_j}{p_j^3} \tag{C.4}$$

$$\overline{BB}(j) = - a_{ij} \frac{C'_j}{p_j^2} \tag{C.5}$$

$$\overline{CC} = \sum_{j=1}^{j=NPS} \left(a_{ij} \frac{C'_j}{p_j^2} \right) \tag{C.6}$$

$$\overline{DD} = \sum_{j=1}^{j=NPS} \left(- a_{ij} \frac{D'_j}{p_j^2} \right) \tag{C.7}$$

Equation C.3 becomes

$$X_{mi} = \left[\sum_{j=1}^{j=NPS} \overline{AA}(j) \sin p_j t + \overline{BB}(j) \cos p_j t \right] + \overline{CC} + \overline{DD} t \tag{C.8}$$

Differentiating,

$$\dot{X}_{mi} = \left[\sum_{j=1}^{j=NPS} p_j \overline{AA}(j) \cos p_j t - p_j \overline{BB}(j) \sin p_j t\right] + \overline{DD} \qquad (C.9)$$

and,

$$\ddot{X}_{mi} = \left[\sum_{j=1}^{j=NPS} - p_j^2 \overline{AA}(j) \sin p_j t - p_j^2 \overline{BB}(j) \cos p_j t\right] \qquad (C.10)$$

The general equations C.8 to C.10 are printed out in an outermost loop from the lumped mass $i = 1$ to the lumped mass $i = NPS$. Also, right after the printout of expressions C.8, C.9, or C.10, the values of the displacements, velocities, or accelerations are computed at equally spaced $(NDIV + 1)$ instants of time from $t = 0$ to $t = C/D$.

FORTRAN Program

The FORTRAN program for the undamped forced motion of rigid frames with lumped masses is shown in Table C. Some explanations for the statements in the program are listed below.

1. *Lines 1 to 4. Dimension Statements.* The static degree of freedom is 5, the number of members is 4, and the number of lumped masses is 2. Note that the user of this program must change the numbers in these dimension statements to suit his data set.

2. *Lines 5 to 37.* Read and print the input data.

3. *Lines 38 to 45.* Build the $[ASA^T]$ matrix.

4. *Lines 46 to 70.* Invert the $[ASA^T]$ matrix.

5. *Lines 71 to 76.* Compute the $[\delta_m M]$ matrix.

6. *Lines 77 to 79.* Place the original $[DM]$ matrix in the check $[CDM]$ matrix.

7. *Line 80.* Initialize the mode number NM to zero.

8. *Line 81.* Initialize the number of iterations NITER to zero. Note that this statement is related to Line 132.

9. *Lines 82 to 128.* Compute the natural frequency and the unitized mode vector. This portion of the program is essentially identical to the computer program in Appendix A.

10. *Lines 129 to 131.* The unitized vector of this mode is normalized and placed in the appropriate column of the $[TA]$ matrix.

11. *Line 132.* Proceed to compute information about the next mode of free vibration.

12. *Lines 133 to 138.* Compute the $\{CP\}$ and $\{DP\}$ vectors by using Eqs. C.1 and C.2.

13. *Lines 139 to 141.* Define NDVP1 and compute DELT which is the time interval used for the numerical evaluation of displacement, velocity, and acceleration at each lumped mass.

14. *Lines 142 to 144.* The reciprocals of p_i^2 and p_i^3 are placed in the $\{PSQ\}$ and $\{PCUB\}$ vectors.

15. *Lines 145.* This is the beginning of the outermost loop which spans to Line 201.

16. *Lines 146 and 147.* Print the lumped mass number.

17. *Lines 148 and 149.* Print the heading for displacement.

18. *Lines 150 to 154.* Compute and print the $\overline{AA}$'s and $\overline{BB}$'s for $j = 1$ to j = NPS by using Eqs. C.4 and C.5.

19. *Lines 155 to 161.* Compute and print the values of $\overline{CC}$ and $\overline{DD}$ by using Eqs. C.6 and C.7.

20. *Lines 162 to 169.* Compute and print the displacement values at the NDVP1 instants of time.

21. *Lines 170 and 171.* Print the heading for velocity.

22. *Lines 172 to 178.* Compute and print Eq. C.9.

23. *Lines 179 to 186.* Compute and print the velocity values at the NDVP1 instants of time.

24. *Lines 187 and 188.* Print the heading for acceleration.

25. *Lines 189 to 192.* Compute and print Eq. C.10.

26. *Lines 193 to 200.* Compute and print the acceleration values at the NDVP1 instants of time.

27. *Line 201.* This is the end of the outermost loop which goes back to Line 145.

28. *Lines 202 and 203.* End of program.

TABLE C

Undamped Forced Motion of Rigid Frames with Lumped Masses

Line No.	Stat. No.	Statement
1		DIMENSION A(5,8),S(4),ASAT(5,5),AMASS(2),INDEX(5),DM(2,2)
2		DIMENSION CDM(2,2),DMX(2),CDMX(2),X(2),PSQ(2),P(2)
3		DIMENSION C(2),D(2),TA(2,2),CP(2),DP(2),AA(2),BB(2)
4		DIMENSION PCUB(2)
5		READ 5, NP,NM,NPS
6	5	FORMAT (3I5)
7		NMT2=2*NM
8		READ 6, ((A(I,J),J=1,NMT2),I=1,NP)
9	6	FORMAT (7F10.4)
10		READ 6, (S(I),I=1,NM)
11		READ 6, (AMASS(I),I=1,NPS)
12		READ 6, (C(I),I=1,NPS)
13		READ 6, (D(I),I=1,NPS)
14		READ 4, NDIV
15	4	FORMAT (I5)
16		PRINT 7
17	7	FORMAT (30H1FORCED MOTION OF RIGID FRAMES//)
18		PRINT 8
19	8	FORMAT (13H0THE MATRIX A)
20		DO 9 I=1,NP
21	9	PRINT 10, I,(A(I,J),J=1,NMT2)
22	10	FORMAT (4H ROW,I3,1X,7E16.8/(8X,7E16.8))
23		PRINT 11
24	11	FORMAT (25H0THE STIFFNESS OF MEMBERS)
25		PRINT 12, (I,S(I),I=1,NM)
26	12	FORMAT (5(5X,I3,E16.8)/)
27		PRINT 13
28	13	FORMAT (18H0THE LUMPED MASSES)
29		PRINT 12, (I,AMASS(I),I=1,NPS)
30		PRINT 201
31	201	FORMAT (13H0THE C VALUES)
32		PRINT 12, (I,C(I),I=1,NPS)
33		PRINT 202
34	202	FORMAT (13H0THE D VALUES)
35		PRINT 12, (I,D(I),I=1,NPS)
36		PRINT 203, NDIV
37	203	FORMAT (24H0DIVIDE TIME PERIOD INTO,I5,11H DIVISIONS)
38		DO 15 I=1,NP
39		DO 15 J=1,NP
40		ASAT(I,J)=0.
41		DO 15 K=1,NM
42		L=2*K-1
43		M=2*K

TABLE C (cont.)

Line No.	Stat. No.	Statement
44		ASAT(I,J)=ASAT(I,J)+A(I,L)*(4.*S(K)*A(J,L)+2.*S(K)*A(J,M))
45	15	ASAT(I,J)=ASAT(I,J)+A(I,M)*(2.*S(K)*A(J,L)+4.*S(K)*A(J,M))
46		DO 16 I=1,NP
47	16	INDEX(I)=0
48	17	AMAX=-1.
49		DO 18 I=1,NP
50		IF (INDEX(I)) 18,19,18
51	19	TEMP=ABSF(ASAT(I,I))
52		IF (TEMP-AMAX) 18,18,20
53	20	ICOL=I
54		AMAX=TEMP
55	18	CONTINUE
56		IF (AMAX) 21,52,22
57	22	INDEX(ICOL)=1
58		PIVOT=ASAT(ICOL,ICOL)
59		ASAT(ICOL,ICOL)=1.0
60		PIVOT=1./PIVOT
61		DO 23 J=1,NP
62	23	ASAT(ICOL,J)=ASAT(ICOL,J)*PIVOT
63		DO 24 I=1,NP
64		IF (I-ICOL) 25,24,25
65	25	TEMP=ASAT(I,ICOL)
66		ASAT(I,ICOL)=0.0
67		DO 26 J=1,NP
68	26	ASAT(I,J)=ASAT(I,J)-ASAT(ICOL,J)*TEMP
69	24	CONTINUE
70		GO TO 17
71	21	NPR=NP-NPS
72		DO 29 I=1,NPS
73		DO 29 J=1,NPS
74		II=I+NPR
75		JJ=J+NPR
76	29	DM(I,J)=ASAT(II,JJ)*AMASS(J)
77		DO 152 I=1,NPS
78		DO 152 J=1,NPS
79	152	CDM(I,J)=DM(I,J)
80		NM=0
81	32	NITER=0
82		DO 33 I=1,NPS
83	33	DMX(I)=1.
84	34	NITER=NITER+1
85		DO 35 I=1,NPS
86	35	X(I)=DMX(I)

TABLE C (cont.)

Line No.	Stat. No.	Statement
87		DO 36 I=1,NPS
88		DMX(I)=0.
89		DO 36 K=1,NPS
90	36	DMX(I)=DMX(I)+DM(I,K)*X(K)
91		DMXMX=-1.
92		DO 37 I=1,NPS
93		IF (ABSF(DMX(I))-DMXMX) 37,37,38
94	38	K=I
95		DMXMX=ABSF(DMX(K))
96	37	CONTINUE
97		DO 39 I=1,NPS
98	39	DMX(I)=DMX(I)/DMX(K)
99		DO 40 I=1,NPS
100		IF (ABSF(X(I)-DMX(I))-0.000001) 40,40,34
101	40	CONTINUE
102		NM=NM+1
103		PSQ(NM)=ABSF(X(K))/DMXMX
104		P(NM)=SQRTF(PSQ(NM))
105		PRINT 42, NITER,NM
106	42	FORMAT (7H0AFTER ,I3,21H ITERATIONS, MODE NO.,I3,12H IS OBTAINED)
107		PRINT 43, P(NM)
108	43	FORMAT (26H0THE CIRCULAR FREQUENCY IS,E16.8)
109		PRINT 47
110	47	FORMAT (26H0THE NODAL DEFLECTIONS ARE)
111		PRINT 12, (I,DMX(I),I=1,NPS)
112		DO 101 I=1,NPS
113		CDMX(I)=0.
114		DO 101 L=1,NPS
115	101	CDMX(I)=CDMX(I)+CDM(I,L)*DMX(L)
116		TEMP=CDMX(K)
117		DO 102 I=1,NPS
118	102	CDMX(I)=CDMX(I)/TEMP
119		PRINT 103
120	103	FORMAT (32H0THE CHECK NODAL DEFLECTIONS ARE)
121		PRINT 12, (I,CDMX(I),I=1,NPS)
122		XTMX=0.
123		DO 53 I=1,NPS
124	53	XTMX=XTMX+DMX(I)*AMASS(I)*DMX(I)
125		FATR=1./(PSQ(NM)*XTMX)
126		DO 54 I=1,NPS
127		DO 54 J=1,NPS
128	54	DM(I,J)=DM(I,J)-FATR*DMX(I)*AMASS(J)*DMX(J)
129		TEMP=1./SQRTF(XTMX)
130		DO 104 I=1,NPS

TABLE C (cont.)

Line No.	Stat. No.	Statement
131	104	TA(I,NM)=DMX(I)*TEMP
132		IF (NM-NPS) 32,301,301
133	301	DO 302 I=1,NPS
134		CP(I)=0.
135		DP(I)=0.
136		DO 302 J=1,NPS
137		CP(I)=CP(I)+TA(J,I)*C(J)
138	302	DP(I)=DP(I)+TA(J,I)*D(J)
139		NDVP1=NDIV+1
140		ANDIV=NDIV
141		DELT=ABSF(C(1)/(D(1)*ANDIV))
142		DO 303 I=1,NPS
143		PCUB(I)=1./(PSQ(I)*P(I))
144	303	PSQ(I)=1./PSQ(I)
145		DO 304 I=1,NPS
146		PRINT 305, I
147	305	FORMAT (19H0AT LUMPED MASS NO.,I4)
148		PRINT 307
149	307	FORMAT (16H DISPLACEMENT)
150		DO 308 J=1,NPS
151		AA(J)=TA(I,J)*DP(J)*PCUB(J)
152		BB(J)=-TA(I,J)*CP(J)*PSQ(J)
153	308	PRINT 309, AA(J),J,BB(J),J
154	309	FORMAT (18X,E20.8,6H SINP(,I2,2H)T,E20.8,6H COSP(,I2,2H)T)
155		CC=0.
156		DD=0.
157		DO 310 K=1,NPS
158		CC=CC+TA(I,K)*CP(K)*PSQ(K)
159	310	DD=DD-TA(I,K)*DP(K)*PSQ(K)
160		PRINT 311, CC,DD
161	311	FORMAT (18X,E20.8,9H CONSTANT,1X,E20.8,8H TIMES T)
162		T=0.
163		DO 401 II=1,NDVP1
164		DISP=CC+DD*T
165		DO 402 J=1,NPS
166	402	DISP=DISP+AA(J)*SINF(P(J)*T)+BB(J)*COSF(P(J)*T)
167		PRINT 403, T,DISP
168	401	T=T+DELT
169	403	FORMAT (10X,2HT=,E12.4,5X,5HDISP=,E20.8)
170		PRINT 312
171	312	FORMAT (12H0 VELOCITY)

TABLE C (cont.)

Line No.	Stat. No.	Statement
172		DO 313 J=1,NPS
173		AA(J)=P(J)*AA(J)
174		BB(J)=−P(J)*BB(J)
175	313	PRINT 314, AA(J),J,BB(J),J
176	314	FORMAT (18X,E20.8,6H COSP(,I2,2H)T,E20.8,6H SINP(,I2,2H)T)
177		PRINT 315, DD
178	315	FORMAT (18X,E20.8,9H CONSTANT)
179		T=0.
180		DO 405 II=1,NDVP1
181		VELO=DD
182		DO 406 J=1,NPS
183	406	VELO=VELO+AA(J)*COSF(P(J)*T)+BB(J)*SINF(P(J)*T)
184		PRINT 407, T,VELO
185	405	T=T+DELT
186	407	FORMAT (10X,2HT=,E12.4,5X,5HVELO=,E20.8)
187		PRINT 316
188	316	FORMAT (16H0 ACCELERATION)
189		DO 317 J=1,NPS
190		AA(J)=−P(J)*AA(J)
191		BB(J)=P(J)*BB(J)
192	317	PRINT 309, AA(J),J,BB(J),J
193		T=0.
194		DO 408 II=1,NDVP1
195		ACCE=0.
196		DO 409 J=1,NPS
197	409	ACCE=ACCE+AA(J)*SINF(P(J)*T)+BB(J)*COSF(P(J)*T)
198		PRINT 410, T,ACCE
199	408	T=T+DELT
200	410	FORMAT (10X,2HT=,E12.4,5X,5HACCE=,E20.8)
201	304	CONTINUE
202	52	STOP
203		END

APPENDIX D

■

Displacement Method of Stability Analysis

Problem Statement

Let NP be the degree of freedom, of which NPR is in rotation and NPS is in sidesway. Let NM be the number of members, of which NM1 and NM2 are member numbers with and without primary axial forces, respectively. The number of internal forces (end moments) is, then, NF = 2 ∗ NM. Given the first-order statics matrix A (NPXNF), the sideway force versus secondary shear force matrix C (NPSXNM1), the member lengths XL (1) ... XL (NM), the member moments of inertia XI (1) ... XI (NM), the primary axial force ratios ROFN(1) ... ROFN(NM1), the modulus of elasticity E, the standard member length XLC, and the standard moment of inertia XIC, obtain the critical standard stability angle $(\phi_{CR})_c$ for the fundamental buckling mode and the corresponding effective length ratios XK (1) ... XK (NM1).

Analysis

In order that the determinant of the stability stiffness matrix $[K] = [A_1 SA_1^T] + [K_2]$ may be computed for a number of trial values of ϕ_c, two subroutines BUASAT and COMDET are separated from the main program. Subroutine BUASAT stands for "building the $[ASA^T]$ matrix including the $[K_2]$ matrix"; and subroutine COMDET stands for "computing the determinant." The ϕ_c value begins at $\phi_c = 1.00$ and is increased by $\Delta\phi_c = 0.10$ each time until the determinant changes sign from positive to negative. Then the correct value of $(\phi_{CR})_c$ to the nearest 0.0001 is obtained by an iterative linear interpolation procedure. Finally, the effective length ratios are computed by $K_m = \pi/[\beta_m(\phi_{CR})_c]$.

FORTRAN Program

The main program and the two subroutines are shown in Tables D.1 to D.3. Explanations for the main program and subroutine BUASAT are itemized below. For the main program,

1. *Lines 1 and 2.* Dimension statements. NP may be as large as 20; NPS, 5; NM, 25; NF, 50. The INDEX array is to keep record of the pivot selection in subroutine COMDET.

2. *Lines 3 to 5.* The program may be used to process any number of data sets at a time.

3. *Lines 6 and 7.* Read fixed point variables as defined. Note that NP = NPR + NPS, NF = 2 ∗ NM, and NM = NM1 + NM2.

4. *Lines 8 to 10.* Zero out the $[A]$ matrix.

5. *Lines 11 to 15.* Read the nonzero elements in the $[A]$ matrix.

6. *Line 16.* If NPS is zero, there is no $[C]$ matrix to be read.

7. *Lines 17 to 19.* Zero out the $[C]$ matrix.

8. *Lines 20 to 23.* Read the nonzero elements in the $[C]$ matrix.

9. *Lines 24 to 29.* Read E, XLC, XIC, $XL(1) \ldots XL(NM)$, $XI(1) \ldots XI(NM)$, and ROFN(1) $\ldots$ ROFN(NM1).

10. *Lines 30 and 31.* Print title.

11. *Lines 32 to 36.* Print the $[A]$ matrix.

12. *Line 37.* If NPS is zero, there is no $[C]$ matrix to be printed.

13. *Lines 38 to 41.* Print the $[C]$ matrix.

14. *Lines 42 to 57.* Print E, XLC, XIC, $XL(1) \ldots XL(NM)$, $XI(1) \ldots XI(NM)$, and ROFN(1) $\ldots$ ROFN(NM1).

15. *Lines 58 and 59.* Compute the β values of the NM1 members with primary axial forces.

16. *Lines 60 to 63.* Compute the determinant for $\phi_c = 1.00$. It is presup-

posed that the determinant at $\phi_c = 1.00$ is positive. If in any problem this determinant happens to be negative, Line 60 must be changed to a lower value of ϕ_c.

17. *Lines 64 to 70.* If determinant is zero, the correct value of $(\phi_{CR})_c$ has been found. If determinant is positive, store ϕ_c value and determinant in PHICA and DETA, go up one increment, and go back to Line 61 or Statement 513. If determinant is negative, store ϕ_c value and determinant in PHICB and DETB.

18. *Lines 71 to 73.* Print the values PHICA and DETA at the left station where DETA is positive, and the values PHICB and DETB at the right station where DETB is negative.

19. *Lines 74 and 75.* Compute the first iterative value of ϕ_c by linear interpolation using the controlling values at the left and right stations. Store this value in TEMP so that it may be compared with the next iterative value of ϕ_c.

20. *Lines 76 to 80.* Compute the determinant for the latest value of ϕ_c.

21. *Lines 81 to 85.* If determinant is now zero, the correct value of $(\phi_{CR})_c$ has been found. If determinant is negative, compute the next iterative value of ϕ_c by interpolating between the present value of ϕ_c and the value of PHICA on the left and then compare the new value of ϕ_c with TEMP in which the old value of ϕ_c has been stored. If determinant is positive, compute the next iterative value of ϕ_c by interpolating between the present value of ϕ_c and the value of PHICB on the right and then compare the new value of ϕ_c with its old value in TEMP. If the comparison in either case is unfavorable, go back to Line 75 or Statement 560.

22. *Lines 86 and 87.* Print the final value of $(\phi_{CR})_c$ which is within a tolerance of 0.0001.

23. *Lines 88 to 93.* Compute and print the final stability stiffness matrix, of which the determinant should be very close to zero.

24. *Lines 94 to 96.* Compute and print the final value of the determinant.

25. *Lines 97 to 102.* Compute and print the effective length ratios of the members with primary axial forces.

26. *Line 103.* Go to Line 3 or Statement 701 and find out if there is another data set.

27. *Lines 104 and 105.* End of main program.

For Subroutine BUASAT,

1. *Lines 1 and 2.* Name of subroutine and all variable names involved in this subroutine.

2. *Lines 3 and 4.* Dimension statement.

3. *Lines 5 to 16.* Accumulate the contributions to the $[ASA^T]$ matrix of the NM1 members with primary axial forces. Note that the end moments of these NM1 members must be numbered first in the F-e diagram. The stiffness coefficients S_{ii} and S_{ij} of the kth member are functions of $\phi_k = \beta_k \, \phi_c$.

4. *Line 17.* If the number of members without primary axial forces is zero, go to Line 27 or Statement 12.

5. *Lines 18 to 26.* Accumulate the contributions to the $[ASA^T]$ matrix of the NM2 members without primary axial forces. Here the stiffness coefficients S_{ii} and S_{ij} are always 4 and 2, respectively.

6. *Line 27.* If there is no sidesway, the $[K_2]$ matrix is zero. Go to Line 35 or Statement 16.

7. *Lines 28 to 34.* Add the $[K_2]$ matrix to the $[ASA^T]$ matrix. Note that

$$[K_2] = - \frac{\phi_c^2 \, EI_c}{L_c^2} \, [C] \, [G] \, [C^T]$$

where

$$[G] = \begin{bmatrix} \dfrac{\alpha_1}{L_1} & & & & \\ & \dfrac{\alpha_2}{L_2} & & & \\ & & \cdot & & \\ & & & \cdot & \\ & & & & \dfrac{\alpha_{NM1}}{L_{NM1}} \end{bmatrix}$$

8. *Lines 35 and 36.* End of subroutine.

TABLE D.1

Stability Analysis of Rigid Frames: Main Program

Line No.	Stat. No.	Statement
1		DIMENSION A(20,50),ASAT(20,20),INDEX(20),C(5,25)
2		DIMENSION ROFN(25),XL(25),XI(25),BETA(25),XK(25)
3	701	READ 101, NDATA

TABLE D.1 (cont.)

Line No.	Stat. No.	Statement
4	101	FORMAT (I5)
5		IF (NDATA) 801,801,102
6	102	READ 103, NP,NPR,NPS,NF,NM,NM1,NM2
7	103	FORMAT (7I5)
8		DO 104 I=1,NP
9		DO 104 J=1,NF
10	104	A(I,J)=0.
11	108	READ 105, I,J,AIJ
12	105	FORMAT (2I5,F15.4)
13		IF (I) 106,106,107
14	107	A(I,J)=AIJ
15		GO TO 108
16	106	IF (NPS) 110,112,110
17	110	DO 111 I=1,NPS
18		DO 111 J=1,NM1
19	111	C(I,J)=0.
20	114	READ 105, I,J,CIJ
21		IF (I) 112,112,113
22	113	C(I,J)=CIJ
23		GO TO 114
24	112	READ 115, E,XLC,XIC
25	115	FORMAT (3F10.4)
26		READ 116, (XL(I),I=1,NM)
27	116	FORMAT (5F10.4)
28		READ 116, (XI(I),I=1,NM)
29		READ 116, (ROFN(I),I=1,NM1)
30		PRINT 201
31	201	FORMAT (35H1STABILITY ANALYSIS OF RIGID FRAMES//)
32		PRINT 202
33	202	FORMAT (13H0THE A MATRIX)
34		DO 203 I=1,NP
35	203	PRINT 204, I,(A(I,J),J=1,NF)
36	204	FORMAT (4H ROW,I3,1X,5E16.8/(8X,5E16.8))
37		IF (NPS) 215,225,215
38	215	PRINT 901
39	901	FORMAT (13H0THE C MATRIX)
40		DO 205 I=1,NPS
41	205	PRINT 204, I,(C(I,J),J=1,NM1)
42	225	PRINT 206, E
43	206	FORMAT (31H0MODULUS OF ELASTICITY IN KSI =,F11.4)

TABLE D.1 (cont.)

Line No.	Stat. No.	Statement
44		PRINT 207, XLC
45	207	FORMAT (28H0STANDARD LENGTH IN INCHES =,F10.4)
46		PRINT 208, XIC
47	208	FORMAT (44H0STANDARD MOMENT OF INERTIA IN INCH FOURTH =,F10.4)
48		PRINT 209
49	209	FORMAT (18H0LENGTH OF MEMBERS)
50		PRINT 210, (I,XL(I),I=1,NM)
51	210	FORMAT (5(5X,I3,E16.8))
52		PRINT 211
53	211	FORMAT (30H0MOMENTS OF INERTIA OF MEMBERS)
54		PRINT 210, (I,XI(I),I=1,NM)
55		PRINT 212
56	212	FORMAT (30H0RATIO OF PRIMARY AXIAL FORCES)
57		PRINT 210, (I,ROFN(I),I=1,NM1)
58		DO 301 I=1,NM1
59	301	BETA(I)=XL(I)/XLC*SQRTF(ROFN(I)*XIC/XI(I))
60		PHIC=1.00
61	513	CALL BUASAT(NP,NM1,BETA,PHIC,E,XI,XL,A,NM2,XIC,XLC,NPS,NPR,C,
62		1ROFN,ASAT)
63		CALL COMDET(NP,ASAT,INDEX,DET,ICOL)
64		IF (DET) 511,601,512
65	512	PHICA=PHIC
66		DETA=DET
67		PHIC=PHIC+0.10
68		GO TO 513
69	511	PHICB=PHIC
70		DETB=DET
71		PRINT 514, PHICA,DETA,PHICB,DETB
72	514	FORMAT (10H0AT PHIC =,E16.8,10X,5HDET =,E16.8/10H at PHIC =,
73		1E16.8,10X,5HDET =,E16.8)
74		PHIC=PHICA+DETA*(PHICB-PHICA)/(DETA-DETB)
75	560	TEMP=PHIC
76		CALL BUASAT(NP,NM1,BETA,PHIC,E,XI,XL,A,NM2,XIC,XLC,NPS,NPR,C,
77		1ROFN,ASAT)
78		CALL COMDET(NP,ASAT,INDEX,DET,ICOL)
79		PRINT 531, PHIC,DET
80	531	FORMAT (10H0AT PHIC =,E16.8,10X,5HDET =,E16.8)
81		IF (DET) 551,601,552
82	551	PHIC=PHICA+DETA*(PHIC-PHICA)/(DETA-DET)
83		IF ((TEMP-PHIC)-0.0001) 601,601,560

TABLE D.1 (cont.)

Line No.	Stat. No.	Statement
84	552	PHIC=PHICB+DETB*(PHICB−PHIC)/(DET−DETB)
85		IF ((PHIC−TEMP)−0.0001) 601,601,560
86	601	PRINT 602, PHIC
87	602	FORMAT (13H0FINAL PHIC =,E16.8)
88		CALL BUASAT(NP,NM1,BETA,PHIC,E,XI,XL,A,NM2,XIC,XLC,NPS,NPR,C,
89		1ROFN,ASAT)
90		PRINT 603
91	603	FORMAT (33H0FINAL STABILITY STIFFNESS MATRIX)
92		DO 604 I=1,NP
93	604	PRINT 204, I,(ASAT(I,J),J=1,NP)
94		CALL COMDET(NP,ASAT,INDEX,DET,ICOL)
95		PRINT 605, DET
96	605	FORMAT (29H0FINAL VALUE OF DETERMINANT =,E16.8)
97		TEMP=3.14159/PHIC
98		DO 661 I=1,NM1
99	661	XK(I)=TEMP/BETA(I)
100		PRINT 662
101	662	FORMAT (24H0EFFECTIVE LENGTH RATIOS)
102		PRINT 210, (I,XK(I),I=1,NM1)
103		GO TO 701
104	801	STOP
105		END

TABLE D.2

Stability Analysis of Rigid Frames: Subroutine BUASAT

Line No.	Stat. No.	Statement
1		SUBROUTINE BUASAT(NP,NM1,BETA,PHIC,E,XI,XL,A,NM2,XIC,XLC,NPS,
2		1NPR,C,ROFN,ASAT)
3		DIMENSION BETA(25),XI(25),XL(25),A(20,50),C(5,25),ROFN(25),AS
4		1AT(20,20)
5		DO 302 I=1,NP
6		DO 302 J=1,NP
7		ASAT(I,J)=0.
8		DO 302 K=1,NM1
9		NFI=2*K−1
10		NFJ=2*K

TABLE D.2 (cont.)

Line No.	Stat. No.	Statement
11		PHI=BETA(K)*PHIC
12		D=2.-2.*COSF(PHI)-PHI*SINF(PHI)
13		SII=E*XI(K)/XL(K)*(PHI*SINF(PHI)-PHI*PHI*COSF(PHI))/D
14		SIJ=E*XI(K)/XL(K)*(PHI*PHI-PHI*SINF(PHI))/D
15	302	ASAT(I,J)=ASAT(I,J)+A(I,NFI)*(SII*A(J,NFI)+SIJ*A(J,NFJ))+A(I,NFJ)*
16		1(SIJ*A(J,NFI)+SII*A(J,NFJ))
17		IF (NM2) 11,12,11
18	11	DO 303 I=1,NP
19		DO 303 J=1,NP
20		DO 303 K=1,NM2
21		MEMNO=(NM1+K)
22		TEMP=E*XI(MEMNO)/XL(MEMNO)
23		NFI=2*NM1+2*K-1
24		NFJ=2*NM1+2*K
25	303	ASAT(I,J)=ASAT(I,J)+TEMP*(A(I,NFI)*(4.*A(J,NFI)+2.*A(J,NFJ))+A
26		1(I,NFJ)*(2.*A(J,NFI)+4.*A(J,NFJ)))
27	12	IF (NPS) 15,16,15
28	15	TEMP=PHIC*PHIC*E*XIC/(XLC*XLC)
29		DO 304 I=1,NPS
30		II=NPR+I
31		DO 304 J=1,NPS
32		JJ=NPR+J
33		DO 304 K=1,NM1
34	304	ASAT(II,JJ)=ASAT(II,JJ)-TEMP*C(I,K)*ROFN(K)/XL(K)*C(J,K)
35	16	RETURN
36		END

TABLE D.3

Stability Analysis of Rigid Frames: Subroutine COMDET

Line No.	Stat. No.	Statement
1		SUBROUTINE COMDET(NP,ASAT,INDEX,DET,ICOL)
2		DIMENSION ASAT(20,20),INDEX(20)
3		DET=1.0
4		DO 401 I=1,NP
5	401	INDEX(I)=0
6	410	AMAX=-1.
7		DO 402 I=1,NP
8		IF (INDEX(I)) 402,403,402
9	403	TEMP=ABSF(ASAT(I,I))

TABLE D.3 (cont.)

Line No.	Stat. No.	Statement
10		IF (TEMP−AMAX) 402,402,404
11	404	ICOL=I
12		AMAX=TEMP
13	402	CONTINUE
14		IF (AMAX) 451,452,405
15	405	INDEX(ICOL)=1
16		PIVOT=ASAT(ICOL,ICOL)
17		ASAT(ICOL,ICOL)=1.0
18		DET=DET*PIVOT
19		PIVOT=1./PIVOT
20		DO 406 J=1,NP
21	406	ASAT(ICOL,J)=ASAT(ICOL,J)*PIVOT
22		DO 407 I=1,NP
23		IF (I−ICOL) 408,407,408
24	408	TEMP=ASAT(I,ICOL)
25		ASAT(I,ICOL)=0.
26		DO 409 J=1,NP
27	409	ASAT(I,J)=ASAT(I,J)−ASAT(ICOL,J)*TEMP
28	407	CONTINUE
29		GO TO 410
30	452	PRINT 453
31	453	FORMAT (24H0ZERO PIVOT IN INVERSION)
32	451	RETURN
33		END

APPENDIX E

■

Stability Analysis of Rigid Frames with Nonuniform Members

Problem Statement

Given the statics matrix $[A]$ of a rigid frame in which the nonuniform members have been subdivided into short uniform segments, the stiffness properties EI/L of the segments, and the second-order stiffness matrix $[K_2]$, find the fundamental buckling load factor with its unitized mode vector, and also as many higher buckling load factors with unitized mode vectors as may be called.

Analysis

In using this computer program it is necessary to arrange the sidesway degree of freedom numbers in such a way that those which are contained in the $[K_2]$ matrix are the last sequence in the global degree of freedom numbers, because the $[\delta_{SS}]$ matrix is taken from the lower right-hand corner of the total $[ASA^T]^{-1}$ matrix.

The configuration of the rigid frame is described by the input matrix $[A]$, which is in the order of the total degree of freedom by twice the number of members, because the bifurcation theory of stability requires that axial deformation must not be considered.

The program is made flexible in that any number of buckling modes may be called for. In the unlikely event that all the modes are called, the $[\delta_{SS}K_2]$ matrix is reduced once more and printed out, so that it may be compared with the original $[\delta_{SS}K_2]$ matrix as being close to a null matrix.

Also, in the computer program, not only the unitized mode vector is printed out together with the buckling load factor, but this unitized vector is used as linear displacements once again, in the original $\{X_S\} = N_{CR}[\delta_{SS}K_2]\{X_S\}$ equation and a new unitized displacement vector computed and printed out. This new vector is called the *check nodal deflections* in the output.

FORTRAN Program

The FORTRAN program for stability analysis of rigid frames with nonuniform members is shown in Table E. The explanations are itemized below.

1. *Lines 1 and 2.* Dimension statements. The degree of freedom may be as large as 24, of which the sidesway degree may be as large as 12. The number of uniform segments may be as large as 18. The $[CDK]$ matrix is used to store the original $[DK]$ matrix, which may be successively reduced for computing higher modes. The $\{CDKX\}$ vector is for the "check nodal deflections." The $\{X\}$ and $\{DKX\}$ vectors are for the assumed sidesway displacements and the resulting unitized displacements, respectively.

2. *Lines 3 to 5.* Program may be used for more than one data set.

3. *Lines 6 and 7.* Read the degree of freedom NP, of which NPR is in rotation and NPS is in sidesway. Read the number of uniform segments NM, and the number of buckling modes required NBMR.

4. *Lines 8 to 11.* Zero out the $[A]$ matrix.

5. *Lines 12 to 16.* Read the nonzero elements in the $[A]$ matrix.

6. *Lines 17 and 18.* Read the $S = EI/L$ values of the uniform segments.

7. *Lines 19 to 21.* Zero out the $[K_2]$ matrix.

8. *Lines 22 to 25.* Read the nonzero elements in the $[K_2]$ matrix.

9. *Lines 26 and 27.* Print title.

10. *Lines 28 to 32.* Print the $[A]$ matrix.

11. *Lines 33 to 36.* Print the $S = EI/L$ values.

12. *Lines 37 to 40.* Print the $[K_2]$ matrix.

13. *Lines 41 to 48.* Build the $[ASA^T]$ matrix.

14. *Lines 49 to 73.* Invert the $[ASA^T]$ matrix.

15. *Lines 74 to 78.* Print the submatrix $[D]$ at the lower right-hand corner of the inverse $[ASA^T]$ matrix.

16. *Lines 79 and 80.* Print the number of modes required NBMR.

17. *Lines 81 to 91.* Compute and print the $[DK]$ matrix.

18. *Lines 92 to 94.* Place the $[DK]$ matrix in $[CDK]$ matrix.

19. *Lines 95 and 96.* Initialize the mode numbers to be sought and the number of iterations.

20. *Lines 97 and 98.* Initialize all sidesway displacements to be equal to unity.

21. *Line 99.* Keep account of the number of iterations required for this mode.

22. *Lines 100 and 101.* Take the unitized $\{DKX\}$ vector as the next $\{X\}$ vector.

23. *Lines 102 to 105.* Compute the $\{DKX\}$ vector.

24. *Lines 106 to 113.* Unitize the just obtained $\{DKX\}$ vector.

25. *Lines 114 to 116.* If a tolerance of 0.000001 between any assumed sidesway deflection and the corresponding element in the unitized $\{DKX\}$ vector is exceeded, proceed with the next iteration.

26. *Lines 117 to 125.* Print out the mode number, the number of iterations, the buckling load factor, and the mode vector.

27. *Lines 126 to 135.* Compute and print the unitized displacement vector by using the original $[DK]$ matrix and the just obtained mode vector.

28. *Line 136.* If NBMR = NPS, proceed to compute the reduced $[DK]$ matrix whether NBM is already equal to NPS or not; if NBMR < NPS, see whether NBM is now equal to NBMR.

29. *Line 137.* If NBMR < NPS and NBM is now equal to NBMR, go to the next data set; if NBMR < NPS and NBM is not yet equal to NBMR, proceed to compute the reduced $[DK]$ matrix.

30. *Lines 138 to 150.* Compute and print the reduced $[DK]$ matrix.

31. *Line 151.* Proceed to solve for the next mode.

32. *Line 152.* Go to the next data set.

33. *Lines 153 and 154.* End of program.

TABLE E

Stability Analysis of Rigid Frames with Nonuniform Members

Line No.	Stat. No.	Statement
1		DIMENSION A(24,36),S(18),XK(12,12),ASAT(24,24),INDEX(24)
2		DIMENSION DK(12,12),CDK(12,12), DKX(12),CDKX(12),X(12)
3	1	READ 2, NDATA
4	2	FORMAT (I5)
5		IF (NDATA) 59,59,3
6	3	READ 5, NP,NPR,NPS,NM,NBMR
7	5	FORMAT (5I5)
8		NMT2=2*NM
9		DO 300 I=1,NP
10		DO 300 J=1,NMT2
11	300	A(I,J)=0.
12	4	READ 301, I,J,AIJ
13	301	FORMAT (2I5,F10.4)
14		IF (I) 302,302,303
15	303	A(I,J)=AIJ
16		GO TO 4
17	302	READ 6, (S(I),I=1,NM)
18	6	FORMAT (5F10.4)
19		DO 71 I=1,NPS
20		DO 71 J=1,NPS
21	71	XK(I,J)=0.
22	75	READ 301, I,J,XKIJ
23		IF (I) 79,79,82
24	82	XK(I,J)=XKIJ
25		GO TO 75
26	79	PRINT 7
27	7	FORMAT (50H1STABILITY OF RIGID FRAMES WITH NONUNIFORM MEMBERS//)
28		PRINT 8
29	8	FORMAT (13H0THE MATRIX A)
30		DO 9 I=1,NP
31	9	PRINT 10, I,(A(I,J),J=1,NMT2)
32	10	FORMAT (4H ROW,I3,1X,5E16.8/(8X,5E16.8))
33		PRINT 11
34	11	FORMAT (25H0THE STIFFNESS OF MEMBERS)
35		PRINT 12, (I,S(I),I=1,NM)
36	12	FORMAT (5(5X,I3,E16.8))
37		PRINT 13
38	13	FORMAT (14H0THE MATRIX K2)

TABLE E (cont.)

Line No.	Stat. No.	Statement
39		DO 14 I=1,NPS
40	14	PRINT 10, I,(XK(I,J),J=1,NPS)
41		DO 15 I=1,NP
42		DO 15 J=1,NP
43		ASAT(I,J)=0.
44		DO 15 K=1,NM
45		L=2*K-1
46		M=2*K
47		ASAT(I,J)=ASAT(I,J)+A(I,L)*(4.*S(K)*A(J,L)+2.*S(K)*A(J,M))
48	15	ASAT(I,J)=ASAT(I,J)+A(I,M)*(2.*S(K)*A(J,L)+4.*S(K)*A(J,M))
49		DO 16 I=1,NP
50	16	INDEX(I)=0
51	17	AMAX=-1.
52		DO 18 I=1,NP
53		IF (INDEX(I)) 18,19,18
54	19	TEMP=ABS(ASAT(I,I))
55		IF (TEMP-AMAX) 18,18,20
56	20	ICOL=I
57		AMAX=TEMP
58	18	CONTINUE
59		IF (AMAX) 21,52,22
60	22	INDEX(ICOL)=1
61		PIVOT=ASAT(ICOL,ICOL)
62		ASAT(ICOL,ICOL)=1.0
63		PIVOT=1./PIVOT
64		DO 23 J=1,NP
65	23	ASAT(ICOL,J)=ASAT(ICOL,J)*PIVOT
66		DO 24 I=1,NP
67		IF (I-ICOL) 25,24,25
68	25	TEMP=ASAT(I,ICOL)
69		ASAT(I,ICOL)=0.0
70		DO 26 J=1,NP
71	26	ASAT(I,J)=ASAT(I,J)-ASAT(ICOL,J)*TEMP
72	24	CONTINUE
73		GO TO 17
74	21	PRINT 123
75	123	FORMAT (13H0THE MATRIX D)
76		NPRP1=NPR+1
77		DO 124 I=NPRP1,NP
78	124	PRINT 10, I,(ASAT(I,J),J=NPRP1,NP)
79		PRINT 125, NBMR
80	125	FORMAT (36H0NUMBER OF BUCKLING MODES REQUIRED =,I5)
81		DO 29 I=1,NPS

TABLE E (cont.)

Line No.	*Stat. No.*	*Statement*
82		DO 29 J=1,NPS
83		DK(I,J)=0.
84		DO 29 K=1,NPS
85		III=I+NPR
86		KKK=K+NPR
87	29	DK(I,J)=DK(I,J)+ASAT(III,KKK)*XK(K,J)
88		PRINT 30
89	30	FORMAT (14H0THE MATRIX DK)
90		DO 31 I=1,NPS
91	31	PRINT 10, I,(DK(I,J),J=1,NPS)
92		DO 152 I=1,NPS
93		DO 152 J=1,NPS
94	152	CDK(I,J)=DK(I,J)
95		NBM=0
96	32	NITER=0
97		DO 33 I=1,NPS
98	33	DKX(I)=1.
99	34	NITER=NITER+1
100		DO 35 I=1,NPS
101	35	X(I)=DKX(I)
102		DO 36 I=1,NPS
103		DKX(I)=0.
104		DO 36 K=1,NPS
105	36	DKX(I)=DKX(I)+DK(I,K)*X(K)
106		DKXMX=-1.
107		DO 37 I=1,NPS
108		IF (ABS(DKX(I))-DKXMX) 37,37,38
109	38	K=I
110		DKXMX=ABS(DKX(K))
111	37	CONTINUE
112		DO 39 I=1,NPS
113	39	DKX(I)=DKX(I)/DKX(K)
114		DO 40 I=1,NPS
115		IF (ABS(X(I)-DKX(I))-0.000001) 40,40,34
116	40	CONTINUE
117		NBM=NBM+1
118		PCR=ABS(X(K))/DKXMX
119		PRINT 42, NITER,NBM
120	42	FORMAT (7H0AFTER ,I3,21H ITERATIONS, MODE NO.,I3,12H IS OBTAINED)
121		PRINT 43, PCR
122	43	FORMAT (28H0THE BUCKLING LOAD FACTOR IS,E16.8)

TABLE E (cont.)

Line No.	Stat. No.	Statement
123		PRINT 47
124	47	FORMAT (26H0THE NODAL DEFLECTIONS ARE)
125		PRINT 12, (I,DKX(I),I=1,NPS)
126		DO 101 I=1,NPS
127		CDKX(I)=0.
128		DO 101 L=1,NPS
129	101	CDKX(I)=CDKX(I)+CDK(I,L)*DKX(L)
130	115	TEMP=CDKX(K)
131		DO 102 I=1,NPS
132	102	CDKX(I)=CDKX(I)/TEMP
133		PRINT 103
134	103	FORMAT (32H0THE CHECK NODAL DEFLECTIONS ARE)
135		PRINT 12, (I,CDKX(I),I=1,NPS)
136		IF (NBMR−NPS) 49,51,51
137	49	IF (NBM−NBMR) 51,52,52
138	51	XTKX=0.
139		DO 53 I=1,NPS
140		DO 53 J=1,NPS
141	53	XTKX=XTKX+XK(J,I)*DKX(J)*DKX(I)
142		FATR=1./(PCR*XTKX)
143		DO 54 I=1,NPS
144		DO 54 J=1,NPS
145		DO 54 K=1,NPS
146	54	DK(I,J)=DK(I,J)−FATR*DKX(I)*XK(J,K)*DKX(K)
147		PRINT 57
148	57	FORMAT (18H0THE NEW DK MATRIX)
149		DO 60 I=1,NPS
150	60	PRINT 10, I,(DK(I,J),J=1,NPS)
151		IF (NBM−NPS) 32,52,52
152	52	GO TO 1
153	59	STOP
154		END

APPENDIX F

Second-Order Analysis of Rigid Frames

Problem Statement

Given (1) for each member in a rigid frame, the 6 global degrees of freedom, the two coordinates of the terminal point referred to the initial point as origin, and the elastic properties EA and EI, and (2) a set of basic loads and a set of load factors: make the first-order analysis and 6 cycles of second-order analysis for each load factor times the basic loads. Make the dimension statements such that the degree of freedom may be as large as 20, the number of members as large as 7, and the number of load factors as large as 5.

FORTRAN Program

The FORTRAN program for the second-order analysis of rigid frames is shown in Table F. Regarding the program, the following explanatory notes may be made.

1. *Lines 1 to 4.* Dimension statements. The 21 dimensioned variables include (1) the fixed coordinates HO(7) and VO(7) and the fixed lengths XLO(7); (2) the fixed EA/L_0 and EI/L_0 values EAOL(7) and EIOL(7); (3) the basic loads

and load factors PBASE(20) and XLDF(5); (4) the global degrees of freedom and the original element statics matrix NPE(7,6) and AO(7,6,3); (5) the changing lengths XL(7); (6) the changing external forces and displacements P(20) and X(21); (7) the changing statics, stiffness, $[SA_0^T]$, and $[ASA_0^T]$ matrices of each member $A(6,3)$, $S(3,3)$, SAT(7,3,6), and EASAT(6,6); (8) the global matrix ASAT(21,21); (9) the record for pivots and row interchanges in matrix inversion INDEX(20,2); (10) the element internal force matrix SATX(3); (11) the axial forces AXF(7); and (12) the values of $(EA/L)\Delta_t$ denoted as DEL(7).

2. *Lines 5 to 7.* This program can execute more than one data set.

3. *Lines 8 and 9.* Read the total degree of freedom NP, the degree of freedom in rotation NPR, the degree of freedom in linear displacement NPS, the number of members NM, and the number of load factors NLF.

4. *Lines 10 to 12.* Read the basic loads and the load factors.

5. *Lines 13 to 18.* Print title and the basic loads.

6. *Lines 19 to 29.* Read and print member information. Compute the original length and the EA/L_0 and EI/L_0 values of each member.

7. *Line 30.* Compute NPP1 = NP + 1.

8. *Line 31.* The beginning of the big loop for each load factor. This loop ends on Line 201.

9. *Line 32.* Initialize the number of iterations. The first-order analysis is represented by NITER = 0.

10. *Lines 33 to 37.* Initialize the axial forces and the external displacements.

11. *Lines 38 to 42.* Print load factor, iteration number, and heading for member information.

12. *Lines 43 and 44.* Compute the loads for this load factor.

13. *Lines 45 to 47.* Zero out the global $[ASA^T]$ matrix.

14. *Line 48.* The beginning of the loop which builds the global $[ASA^T]$ matrix by the direct element method. This loop ends on Line 131.

15. *Lines 49 to 53.* Compute the new length and the new cosine and sine functions on the basis of the joint displacements at the end of the preceding cycle.

16. *Lines 54 to 61.* Compute Δ_t according to Eq. 6.3.7b and adjust the external loads according to Eq. 6.6.4.

17. *Lines 62 to 81.* Build the element statics matrix $[A]$ according to Fig. 6.2.2 and Eq. 6.2.1, except the axial force has been placed in the first column, instead of the third column.

18. *Lines 82 to 85.* If NITER = 0, store the element $[A]$ matrix in a 3-di-

mensional $[A_0]$ matrix in order that this information may be used in all cycles of second-order analysis.

19. *Lines 86 to 113.* Build the 3×3 element $[S]$ matrix. Note that Formulas 6.5.15 and 6.5.16 are used for tension members; and Formulas 6.5.27 and 6.5.28, for compression members.

20. *Lines 114 and 115.* Print member information including its new geometry and stiffness coefficients.

21. *Lines 116 to 120.* Compute the element $[SA^T]$ matrix and store it in memory for use in computing internal forces.

22. *Lines 121 to 125.* Compute the element $[ASA^T]$ matrix.

23. *Lines 126 to 130.* Feed the contribution of the element $[ASA^T]$ matrix into the global $[ASA^T]$ matrix.

24. *Line 131.* End of the loop started on Line 48.

25. *Line 132 and 133.* Install the column matrix $\{P\}$ modified in Lines 58 to 61.

26. *Lines 134 to 180.* The global $[ASA^T]$ matrix is inverted by using the inversion program of Appendix B in *Matrix Methods of Structural Analysis*. Note that the pivot location for each Gauss-Jordan elimination is printed out.

27. *Lines 181 to 183.* The $(NP + 1)$th column contains the displacements $\{X\}$.

28. *Lines 184 to 186.* Print the heading for the axial force, the two end moments, and the shear force acting on each member.

29. *Lines 187 and 188.* Place the joint displacements in the NPP1th column of $[ASA^T]$ in $\{X\}$.

30. *Lines 189 to 197.* Compute the three independent internal forces for each member and print them. Note Line 194 wherein the effect of Δ_t on the axial force is considered.

31. *Lines 198 to 200.* If number of iterations in second-order analysis is already 6, go ahead and begin with the first-order analysis for the next load factor.

32. *Line 201.* End of the big loop started on Line 31.

33. *Line 202.* Execute the next data set.

34. *Lines 203 and 204.* End of program.

TABLE F
Second-Order Analysis of Rigid Frames

Line No.	Stat. No.	Statement
1		DIMENSION HO(7),VO(7),XLO(7),XL(7),EAOL(7),EIOL(7),NPE(7,6)
2		DIMENSION AO(7,6,3),XLDF(5),PBASE(20),P(20),X(21)
3		DIMENSION A(6,3),S(3,3),SAT(7,3,6),EASAT(6,6),ASAT(21,21)
4		DIMENSION INDEX(20,2),SATX(3),AXF(7),DEL(7)
5	1	READ 101, NDATA
6	101	FORMAT (I5)
7		IF (NDATA) 601,601,102
8	102	READ 103, NP,NPR,NPS,NM,NLF
9	103	FORMAT (5I5)
10		READ 104, (PBASE(I),I=1,NP)
11	104	FORMAT (5F10.4)
12		READ 104, (XLDF(I),I=1,NLF)
13		PRINT 121
14	121	FORMAT (38H1SECOND ORDER ANALYSIS OF RIGID FRAMES//)
15		PRINT 122
16	122	FORMAT (16H0THE BASIC LOADS/)
17		PRINT 123, (I,PBASE(I),I=1,NP)
18	123	FORMAT (5(5X,I3,E16.7)/)
19		PRINT 124
20	124	FORMAT (31H0MEMBER NP1 NP2 NP3 NP4 NP5 NP6,7X,1HH,11X, 1HV,11X,
21		12HEA,11X,2HEI/)
22		DO 125 K=1,NM
23		READ 126, MEMNO,(NPE(K,J),J=1,6),HO(K),VO(K),EA,EI
24	126	FORMAT (7I5,4F10.4)
25		PRINT 127, MEMNO,(NPE(K,J),J=1,6),HO(K),VO(K),EA,EI
26	127	FORMAT (1H ,2I5,5I4,4F12.1)
27		XLO(K)=SQRTF(HO(K)*HO(K)+VO(K)*VO(K))
28		EAOL(K)=EA/XLO(K)
29	125	EIOL(K)=EI/XLO(K)
30		NPP1=NP+1
31		DO 201 ILF=1,NLF
32		NITER=0
33		DO 202 K=1,NM
34	202	AXF(K)=0.
35		DO 203 J=1,NP
36	203	X(J)=0.
37		X(NPP1)=0.
38	503	PRINT 205, XLDF(ILF),NITER
39	205	FORMAT (14H1LOAD FACTOR =,F5.2,10X,7HNITER =,I5/)

TABLE F (cont.)

Line No.	Stat. No.	Statement
40		PRINT 206
41	206	FORMAT (1H0,11X,1HH,15X,1HV,15X,1HL,14X,3HCOS,13X,3HSIN,13X,
42		13HSII,13X,3HSIJ/)
43		DO 204 J=1,NP
44	204	P(J)=XLDF(ILF)*PBASE(J)
45		DO 211 J=1,NPP1
46		DO 211 L=1,NPP1
47	211	ASAT(J,L)=0.
48		DO 215 K=1,NM
49		H=HO(K)+X(NPE(K,5))−X(NPE(K,2))
50		V=VO(K)+X(NPE(K,6))−X(NPE(K,3))
51		XL(K)=SQRTF(H*H+V*V)
52		CS=H/XL(K)
53		SN=V/XL(K)
54		DELT=((H−HO(K))**2+(V−VO(K))**2−(XL(K)−XLO(K))**2)/(2.*XLO(K))
55		DEL(K)=DELT*EAOL(K)
56		PSH=EAOL(K)*DELT*CS
57		PSV=EAOL(K)*DELT*SN
58		P(NPE(K,2))=P(NPE(K,2))+PSH
59		P(NPE(K,3))=P(NPE(K,3))+PSV
60		P(NPE(K,5))=P(NPE(K,5))−PSH
61		P(NPE(K,6))=P(NPE(K,6))−PSV
62		SNOL=SN/XL(K)
63		CSOL=CS/XL(K)
64		A(1,1)=0.
65		A(1,2)=1.
66		A(1,3)=0.
67		A(2,1)=−CS
68		A(2,2)=SNOL
69		A(2,3)=SNOL
70		A(3,1)=−SN
71		A(3,2)=−CSOL
72		A(3,3)=−CSOL
73		A(4,1)=0.
74		A(4,2)=0.
75		A(4,3)=1.
76		A(5,1)=CS
77		A(5,2)=−SNOL
78		A(5,3)=−SNOL
79		A(6,1)=SN
80		A(6,2)=CSOL
81		A(6,3)=CSOL
82		IF (NITER) 233,233,234

TABLE F (cont.)

Line No.	Stat. No.	*Statement*
83	233	DO 235 L=1,6
84		DO 235 M=1,3
85	235	AO(K,L,M)=A(L,M)
86	234	S(1,1)=EAOL(K)
87		S(1,2)=0.
88		S(1,3)=0.
89		S(2,1)=0.
90		S(3,1)=0.
91		IF (AXF(K)) 242,241,242
92	241	SII=4.*EIOL(K)
93		SIJ=2.*EIOL(K)
94		GO TO 261
95	242	Q=SQRTF(ABSF(AXF(K))*XLO(K)/EIOL(K))
96		IF (Q-.01) 243,243,244
97	243	IF (AXF(K)) 251,241,252
98	251	SII=4.*EIOL(K)*(1.-Q*Q/10.)/(1.-Q*Q/15.)
99		SIJ=2.*EIOL(K)*(1.-Q*Q/20.)/(1.-Q*Q/15.)
100		GO TO 261
101	252	SII=4.*EIOL(K)*(1.+Q*Q/10.)/(1.+Q*Q/15.)
102		SIJ=2.*EIOL(K)*(1.+Q*Q/20.)/(1.+Q*Q/15.)
103		GO TO 261
104	244	IF (AXF(K)) 253,241,254
105	253	SII=EIOL(K)*Q*(SINF(Q)-Q*COSF(Q))/(2.-2.*COSF(Q)-Q*SINF(Q))
106		SIJ=EIOL(K)*(Q*Q-Q*SINF(Q))/(2.-2.*COSF(Q)-Q*SINF(Q))
107		GO TO 261
108	254	SII=EIOL(K)*Q*(Q*COSHF(Q)-SINHF(Q))/(2.-2.*COSHF(Q)+Q*SINHF(Q))
109		SIJ=EIOL(K)*(Q*SINHF(Q)-Q*Q)/(2.-2.*COSHF(Q)+Q*SINHF(Q))
110	261	S(2,2)=SII
111		S(3,3)=SII
112		S(2,3)=SIJ
113		S(3,2)=SIJ
114		PRINT 262, K,H,V,XL(K),CS,SN,SII,SIJ
115	262	FORMAT (I5,7E16.8)
116		DO 281 L=1,3
117		DO 281 M=1,6
118		SAT(K,L,M)=0.
119		DO 281 N=1,3
120	281	SAT(K,L,M)=SAT(K,L,M)+S(L,N)*AO(K,M,N)
121		DO 282 L=1,6
122		DO 282 M=1,6
123		EASAT(L,M)=0.
124		DO 282 N=1,3
125	282	EASAT(L,M)=EASAT(L,M)+A(L,N)*SAT(K,N,M)

TABLE F (cont.)

Line No.	Stat. No.	Statement
126		DO 283 L=1,6
127		L1=NPE(K,L)
128		DO 283 M=1,6
129		M1=NPE(K,M)
130	283	ASAT(L1,M1)=ASAT(L1,M1)+EASAT(L,M)
131	215	CONTINUE
132		DO 291 J=1,NP
133	291	ASAT(J,NPP1)=P(J)
134		DO 301 I=1,NP
135	301	INDEX(I,1)=0
136		II=0
137	302	AMAX=-1.
138		DO 303 I=1,NP
139		IF (INDEX(I,1)) 303,304,303
140	304	DO 305 J=1,NP
141		IF (INDEX(J,1)) 305,306,305
142	306	TEMP=ABSF(ASAT(I,J))
143		IF (TEMP-AMAX) 305,305,307
144	307	IROW=I
145		ICOL=J
146		AMAX=TEMP
147	305	CONTINUE
148	303	CONTINUE
149		IF (AMAX) 401,1,309
150	309	INDEX(ICOL,1)=IROW
151		PRINT 311, IROW,ICOL
152	311	FORMAT (20X,6HIROW =,I5,10X,6HICOL =,I5)
153		IF (IROW-ICOL) 312,313,312
154	312	DO 314 J=1,NPP1
155		TEMP=ASAT(IROW,J)
156		ASAT(IROW,J)=ASAT(ICOL,J)
157	314	ASAT(ICOL,J)=TEMP
158		II=II+1
159		INDEX(II,2)=ICOL
160	313	PIVOT=ASAT(ICOL,ICOL)
161		ASAT(ICOL,ICOL)=1.
162		PIVOT=1./PIVOT
163		DO 316 J=1,NPP1
164	316	ASAT(ICOL,J)=ASAT(ICOL,J)*PIVOT
165		DO 317 I=1,NP
166		IF (I-ICOL) 318,317,318
167	318	TEMP=ASAT(I,ICOL)
168		ASAT(I,ICOL)=0.
169		DO 319 J=1,NPP1
170	319	ASAT(I,J)=ASAT(I,J)-ASAT(ICOL,J)*TEMP

TABLE F (cont.)

Line No.	Stat. No.	Statement
171	317	CONTINUE
172		GO TO 302
173	320	ICOL=INDEX(II,2)
174		IROW=INDEX(ICOL,1)
175		DO 321 I=1,NP
176		TEMP=ASAT(I,IROW)
177		ASAT(I,IROW)=ASAT(I,ICOL)
178	321	ASAT(I,ICOL)=TEMP
179		II=II−1
180	401	IF (II) 320,402,320
181	402	PRINT 406
182	406	FORMAT (12H0VALUES OF X/)
183		PRINT 123, (I,ASAT(I,NPP1),I=1,NP)
184		PRINT 414
185	414	FORMAT (7H0MEMBER,8X,11HAXIAL FORCE,5X,18HINITIAL END MOMENT,2X,
186		119HTERMINAL END MOMENT,6X,11HSHEAR FORCE/)
187		DO 502 J=1,NP
188	502	X(J)=ASAT(J,NPP1)
189		DO 421 K=1,NM
190		DO 423 L=1,3
191		SATX(L)=0.
192		DO 423 M=1,6
193	423	SATX(L)=SATX(L)+SAT(K,L,M)*X(NPE(K,M))
194		AXF(K)=SATX(1)+DEL(K)
195		V=(SATX(2)+SATX(3))/XL(K)
196	421	PRINT 425, K,AXF(K),SATX(2),SATX(3),V
197	425	FORMAT (I6,4X,4E20.8)
198		IF (NITER−6) 501,201,201
199	501	NITER=NITER+1
200		GO TO 503
201	201	CONTINUE
202		GO TO 1
203	601	STOP
204		END

APPENDIX G

Plane Stress Analysis (Rectangular Element with Linear Edge Displacement)

Problem Statement

Write a FORTRAN program for plane stress analysis using rectangular elements with linear edge displacement as described in Sec. 8.5. Input data include (1) the degree of freedom NP, the number of elements NELMT, the number of loading conditions NLC, the modulus of elasticity E, the Poisson's ratio μ, and the plate thickness t; (2) for each element, the lengths of sides a and b and the eight degrees of freedom in the order listed in Fig. 8.5.1; and (3) the external-force matrix $P(NP \times NLC)$. Output required includes (1) the displacement matrix $X(NP \times NLC)$; (2) for each element, the stress equations for σ_x, σ_y, and τ_{xy} and the displacement equations for u and v as functions of x and y referred to the center of the element as origin; and (3) the check matrix $P(NP \times NLC)$ as computed from accumulating the resistance offered by the stresses in each element. Make the dimension statements such that the degree of freedom NP and the number of loading conditions NLC may be as large as 150 and 2 respectively.

FORTRAN Program

Regarding the FORTRAN program, the following explanations are offered.

1. *Lines 1 and 2.* In the dimension statements; EASAT (8,8) is for building the stiffness matrix of each element; NPE (8) is for the 8 global degrees of freedom of each element; and INDEX (150) is for keeping the record of pivot selection in the inversion process.

2. *Lines 3 to 5.* The program, on each compilation, may be used to run more than one data set.

3. *Lines 6 and 7.* Read the degree of freedom NP, the number of elements NELMT, the number of loading conditions NLC, the modulus of elasticity E, the Poisson's ratio PR, and the plate thickness T.

4. *Lines 8 to 11.* Zero out the $[ASA^T]$ matrix. Note that the extra row and column are for the restraint.

5. *Lines 12 to 17.* Print title and heading for the finite elements.

6. *Lines 18 to 20.* Read the 8 global degrees of freedom in the order listed in Fig. 8.5.1 and the lengths of sides A and B of each element until a blank card is hit.

7. *Lines 21 and 22.* Print the information for each element as obtained in Line 18.

8. *Lines 23 to 37.* Compute those constants which are to be used in establishing the stiffness matrix of the element.

9. *Lines 38 to 73.* Establish the lower triangular portion of the element stiffness matrix.

10. *Lines 74 to 77.* Project the lower triangular portion to the upper triangular portion of the element stiffness matrix.

11. *Lines 78 to 82.* Feed the contribution of this element into the global stiffness matrix.

12. *Lines 83.* Proceed to the next element.

13. *Lines 84 to 108.* Invert the global stiffness matrix.

14. *Lines 109 to 111.* Zero out the $[P]$ matrix.

15. *Lines 112 to 116.* Read the nonzero elements in the $[P]$ matrix.

16. *Lines 117 to 121.* Print the $[P]$ matrix.

17. *Lines 122 to 130.* Compute and print the $[X]$ matrix.

18. *Lines 131 to 133.* Zero out the $[P]$ matrix to make room for the check $[P]$ matrix. Note that the extra row is for the restraint.

19. *Lines 134 to 136.* Initialize the loading condition number so that output for element stresses and displacements, as well as for the check [P] matrix can be obtained for one loading condition at a time.

20. *Line 137.* Zero out the displacement at the restraint.

21. *Lines 138 and 139.* Read the element information. Note that as many sets of element information as there are loading conditions must be provided. Each set is identical with the initial set used in Line 18.

22. *Lines 140 to 166.* Compute and print the stresses in each element using the following formulas:

$$\sigma_x = A_{11} + A_{12}x + A_{13}y$$
$$\sigma_y = A_{21} + A_{22}x + A_{23}y$$
$$\tau_{xy} = A_{31} + A_{32}x + A_{33}y$$

in which

$$A_{11} = \frac{E}{1 - \mu^2}\left[\frac{1}{2a}(X_1 - X_3 - X_5 + X_7) + \frac{\mu}{2b}(X_2 + X_4 - X_6 - X_8)\right]$$

$$A_{12} = \frac{E}{1 - \mu^2}\left[\frac{\mu}{ab}(X_2 - X_4 + X_6 - X_8)\right]$$

$$A_{13} = \frac{E}{1 - \mu^2}\left[\frac{1}{ab}(X_1 - X_3 + X_5 - X_7)\right]$$

$$A_{21} = \frac{E}{1 - \mu^2}\left[\frac{1}{2b}(X_2 + X_4 - X_6 - X_8) + \frac{\mu}{2a}(X_1 - X_3 - X_5 + X_7)\right]$$

$$A_{22} = \frac{E}{1 - \mu^2}\left[\frac{1}{ab}(X_2 - X_4 + X_6 - X_8)\right]$$

$$A_{23} = \frac{E}{1 - \mu^2}\left[\frac{\mu}{ab}(X_1 - X_3 + X_5 - X_7)\right]$$

$$A_{31} = \frac{E}{4ab(1 + \mu)}\left[a(X_1 + X_3 - X_5 - X_7) + b(X_2 - X_4 - X_6 + X_8)\right]$$

$$A_{32} = \frac{E}{2ab(1+\mu)} (X_1 - X_3 + X_5 - X_7)$$

$$A_{33} = \frac{E}{2ab(1+\mu)} (X_2 - X_4 + X_6 - X_8)$$

The above formulas can be conveniently obtained from Eq. 8.5.7.

23. *Lines 167 to 182.* Compute and print the displacements in each element using the following formulas:

$$u = \alpha_1 x + \alpha_2 xy + \alpha_3 y + \alpha_4$$
$$v = \alpha_5 x + \alpha_6 xy + \alpha_7 y + \alpha_8$$

in which

$$\alpha_1 = (X_1 - X_3 - X_5 + X_7)/(2a)$$
$$\alpha_2 = (X_1 - X_3 + X_5 - X_7)/(ab)$$
$$\alpha_3 = (X_1 + X_3 - X_5 - X_7)/(2b)$$
$$\alpha_4 = (X_1 + X_3 + X_5 + X_7)/4$$
$$\alpha_5 = (X_2 - X_4 - X_6 + X_8)/(2a)$$
$$\alpha_6 = (X_2 - X_4 + X_6 - X_8)/(ab)$$
$$\alpha_7 = (X_2 + X_4 - X_6 - X_8)/(2b)$$
$$\alpha_8 = (X_2 + X_4 + X_6 + X_8)/4$$

The above formulas are identical to Eqs. 8.5.1 and 8.5.3.

24. *Lines 183 to 198.* The stresses within each element should yield a set of 8 nodal forces to satisfy equilibrium. These nodal forces are fed into the check [P] matrix for the loading condition. The nodal forces are:

$$P_1 = \frac{t}{2}\left(bA_{11} + \frac{b^2}{6}A_{13} + aA_{31} + \frac{a^2}{6}A_{32}\right)$$

$$P_2 = \frac{t}{2}\left(aA_{21} + \frac{a^2}{6}A_{22} + bA_{31} + \frac{b^2}{6}A_{33}\right)$$

$$P_3 = \frac{t}{2}\left(-bA_{11} - \frac{b^2}{6}A_{13} + aA_{31} - \frac{a^2}{6}A_{32}\right)$$

$$P_4 = \frac{t}{2}\left(aA_{21} - \frac{a^2}{6}A_{22} - bA_{31} - \frac{b^2}{6}A_{33}\right)$$

$$P_5 = \frac{t}{2}\left(-bA_{11} + \frac{b^2}{6}A_{13} - aA_{31} + \frac{a^2}{6}A_{32}\right)$$

$$P_6 = \frac{t}{2}\left(-aA_{21} + \frac{a^2}{6}A_{22} - bA_{31} + \frac{b^2}{6}A_{33}\right)$$

$$P_7 = \frac{t}{2}\left(bA_{11} - \frac{b^2}{6}A_{13} - aA_{31} - \frac{a^2}{6}A_{32}\right)$$

$$P_8 = \frac{t}{2}\left(-aA_{21} - \frac{a^2}{6}A_{22} + bA_{31} - \frac{b^2}{6}A_{33}\right)$$

The above formulas may be derived by applying the reciprocal energy theorem between the real finite element with known stresses and strains and the finite element in each of the 8 basic Q-Y modes described by Eqs. 8.5.6 and 8.5.7. For instance, P_3 of the real finite element can be obtained from

$$P_3 * Y_3 = \iint[\sigma \text{ in } Y_3 \text{ mode}]^T \{\text{real } e\} t\, dydx$$

$$= \iint[e \text{ in } Y_3 \text{ mode}]^T \{\text{real } \sigma\} t\, dydx$$

$$= \int_{-a/2}^{+a/2} \int_{-b/2}^{+b/2} \left[\left(-\frac{1}{2a} - \frac{y}{ab}\right) Y_3 \left(A_{11} + A_{12}x + A_{13}y\right)\right.$$

$$\left. + \left(\frac{1}{2b} - \frac{x}{ab}\right) Y_3 (A_{31} + A_{32}x + A_{33}y)\right] t\, dydx$$

$$P_3 = \frac{t}{2}\left(-bA_{11} - \frac{b^2}{6}A_{13} + aA_{31} - \frac{a^2}{6}A_{32}\right)$$

25. *Line 199.* Go to the next element and compute stresses, displacements, and its contribution to the check [P] matrix.

26. *Lines 200 to 203.* Print the check [P] matrix. Comparison of the check [P] matrix with the original [P] matrix constitutes a grand check of the accuracy of the arithmetic performed by the computer.

27. *Line 204.* Go to the next data set.

28. *Lines 205 and 206.* End of program.

TABLE G
Plane Stress Analysis

Line No.	Stat. No.	Statement
1		DIMENSION EASAT(8,8),NPE(8),ASAT(151,151),INDEX(150),P(151,2)
2		DIMENSION X(151,2)
3	901	READ 902, III
4	902	FORMAT (I5)
5		IF (III) 1111,1111,903
6	903	READ 101, NP,NELMT,NLC,E,PR,T
7	101	FORMAT (3I5,3F10.4)
8		NPP1=NP+1
9		DO 102 I=1,NPP1
10		DO 102 J=1,NPP1
11	102	ASAT(I,J)=0.
12		PRINT 103
13	103	FORMAT (78H1PLANE STRESS ANALYSIS USING RECTANGULAR ELEMENT WIT
14		1H LINEAR EDGE DISPLACEMENT//)
15		PRINT 104
16	104	FORMAT (46H0NELMT NP1 NP2 NP3 NP4 NP5 NP 6 NP7 NP8, 5X, 1HA
17		1,9X,1HB)
18	105	READ 106, NELMT,(NPE(I),I=1,8),A,B
19	106	FORMAT (9I5,2F10.4)
20		IF (NELMT) 302,302,107
21	107	PRINT 108, NELMT,(NPE(I),I=1,8),A,B
22	108	FORMAT (1H ,9I5,2F10.4)
23		C=A/B
24		D=B/A
25		G=C*(1.-PR)
26		H=D*(1.-PR)
27		AA=4.*D+2.*G
28		BB=1.5*(1.+PR)
29		CC=-4.*D+G
30		DD=1.5*(1.-3.*PR)
31		EE=-2.*D-G
32		FF=2.*D-2.*G
33		AAA=4.*C+2.*H
34		CCC=-4.*C+H
35		EEE=-2.*C-H
36		FFF=2.*C-2.*H
37		CM=(E*T)/(12.*(1.-PR*PR))
38		EASAT(1,1)=AA
39		EASAT(2,1)=BB

TABLE G (cont.)

Line No.	Stat. No.	Statement
40		EASAT(2,2)=AAA
41		EASAT(3,1)=CC
42		EASAT(3,2)=DD
43		EASAT(3,3)=AA
44		EASAT(4,1)=-DD
45		EASAT(4,2)=FFF
46		EASAT(4,3)=-BB
47		EASAT(4,4)=AAA
48		EASAT(5,1)=EE
49		EASAT(5,2)=-BB
50		EASAT(5,3)=FF
51		EASAT(5,4)=DD
52		EASAT(5,5)=AA
53		EASAT(6,1)=-BB
54		EASAT(6,2)=EEE
55		EASAT(6,3)=-DD
56		EASAT(6,4)=CCC
57		EASAT(6,5)=BB
58		EASAT(6,6)=AAA
59		EASAT(7,1)=FF
60		EASAT(7,2)=-DD
61		EASAT(7,3)=EE
62		EASAT(7,4)=BB
63		EASAT(7,5)=CC
64		EASAT(7,6)=DD
65		EASAT(7,7)=AA
66		EASAT(8,1)=DD
67		EASAT(8,2)=CCC
68		EASAT(8,3)=BB
69		EASAT(8,4)=EEE
70		EASAT(8,5)=-DD
71		EASAT(8,6)=FFF
72		EASAT(8,7)=-BB
73		EASAT(8,8)=AAA
74		DO 202 I=1,7
75		II=I+1
76		DO 202 J=II,8
77	202	EASAT(I,J)=EASAT(J,I)
78		DO 203 I=1,8
79		NS1=NPE(I)
80		DO 203 J=1,8
81		NS2=NPE(J)
82	203	ASAT(NS1,NS2)=ASAT(NS1,NS2)+EASAT(I,J)*CM
83		GO TO 105

TABLE G (cont.)

Line No.	Stat. No.	Statement
84	302	DO 303 I=1,NP
85	303	INDEX(I)=0
86	304	AMAX=-1.
87		DO 307 I=1,NP
88		IF (INDEX(I)) 307,305,307
89	305	TEMP=ABS(ASAT(I,I))
90		IF (TEMP-AMAX) 307,307,306
91	306	ICOL=I
92		AMAX=TEMP
93	307	CONTINUE
94		IF (AMAX) 401,701,308
95	308	INDEX(ICOL)=1
96		PIVOT=ASAT(ICOL,ICOL)
97		ASAT(ICOL,ICOL)=1.
98		PIVOT=1./PIVOT
99		DO 309 J=1,NP
100	309	ASAT(ICOL,J)=ASAT(ICOL,J)*PIVOT
101		DO 312 I=1,NP
102		IF (I-ICOL) 310,312,310
103	310	TEMP=ASAT(I,ICOL)
104		ASAT(I,ICOL)=0.
105		DO 311 J=1,NP
106	311	ASAT(I,J)=ASAT(I,J)-ASAT(ICOL,J)*TEMP
107	312	CONTINUE
108		GO TO 304
109	401	DO 402 I=1,NP
110		DO 402 J=1,NLC
111	402	P(I,J)=0.
112	403	READ 404, I,J,PIJ
113	404	FORMAT (2I5,F10.4)
114		IF (I) 406,406,405
115	405	P(I,J)=PIJ
116		GO TO 403
117	406	PRINT 407
118	407	FORMAT (13H0THE MATRIX P)
119		DO 408 I=1,NP
120	408	PRINT 409, I,(P(I,J),J=1,NLC)
121	409	FORMAT (4H ROW,I3,1X,4E16.8/(8X,4E16.8))
122		DO 501 I=1,NP
123		DO 501 J=1,NLC
124		X(I,J)=0.
125		DO 501 K=1,NP
126	501	X(I,J)=X(I,J)+ASAT(I,K)*P(K,J)
127		PRINT 502

TABLE G (cont.)

Line No.	Stat. No.	Statement
128	502	FORMAT (13H0THE MATRIX X)
129		DO 503 I=1,NP
130	503	PRINT 409, I,(X(I,J),J=1,NLC)
131		DO 611 I=1,NPP1
132		DO 611 J=1,NLC
133	611	P(I,J)=0.
134		JJ=0
135	601	JJ=JJ+1
136		IF (JJ-NLC) 602,602,801
137	602	X(NPP1,JJ)=0.
138	610	READ 106, NELMT,N1,N2,N3,N4,N5,N6,N7,N8,A,B
139		IF (NELMT) 601,601,603
140	603	C1=E/(1.-PR*PR)
141		C2=X(N1,JJ)-X(N3,JJ)-X(N5,JJ)+X(N7,JJ)
142		C3=X(N2,JJ)+X(N4,JJ)-X(N6,JJ)-X(N8,JJ)
143		C4=X(N2,JJ)-X(N4,JJ)+X(N6,JJ)-X(N8,JJ)
144		C5=X(N1,JJ)-X(N3,JJ)+X(N5,JJ)-X(N7,JJ)
145		C6=X(N1,JJ)+X(N3,JJ)-X(N5,JJ)-X(N7,JJ)
146		C7=X(N2,JJ)-X(N4,JJ)-X(N6,JJ)+X(N8,JJ)
147		C8=E/(4.*A*B*(1.+PR))
148		A11=C1*((C2/(2.*A))+(PR*C3)/(2.*B))
149		A12=(C1*PR*C4)/(A*B)
150		A13=(C1*C5)/(A*B)
151		A21=C1*((PR*C2)/(2.*A)+(C3/(2.*B)))
152		A22=(C1*C4)/(A*B)
153		A23=(C1*PR*C5)/(A*B)
154		A31=C8*(A*C6+B*C7)
155		A32=2.*C8*C5
156		A33=2.*C8*C4
157		PRINT 605, JJ
158	605	FORMAT (22H0LOADING CONDITION NO.,I5)
159		PRINT 606, NELMT
160	606	FORMAT (12H0ELEMENT NO.,I5)
161		PRINT 5001, A11,A12,A13
162	5001	FORMAT (9H0SIGMA X=,E15.7,6H + (,E15.7,9H) X + (,E15.7, 3H) Y)
163		PRINT 5002, A21,A22,A23
164	5002	FORMAT (9H0SIGMA Y=,E15.7,6H + (,E15.7,9H) X + (, E15.7,3H) Y)
165		PRINT 5003, A31,A32,A33
166	5003	FORMAT (9H0TAU XY=,E15.7,6H + (,E15.7,9H) X + (, E15.7,3H) Y)
167		C9=X(N1,JJ)+X(N3,JJ)+X(N5,JJ)+X(N7,JJ)

TABLE G (cont.)

Line No.	Stat. No.	Statement
168		C10=X(N2,JJ)+X(N4,JJ)+X(N6,JJ)+X(N8,JJ)
169		B11=C2*(1./(2.*A))
170		B12=C5*(1./(A*B))
171		B13=C6*(1./(2.*B))
172		B14=C9*0.25
173		B21=C7*(1./(2.*A))
174		B22=C4*(1./(A*B))
175		B23=C3*(1./(2.*B))
176		B24=C10*0.25
177		PRINT 5004, B11,B12,B13,B14
178	5004	FORMAT (7H0UX= (,E15.7,9H) X + (,E15.7,
179		10H) XY + (,E15.7,19H) Y + (,E15.7,1H))
180		PRINT 5005. B21,B22,B23,B24
181	5005	FORMAT (7H0UY= (,E15.7,9H) X + (,E15.7,10H) XY + (,E
182		15.7,19H) Y + (,E15.7,1H))
183		P(N1,JJ)=P(N1,JJ)+(0.5*T)*(B*A11+A*A31+(1./6.)*A*A*A32+(1./6.)
184		1*B*B*A13)
185		P(N2,JJ)=P(N2,JJ)+0.5*T*(A*A21+B*A31+(1./6.)*A*A*A22+(1./6.)*B
186		1*B*A33)
187		P(N3,JJ)=P(N3,JJ)+(0.5*T)*(-B*A11+A*A31-(1./6.)*A*A*A32-(1./6.
188		1)*B*B*A13)
189		P(N4,JJ)=P(N4,JJ)+(0.5*T)*(A*A21-B*A31-(1./6.)*A*A*A22-(1./6.)
190		1*B*B*A33)
191		P(N5,JJ)=P(N5,JJ)+(.5*T)*(-B*A11-A*A31+(1./6.)*A*A*A32+(1./6.)
192		1*B*B*A13)
193		P(N6,JJ)=P(N6,JJ)+(0.5*T)*(-A*A21-B*A31+(1./6.)*A*A*A22+(1./6.
194		1)*B*B*A33)
195		P(N7,JJ)=P(N7,JJ)+(0.5*T)*(B*A11-A*A31-(1./6.)*A*A*A32-(1./6.)*B
196		1*B*A13)
197		P(N8,JJ)=P(N8,JJ)+(0.5*T)*(B*A31-A*A21-(1./6.)*A*A*A22-(1./6.)
198		1*B*B*A33)
199		GO TO 610
200	801	PRINT 802
201	802	FORMAT (29H0STATICS CHECK. THE P MATRIX)
202		DO 803 I=1,NP
203	803	PRINT 409, I,(P(I,J),J=1,NLC)
204	701	GO TO 901
205	1111	STOP
206		END

APPENDIX   H

Plate Bending Analysis

Problem Statement

Write a computer program for the elastic analysis of plates in bending using the rectangular finite element described in Secs. 9.4 to 9.6. Input data includes: (1) the degree of freedom NP, the number of rectangular finite elements NELMT, the number of loading conditions NLC, the modulus of elasticity E, the Poisson's ratio μ, and the plate thickness t; (2) for each element, the 12 global degree of freedom numbers corresponding to the 12 local degree of freedom numbers in Fig. 9.4.1, and the lengths of sides a and b; and (3) the external-force matrix $P(\text{NP} \times \text{NLC})$. Output is to include: (1) at the option of the analyst, the element stiffness matrix of each element, the global stiffness matrix and its inverse; (2) the displacement matrix $X(\text{NP} \times \text{NLC})$; and (3) for each loading condition and for each element, the numerical values of the 12 coefficients in the displacement equation, and the equations for M_x, M_y, and M_{xy} in numerical form in terms of the coordinates x and y referred to the center of the rectangle as origin.

FORTRAN Program

The entire computer program includes a main program and three subroutines named STIFF, STATIC, and INVTRN. The main program reads and prints the input data, calls the subroutine STIFF to build the global stiffness matrix, and then calls the subroutine STATIC to yield the required output. The subroutine STATIC calls on the subroutine INVTRN to invert the global stiffness matrix. Explanations for the main program and the subroutines STIFF and STATIC are made below according to the numbers shown at the head of each statement. For the main program,

1. *Lines 1 and 2.* Dimension and common statements. The degree of freedom NP may be as large as 19; the number of elements NELMT, 4; and the number of loading conditions NLC, 2. The user must modify the dimension statement if these limits are exceeded. The matrix NPM has NELMT rows and 12 columns; it keeps a record of the global degrees of freedom of the elements. The program may be modified to eliminate this matrix; then two data sets for element information would be required, one in Subroutine STIFF and the other in Subroutine STATIC.

2. *Lines 3 and 4.* Read the degree of freedom NP, the number of elements NELMT, the number of loading conditions NLC, the modulus of elasticity E, the Poisson's ratio PR, and the plate thickness T.

3. *Line 5.* Ready for next data set.

4. *Lines 6 and 7.* Print title.

5. *Lines 8 to 16.* Print NP, NELMT, E, PR, and T.

6. *Lines 17 to 30.* Read and print the 12 global degrees of freedom and the sides *a* and *b* of all the finite elements.

7. *Lines 31 to 43.* Zero out the $[P]$ matrix; read the nonzero elements in it; and print the $[P]$ matrix.

8. *Line 44.* Call Subroutine STIFF to build the global stiffness matrix.

9. *Line 45.* Call Subroutine STATIC to yield the desired output.

10. *Line 46.* Go to the next data set.

11. *Lines 47 and 48.* End of main program.

For Subroutine STIFF,

1. *Lines 1 to 4.* Subroutine name, dimension and common statements.

2. *Lines 5 to 8.* Zero out the $[ASA^T]$ matrix. Note the extra row and column for the restraint.

3. *Lines 9 to 11.* Zero out the storage for the element stiffness matrix.

4. *Line 12.* Beginning of the big loop for feeding each element stiffness matrix into the global stiffness matrix.

5. *Lines 13 to 43.* Compute the required quantities T1 to T24 within the element stiffness matrix according to the formulas in Sec. 9.6. Note that $T19 = T20 = T22 = 0$.

6. *Lines 44 to 109.* Fill in the nonzero quantities in the lower triangular matrix of the $[EK]$ matrix.

7. *Lines 110 to 113.* Reflect the lower triangular matrix into the upper triangular matrix.

8. *Lines 114 to 118.* Print the element stiffness matrix. Cards 114 to 117 should be pulled out if such print is not needed.

9. *Lines 119 to 123.* Feed the element stiffness matrix into the global stiffness matrix.

10. *Line 124.* End of the big loop started at Line 12.

11. *Lines 125 to 128.* Print the global stiffness matrix. Pull out these cards if such print is not needed.

12. *Lines 129 and 130.* End of this subroutine.

For Subroutine STATIC,

1. *Lines 1 to 4.* Subroutine name, dimension and common statements.

2. *Line 5.* Call on subroutine INVTRN to invert the global stiffness matrix.

3. *Lines 6 to 10.* Print the inverse of the global stiffness matrix. Pull out cards 6 to 9 if such print is not needed.

4. *Lines 11 to 19.* Compute and print the $[X]$ matrix.

5. *Line 20.* Beginning of outer loop for each successive element.

6. *Lines 21 to 32.* Get the 12 global degree of freedom numbers corresponding to the 12 local degree of freedom numbers.

7. *Lines 33 and 34.* Get the lengths of sides a and b of this element.

8. *Line 35.* Define NPP1 = NP + 1.

9. *Line 36.* Beginning of inner loop for each successive loading condition.

10. *Line 37.* Zero out the displacement at the restraint.

11. *Lines 38 to 49.* Define the 12 quantities such as $X1P4 = X_1$ plus X_4, $X9M12 = X_9$ minus X_{12}, etc.

12. *Lines 50 to 66.* Compute the 12 coefficients α_1 to α_{12} which appear in the displacement equation 9.5.4.

13. *Lines 67 to 78.* Print the displacement equation.

14. *Lines 79 to 93.* Compute the coefficients in the equations for the stress resultants M_x, M_y, and M_{xy}. These equations are

$$M_x = A_{11} + A_{12}x + A_{13}y + A_{14}xy$$
$$M_y = A_{21} + A_{22}x + A_{23}y + A_{24}xy$$
$$M_{xy} = A_{31} + A_{32}x + A_{33}y + A_{34}x^2 + A_{35}y^2$$

in which

$$A_{11} = \frac{EI}{1-\mu^2}(-2\alpha_4 - 2\mu\alpha_6) \qquad A_{21} = \frac{EI}{1-\mu^2}(-2\mu\alpha_4 - 2\alpha_6)$$

$$A_{12} = \frac{EI}{1-\mu^2}(-6\alpha_7 - 2\mu\alpha_9) \qquad A_{22} = \frac{EI}{1-\mu^2}(-6\mu\alpha_7 - 2\alpha_9)$$

$$A_{13} = \frac{EI}{1-\mu^2}(-2\alpha_8 - 6\mu\alpha_{10}) \qquad A_{23} = \frac{EI}{1-\mu^2}(-2\mu\alpha_8 - 6\alpha_{10})$$

$$A_{14} = \frac{EI}{1-\mu^2}(-6\alpha_{11} - 6\mu\alpha_{12}) \qquad A_{24} = \frac{EI}{1-\mu^2}(-6\mu\alpha_{11} - 6\alpha_{12})$$

$$A_{31} = \frac{EI}{2(1+\mu)}(-2\alpha_5)$$

$$A_{32} = \frac{EI}{2(1+\mu)}(-4\alpha_8)$$

$$A_{33} = \frac{EI}{2(1+\mu)}(-4\alpha_9)$$

$$A_{34} = \frac{EI}{2(1+\mu)}(-6\alpha_{11})$$

$$A_{35} = \frac{EI}{2(1+\mu)}(-\alpha_{12})$$

Expressions for the 13 constants shown above have been derived by substituting Eq. 9.5.2 into Eq. 9.2.9.

15. *Lines 94 to 105.* Print the equations for the stress resultants M_x, M_y, and M_{xy}.

16. *Line 106.* End of both inner and outer loops started at Lines 36 and 20.

17. *Lines 107 and 108.* End of this subroutine.

TABLE H.1

Plate Bending Analysis: Main Program

Line No.	Stat. No.	Statement
1		DIMENSION NPM(4,12),A(4),B(4),P(19,2),ASAT(20,20)
2		COMMON NP,NELMT,NPM,A,B,E,PR,T,ASAT,NLC,P
3	10	READ 100, NP,NELMT,NLC,E,PR,T
4	100	FORMAT (3I5,3F10.4)
5		IF (NP) 901,901,101
6	101	PRINT 102
7	102	FORMAT ('1ELASTIC ANALYSIS OF PLATES USING FINITE ELEMENT METHOD.')
8		PRINT 111, NP,NELMT
9	111	FORMAT ('0TOTAL DEGREES OF FREEDOM =',I3,4X,
10		1' TOTAL NOS. OF ELEMENTS =',I3)
11		PRINT 112, E
12	112	FORMAT ('0MODULUS OF ELASTICITY OF PLATE =',E16.8)
13		PRINT 113, PR
14	113	FORMAT ('0POISSON's RATIO OF PLATE =',F6.4)
15		PRINT 114, T
16	114	FORMAT ('0THICKNESS OF PLATE =',F8.4,////)
17		DO 121 I=1,NELMT
18	121	READ 122, (NPM(I,J),J=1,12),A(I),B(I)
19	122	FORMAT (12I4,2F10.4)
20		PRINT 123
21	123	FORMAT ('0NELMT NP1 NP2 NP3 NP4 NP5 NP6 N
22		1 P7 NP8 NP9 NP10 NP11 NP12')
23		DO 124 I=1,NELMT
24	124	PRINT 125, I,(NPM(I,J),J=1,12)
25	125	FORMAT (1H ,10I5,3I6)
26		PRINT 128
27	128	FORMAT (////'0NELMT',5X,1HA,9X,1HB)
28		DO 129 I=1,NELMT
29	129	PRINT 130, I,A(I),B(I)
30	130	FORMAT (I6,2F10.4)
31		DO 201 I=1,NP
32		DO 201 J=1,NLC
33	201	P(I,J)=0.
34	202	READ 203, I,J,PIJ
35	203	FORMAT (2I5,F10.4)
36		IF (I) 205,205,204
37	204	P(I,J)=PIJ
38		GO TO 202
39	205	PRINT 206
40	406	FORMAT ('1THE LOAD MATRIX P')

TABLE H.1 (cont.)

Line No.	Stat. No.	Statement
41		DO 207 I=1,NP
42	207	PRINT 208, I,(P(I,J),J=1,NLC)
43	208	FORMAT (4H ROW,I3,1X,4E16.8/(8X,4E16.8))
44		CALL STIFF
45		CALL STATIC
46		GO TO 10
47	901	STOP
48		END

TABLE H.2

Plate Bending Analysis: Subroutine STIFF

Line No.	Stat. No.	Statement
1		SUBROUTINE STIFF
2		DIMENSION NPM(4,12),A(4),B(4),P(19,2),ASAT(20,20)
3		DIMENSION EK(12,12)
4		COMMON NP,NELMT,NPM,A,B,E,PR,T,ASAT,NLC,P
5		NPP1=NP+1
6		DO 101 I=1,NPP1
7		DO 101 J=1,NPP1
8	101	ASAT(I,J)=0.
9		DO 110 I=1,12
10		DO 110 J=1,12
11	110	EK(I,J)=0.
12		DO 251 II=1,NELMT
13		AI=A(II)
14		BI=B(II)
15		C1=AI/BI
16		C2=1./C1
17		C3=C1*(1.-PR)
18		C4=C2*(1.-PR)
19		C5=(E*T*T*T)/(1.-PR*PR)
20		C6=1.+4.*PR
21		C7=1.-PR
22		C8=14.-4.*PR
23		T1=C5*(C1/9.+C4/45.)
24		T2=C5*(C2/9.+C3/45.)
25		T3=C5*(C1/18.-C4/45.)
26		T4=C5*(C2/18.-C3/45.)

TABLE H.2 (cont.)

Line No.	Stat. No.	Statement
27		T5=C5*(C1/18.-C4/180.)
28		T6=C5*(C2/18.-C3/180.)
29		T7=C5*(C1/36.+C4/180.)
30		T8=C5*(C2/36.+C3/180.)
31		T9=C5*(C1/(6.*BI)+C6/(60.*AI))
32		T10=C5*(C2/(6.*AI)+C6/(60.*BI))
33		T11=C5*(C1/(12.*BI)-C6/(60.*AI))
34		T12=C5*(C2/(12.*AI)-C6/(60.*BI))
35		T13=C5*(C1/(12.*BI)-C7/(60.*AI))
36		T14=C5*(C2/(12.*AI)-C7/(60.*BI))
37		T15=C5*(C1/(6.*BI)+C7/(60.*AI))
38		T16=C5*(C2/(6.*AI)+C7/(60.*BI))
39		T17=C5*(-C2/(3.*AI*AI)+C1/(6.*BI*BI)-C8/(60.*AI*BI))
40		T18=C5*(-C1/(3.*BI*BI)+C2/(6.*AI*AI)-C8/(60.*AI*BI))
41		T21=C5+PR/12.
42		T23=C5*(C2/(3.*AI*AI)+C1/(3.*BI*BI)+C8/(60.*AI*BI))
43		T24=C5*(-C2/(6.*AI*AI)-C1/(6.*BI*BI)+C8/(60.*AI*BI))
44		EK(1,1)=T1
45		EK(2,1)=-T21
46		EK(2,2)=T2
47		EK(3,1)=T9
48		EK(3,2)=-T10
49		EK(3,3)=T23
50		EK(4,1)=T3
51		EK(4,3)=T11
52		EK(4,4)=T1
53		EK(5,2)=T6
54		EK(5,3)=-T16
55		EK(5,4)=T21
56		EK(5,5)=T2
57		EK(6,1)=T11
58		EK(6,2)=T16
59		EK(6,3)=T17
60		EK(6,4)=T9
61		EK(6,5)=T10
62		EK(6,6)=T23
63		EK(7,1)=T7
64		EK(7,3)=T13
65		EK(7,4)=T5
66		EK(7,6)=T15
67		EK(7,7)=T1
68		EK(8,2)=T8
69		EK(8,3)=-T14
70		EK(8,5)=T4
71		EK(8,6)=T12
72		EK(8,7)=-T21

TABLE H.2 (cont.)

Line No.	Stat. No.	Statement
73		EK(8,8)=T2
74		EK(9,1)=−T13
75		EK(9,2)=T14
76		EK(9,3)=T24
77		EK(9,4)=−T15
78		EK(9,5)=T12
79		EK(9,6)=T18
80		EK(9,7)=−T9
81		EK(9,8)=T10
82		EK(9,9)=T23
83		EK(10,1)=T5
84		EK(10,3)=T15
85		EK(10,4)=T7
86		EK(10,6)=T13
87		EK(10,7)=T3
88		EK(10,9)=−T11
89		EK(10,10)=T1
90		EK(11,2)=T4
91		EK(11,3)=−T12
92		EK(11,5)=T8
93		EK(11,6)=T14
94		EK(11,8)=T6
95		EK(11,9)=T16
96		EK(11,10)=T21
97		EK(11,11)=T2
98		EK(12,1)=−T15
99		EK(12,2)=−T12
100		EK(12,3)=T18
101		EK(12,4)=−T13
102		EK(12,5)=−T14
103		EK(12,6)=T24
104		EK(12,7)=−T11
105		EK(12,8)=T16
106		EK(12,9)=T17
107		EK(12,10)=−T9
108		EK(12,11)=−T10
109		EK(12,12)=T23
110		DO 205 I=1,11
111		IP1=I+1
112		DO 205 J=IP1,12
113	205	EK(I,J)=EK(J,I)
114		PRINT 206, II
115	206	FORMAT ('1THE STIFFNESS MATRIX FOR ELEMENT NO.',I3)
116		DO 207 I=1,12

TABLE H.2 (cont.)

Line No.	Stat. No.	Statement
117	207	PRINT 208, I,(EK(I,J),J=1,12)
118	208	FORMAT (4H ROW,I3,1X,4E16.8/(8X,4E16.8))
119		DO 211 I=1,12
120		NS1=NPM(II,I)
121		DO 211 J=1,12
122		NS2=NPM(II,J)
123	211	ASAT(NS1,NS2)=ASAT(NS1,NS2)+EK(I,J)
124	251	CONTINUE
125		PRINT 1001
126	1001	FORMAT ('1THE GLOBAL STIFFNESS MATRIX')
127		DO 1002 I=1,NP
128	1002	PRINT 208, I,(ASAT(I,J),J=1,NP)
129		RETURN
130		END

TABLE H.3

Plate Bending Analysis: Subroutine STATIC

Line No.	Stat. No.	Statement
1		SUBROUTINE STATIC
2		DIMENSION NPM(4,12),A(4),B(4),P(19,2),ASAT(20,20)
3		DIMENSION X(20,2)
4		COMMON NP,NELMT,NPM,A,B,E,PR,T,ASAT,NLC,P
5		CALL INVTRN(ASAT,NP)
6		PRINT 10
7	10	FORMAT ('1THE INVERSE OF GLOBAL ASAT MATRIX')
8		DO 11 I=1,NP
9	11	PRINT 12, I,(ASAT(I,J),J=1,NP)
10	12	FORMAT (4H ROW,I3,1X,4E16.8/(8X,4E16.8))
11		DO 101 I=1,NP
12		DO 101 J=1,NLC
13		X(I,J)=0.
14		DO 101 K=1,NP
15	101	X(I,J)=X(I,J)+ASAT(I,K)*P(K,J)
16		PRINT 102
17	102	FORMAT ('1THE DISPLACEMENT MATRIX')
18		DO 103 I=1,NP
19	103	PRINT 12, I,(X(I,J),J=1,NLC)

TABLE H.3 (cont.)

Line No.	Stat. No.	Statement
20		DO 251 II=1,NELMT
21		N1=NPM(II,1)
22		N2=NPM(II,2)
23		N3=NPM(II,3)
24		N4=NPM(II,4)
25		N5=NPM(II,5)
26		N6=NPM(II,6)
27		N7=NPM(II,7)
28		N8=NPM(II,8)
29		N9=NPM(II,9)
30		N10=NPM(II,10)
31		N11=NPM(II,11)
32		N12=NPM(II,12)
33		AI=A(II)
34		BI=B(II)
35		NPP1=NP+1
36		DO 251 JJ=1,NLC
37		X(NPP1,JJ)=0.
38		X1P4=X(N1,JJ)+X(N4,JJ)
39		X1M4=X(N1,JJ)−X(N4,JJ)
40		X7P10=X(N7,JJ)+X(N10,JJ)
41		X7M10=X(N7,JJ)−X(N10,JJ)
42		X2P5=X(N2,JJ)+X(N5,JJ)
43		X2M5=X(N2,JJ)−X(N5,JJ)
44		X8P11=X(N8,JJ)+X(N11,JJ)
45		X8M11=X(N8,JJ)−X(N11,JJ)
46		X3P6=X(N3,JJ)+X(N6,JJ)
47		X3M6=X(N3,JJ)−X(N6,JJ)
48		X9P12=X(N9,JJ)+X(N12,JJ)
49		X9M12=X(N9,JJ)−X(N12,JJ)
50		ALP1=(BI/16.)*(X1P4−X7P10)+(AI/16.)*(−X2M5+X8M11)+.25* (X3P6+X9P12)
51		ALP2=(BI/(8.*AI))*(X1M4+X7M10)+.125*(−X2P5−X8P11)+(.75/AI)* (X3M6−X
52		19M12)
53		ALP3=.125*(X1P4+X7P10)+(AI/(8.*BI))*(−X2M5−X8M11)+(.75/BI)* (X3P6−X
54		19P12)
55		ALP4=(.25/AI)*(X2M5−X8M11)
56		ALP5=(.25/AI)*(X1M4−X7M10)+(.25/BI)*(X2P5+X8P11)+(2./(AI*BI))* (X3
57		1M6+X9M12)

TABLE H.3 (cont.)

Line No.	Stat. No.	Statement
58		ALP6=(.25/BI)*(−X1P4+X7P10)
59		ALP7=(.5/(AI*AI))*(X2P5+X8P11)+(1./(AI**3))*(−X3M6+X9M12)
60		ALP8=(.5/(AI*BI))*(X2M5+X8M11)
61		ALP9=(0.5/(AI*BI))*(−X1M4−X7M10)
62		ALP10=(.5/(BI*BI))*(−X1P4−X7P10)+(1./(BI**3))*(−X3P6+X9P12)
63		ALP11=(1./(AI*AI*BI))*(X2P5−X8P11)+(2./(AI*AI*AI*BI))*(−X3M6−
		X9M12
64		1)
65		ALP12=(1./(AI*BI*BI))*(−X1M4+X7M10)+(2./(AI*BI*BI*BI))*(−X3M6−
		X9M1
66		12)
67		PRINT 201, II,JJ
68	201	FORMAT (////'0DISPLACEMENT EQUATION FOR ELEMENT NO. ',I3,6X,
69		1' LOADING CONDITION NO.',I3)
70		PRINT 202, ALP1,ALP2,ALP3,ALP4
71	202	FORMAT (1H0,E15.8,4H + (,E15.8,8H) X + (,E15.8,8H) Y + (, E15.8,
72		17H) X**2)
73		PRINT 203, ALP5,ALP6,ALP7,ALP8
74	203	FORMAT (4H0+ (,E15.8,10H) X*Y + (,E15.8,11H) Y**2 + (, E15.8,11
75		1H) X**3 + (,E15.8,8H) X*X*Y)
76		PRINT 204, ALP9,ALP10,ALP11,ALP12
77	204	FORMAT (4H0+ (,E15.8,12H) X*Y*Y + (,E15.8,11H) Y**3 + (, E15.8
78		1,14H) X*X*X*Y + (,E15.8,10H) X*Y*Y*Y)
79		CC=(E*T*T*T)/(12.*(1.−PR*PR))
80		A11=CC*(−2.*ALP4−2.*PR*ALP6)
81		A12=CC*(−6.*ALP7−2.*PR*ALP9)
82		A13=CC*(−2.*ALP8−6.*PR*ALP10)
83		A14=CC*(−6.*ALP11−6.*PR*ALP12)
84		A21=CC*(−2.*PR*ALP4−2.*ALP6)
85		A22=CC*(−6.*PR*ALP7−2.*ALP9)
86		A23=CC*(−2.*PR*ALP8−6.*ALP10)
87		A24=CC*(−6.*PR*ALP11−6.*ALP12)
88		CCC=(E*T*T*T)/(24.*(1.+PR))
89		A31=−2.*ALP5*CCC
90		A32=−4.*ALP8*CCC
91		A33=−4.*ALP9*CCC
92		A34=−6.*ALP11*CCC
93		A35=−6.*ALP12*CCC
94		PRINT 301, II,JJ
95	301	FORMAT ('0EQUATION FOR MOMENTS FOR ELEMENT NO.',I3,6X,

TABLE H.3 (cont.)

Line No.	Stat. No.	Statement
96		1' LOADING CONDITION NO.',I3)
97		PRINT 302, A11,A12,A13,A14
98	302	FORMAT (5H0MX =,E15.8,4H + (,E15.8,8H) X + (,E15.8,8H) Y + (
99		1,E15.8,6H) X*Y)
100		PRINT 303, A21,A22,A23,A24
101	303	FORMAT (5H0MY =,E15.8,4H + (,E15.8,8H) X + (,E15.8,8H) Y + (
102		1,E15.8,6H) X*Y)
103		PRINT 304, A31,A32,A33,A34,A35
104	304	FORMAT (6H0MXY =,E15.8,4H + (,E15.8,8H) X + (,E15.8,8H) Y + (
105		1,E15.8,10H) X*X + (,E15.8,6H) Y*Y)
106	251	CONTINUE
107		RETURN
108		END

TABLE H.4

Plate Bending Analysis: Subroutine INVTRN

Line No.	Stat. No.	Statement
1		SUBROUTINE INVTRN (ASAT,NP)
2		DIMENSION ASAT(20,20),INDEX(19)
3		DO 113 I=1,NP
4	113	INDEX(I)=0
5	114	AMAX=-1.
6		DO 115 I=1,NP
7		IF (INDEX(I)) 115,116,115
8	116	TEMP=ABS(ASAT(I,I))
9		IF (TEMP-AMAX) 115,115,117
10	117	ICOL=I
11		AMAX=TEMP
12	115	CONTINUE
13		IF (AMAX) 118,124,119
14	119	INDEX(ICOL)=1
15		PIVOT=ASAT(ICOL,ICOL)
16		ASAT(ICOL,ICOL)=1.0
17		PIVOT=1./PIVOT
18		DO 120 J=1,NP
19	120	ASAT(ICOL,J)=ASAT(ICOL,J)*PIVOT
20		DO 121 I=1,NP
21		IF (I-ICOL) 122,121,122
22	122	TEMP=ASAT(I,ICOL)
23		ASAT(I,ICOL)=0.0
24		DO 123 J=1,NP

TABLE H.4 (cont.)

Line No.	Stat. No.	Statement
25	123	ASAT(I,J)=ASAT(I,J)−ASAT(ICOL,J)*TEMP
26	121	CONTINUE
27		GO TO 114
28	124	PRINT 125
29	125	FORMAT (14H0PIVOT IS ZERO)
30		STOP
31	118	CONTINUE
32		RETURN
33		END

APPENDIX I

■

Minimizing a Linear Function by Simplex Method

Problem Statement

Given the first matrix form of a minimization problem as described in Sec. 10.6, make as many Gauss-Jordan substitutions as needed, to arrive at a conclusion whether the solution is trivial, indeterminate, infeasible, or successful. For each substitution, print the pivot location, the reduced matrix form, the values of the N design variables, and the M slack variables, and the merit function. Make the dimension statement so that N and M may be as large as 4 and 8, respectively. Also, as a safety measure, limit the maximum number of Gauss-Jordan substitutions to 20.

FORTRAN Program

The FORTRAN program for minimizing a linear function by the simplex method beginning with the first matrix form as described in Sec. 10.6 is shown in Table I.1. Regarding the program, the following explanatory notes are made.

1. *Line 1.* Dimension statement is for $N = 4$ and $M = 8$.

2. *Lines 2 to 4.* Program may be used to solve as many data sets as provided.

3. *Lines 5 to 10.* Read N, M, and A $(M + 1, N + M + 1)$.

4. *Lines 11 and 12.* Print title.

5. *Line 13.* Initialize the number of Gauss-Jordan substitutions NSUB to zero.

6. *Lines 14 to 18.* Print the first matrix form.

7. *Lines 19 and 20.* Initialize the values of the N design variables.

8. *Lines 21 to 25.* Equate the slack variables to the values in the last column of the first matrix form.

9. *Lines 26 to 29.* Print the initial $(N + M)$ values of x.

10. *Lines 30 to 35.* Initialize all values of NIN(1) to NIN(M) and of INDEX(1) to INDEX(N+M).

11. *Line 36.* As a safety measure, limit NSUB to 20. Note that the number 20 may be changed to suit a particular problem.

12. *Lines 37 to 39.* Find out if all values in the first M rows of the last column are nonnegative.

13. *Line 40.* If the answer to Lines 37 to 39 is yes, and if no substitution has yet been made, solution is TRIVIAL and stop.

14. *Lines 41 to 44.* If the answer to Lines 37 to 39 is yes, and if at least one substitution has been made, and if some value of A $(M + 1, J)$ where INDEX(J) = 1 is zero, solution is INDETERMINATE and stop.

15. *Line 45.* If the answer to Lines 37 to 39 is yes, if at least one substitution has been made, and if none of the values A $(M + 1, J)$ where INDEX(J)=1 is zero, solution is SUCCESSFUL and stop.

16. *Line 46.* When Line 38 indicates that there is at least one negative value in the first M rows of the last column, the search for the best eligible pivot begins here.

17. *Lines 47 to 50.* Search for a positive A (MP1, J) when INDEX (J)=1.

18. *Lines 51 to 60.* Search for the pivot in this particular column to give the minimum increase in the merit function. This increase is equal to TEMP3.

19. *Line 61.* Complete search for the best pivot in all eligible columns with a positive A (MP1, J).

20. *Line 62.* If there is no eligible pivot, solution is INFEASIBLE and stop.

21. *Line 63.* Begin the process of Gauss-Jordan substitution.

22. *Lines 64 to 68.* Check with the tabulated effects of the reduction in Sec. 10.8.

23. *Lines 69 to 80.* The Gauss-Jordan substitution is actually carried out.

24. *Lines 81 to 83.* Enter the newly found values of x.

25. *Line 84.* Enter the new merit function.

26. *Lines 85 to 93.* Print IROW, ICOL, NSUB, $[A]$, $\{X\}$, and z.

27. *Line 94.* Go to Line 36 or Statement 501.

28. *Lines 95 to 106.* Print the conclusive remark and the total number of substitutions made.

29. *Lines 107 and 108.* End of program.

Discussion

A close examination of the intermediate matrix form and its new form subsequent to a Gauss-Jordan substitution, as shown in Sec. 10.7, reveals that there are M columns in either form containing nothing else but the quantities zero or one. This is a waste of storage space.

Similar to the technique employed in matrix inversion where the inverse takes the place of the original matrix without need of installing an extra panel of unit matrix at the outset, it is possible to work through the simplex algorithm within the storage of $(M + 1)$ rows by $(N + 1)$ columns. This would require the use of the INDEX(J) array, for $J = 1$ to $J = N$, to record the nonzero design or slack variables. For instance, for the intermediate matrix form in Sec. 10.7, INDEX(1) and INDEX(2) would be equal to 2 and 3; but they would become 2 (unchanged) and 5 after the reduction.

This more sophisticated version of Table I.1 is shown in Table I.2. Note the following corrections which are required to change Table I.1 to Table I.2.

1. Change the $A\,(9,13)$ and INDEX(12) in Line 1 to $A\,(9,5)$ and INDEX(4), because there are now only $(N + 1)$ columns in the A matrix and only N columns in the $(M + 1)$th row before the $(-z)$ value.
2. Change Line 8 from NPMP1 $= N + M + 1$ to NP1 $= N + 1$ because $(N + M + 1)$ is no longer needed.
3. Change the NPMP1 in Lines 9, 17, 25, 38, 53, 70, 76, 83, 84, and 89 to NP1.
4. Delete Lines 21, 34, 35, 42, 48, 68, 77, and 79.
5. Change the NPMP1 in Line 32 and the NPM in Line 41 to N.
6. Change the 1 in Line 33 to I.
7. Delete the statement number 227 in Line 43.
8. Change the NPM in Line 47 to N.
9. Delete the statement number 305 in Line 49.
10. Change Line 66 from NIN(IROW) = ICOL to NIN(IROW) = INDEX(ICOL).

11. Change Line 67 from INDEX(ICOL) = 0 to INDEX(ICOL) = NTEMP.
12. Add A(IROW, ICOL) = 1.0 between Lines 69 and 70.
13. Change the statement number in Line 78 from 327 to 326.

A still more sophisticated version of Table I.2 is shown in Table I.3. It is found that the number of Gauss-Jordan substitutions is smaller when Table I.3 is used instead of Table I.2. For instance, only 4, instead of 12, substitutions are needed to arrive at the same conclusion for the linear programming problem in Example 11.5.1 in Chapter 11.

The reason for the reduction of substitution numbers is that, in Table I.2, the pivot is selected each time on the basis of raising the merit function the least amount, but in Table I.3 the pivot is selected each time on the basis of raising the merit function the most amount, so long as there is assurance that the minimum merit function is not passed over. This assurance is secured by making sure that the cost factors—e.g., the quantities in the locations (4,2) and (4,5) in the matrix table of Sec. 10.8—are all positive before a pivot is accepted for use. The last equation in this matrix table reads:

$$0. * X_1 + A'(4,2) * X_2 + 0. * X_3 + 0. * X_4 + A'(4,5) * X_5 = z - A'(4,6)$$

When $A'(4,2)$ and $A'(4,5)$ are positive, and since X_2 and X_5 are to be positive in the final solution, the minimum merit function z has not passed over the quantity $A'(4,6)$.

Thus the only difference between Table I.2 and Table I.3 is in the pivot selection. Lines 1 to 41 of Table I.3 are the same as Lines 1 to 41 of Table I.2. Only Lines 42 to 57 of Table I.2 have been changed to Lines 42 to 58 of Table I.3. Lines 59 to 102 of Table I.3 are again the same as Lines 58 to 101 of Table I.2.

TABLE I.1

Minimizing A Linear Function By Simplex Method

Line No.	Stat. No.	Statement
1		DIMENSION A(9,13),X(12),NIN(8),INDEX(12)
2	1	READ 2, NDATA
3	2	FORMAT (I5)
4		IF (NDATA) 4,4,3
5	3	READ 101, N,M
6	101	FORMAT (2I5)
7		MP1=M+1
8		NPMP1=N+M+1

TABLE I.1 (cont.)

Line No.	Stat. No.	Statement
9		READ 102, ((A(I,J),J=1,NPMP1),I=1,MP1)
10	102	FORMAT (5F10.4)
11		PRINT 201
12	201	FORMAT (31H1FIND MINIMUM VALUE OF FUNCTION/)
13		NSUB=0
14		PRINT 202, NSUB
15	202	FORMAT (20H0THE MATRIX A NSUB=,I3/)
16		DO 203 I=1,MP1
17	203	PRINT 204, I,(A(I,J),J=1,NPMP1)
18	204	FORMAT (4H ROW,I3,1X,7E16.8/(8X,7E16.8))
19		DO 205 I=1,N
20	205	X(I)=0.
21		NP1=N+1
22		NPM=N+M
23		DO 206 I=NP1,NPM
24		II=I−N
25	206	X(I)=A(II,NPMP1)
26		PRINT 207
27	207	FORMAT (16H0THE VALUES OF X/)
28		PRINT 208, (I,X(I),I=1,NPM)
29	208	FORMAT (5(5X,I3,E16.8))
30		DO 209 I=1,M
31	209	NIN(I)=N+I
32		DO 210 I=1,NPM
33	210	INDEX(I)=1
34		DO 211 I=NP1,NPM
35	211	INDEX(I)=0
36	501	IF (NSUB−20) 502,502,1
37	502	DO 215 I=1,M
38		IF (A(I,NPMP1)) 216,215,215
39	215	CONTINUE
40		IF (NSUB−1) 701,217,217
41	217	DO 225 J=1,NPM
42		IF (INDEX(J)) 227,225,227
43	227	IF (A(MP1,J)) 225,711,225
44	225	CONTINUE
45		GO TO 721
46	216	AMIN=1.0E08
47		DO 302 J=1,NPM

TABLE I.1 (cont.)

Line No.	Stat. No.	Statement
48		IF (INDEX(J)) 305,302,305
49	305	IF (A(MP1,J)) 302,306,306
50	306	TEMP1=A(MP1,J)
51		DO 313 I=1,M
52		IF (A(I,J)) 307,313,313
53	307	TEMP2=A(I,NPMP1)/A(I,J)
54		IF (TEMP2) 313,313,314
55	314	TEMP3=TEMP1*TEMP2
56		IF (TEMP3−AMIN) 315,313,313
57	315	ICOL=J
58		IROW=I
59		AMIN=TEMP3
60	313	CONTINUE
61	302	CONTINUE
62		IF (AMIN −1.0E07) 317,317,731
63	317	NSUB=NSUB+1
64		NTEMP=NIN(IROW)
65		X(NTEMP)=0.
66		NIN(IROW)=ICOL
67		INDEX(ICOL)=0
68		INDEX(NTEMP)=1
69		PIVOT=1./A(IROW,ICOL)
70		DO 322 J=1,NPMP1
71	322	A(IROW,J)=A(IROW,J)*PIVOT
72		DO 323 I=1,MP1
73		IF (I−IROW) 325,323,325
74	325	TEMP=A(I,ICOL)
75		A(I,ICOL)=0.
76		DO 326 J=1,NPMP1
77		IF (INDEX(J)) 327,326,327
78	327	A(I,J)=A(I,J)−A(IROW,J)*TEMP
79	326	CONTINUE
80	323	CONTINUE
81		DO 331 I=1,M
82		NTEMP=NIN(I)
83	331	X(NTEMP)=A(I,NPMP1)
84		Z=−A(MP1,NPMP1)
85		PRINT 401, IROW,ICOL
86	401	FORMAT (9H0PIVOT AT,5X,5HIROW=,I3,5X,5HICOL=,I3/)
87		PRINT 202, NSUB
88		DO 402 I=1,MP1
89	402	PRINT 204, I,(A(I,J),J=1,NPMP1)

TABLE I.1 (cont.)

Line No.	Stat. No.	Statement
90		PRINT 207
91		PRINT 208, (I,X(I),I=1,NPM)
92		PRINT 403, Z
93	403	FORMAT (20H0VALUE OF FUNCTION =,E16.8/)
94		GO TO 501
95	701	PRINT 702, NSUB
96	702	FORMAT (27H0SOLUTION IS TRIVIAL NSUB=,13)
97		GO TO 1
98	711	PRINT 712, NSUB
99	712	FORMAT (33H0SOLUTION IS INDETERMINATE NSUB=,13)
100		GO TO 1
101	721	PRINT 722, NSUB
102	722	FORMAT (30H0SOLUTION IS SUCCESSFUL NSUB=,13)
103		GO TO 1
104	731	PRINT 732, NSUB
105	732	FORMAT (28H0NO FEASIBLE SOLUTION NSUB=,13)
106		GO TO 1
107	4	STOP
108		END

TABLE I.2

Minimizing a Linear Function by Simplex Method

Line No.	Stat. No.	Statement
1		DIMENSION A(9,5),X(12),NIN(8),INDEX(4)
2	1	READ 2, NDATA
3	2	FORMAT (I5)
4		IF (NDATA) 4,4,3
5	3	READ 101, N,M
6	101	FORMAT (2I5)
7		MP1=M+1
8		NP1=N+1
9		READ 102, ((A(I,J),J=1,NP1),I=1,MP1)
10	102	FORMAT (5F10.4)
11		PRINT 201
12	201	FORMAT (31H1FIND MINIMUM VALUE OF FUNCTION/)
13		NSUB=0
14		PRINT 202, NSUB
15	202	FORMAT (20H0THE MATRIX A NSUB=,13/)

TABLE I.2 (cont.)

Line No.	Stat. No.	Statement
16		DO 203 I=1,MP1
17	203	PRINT 204, I,(A(I,J),J=1,NP1)
18	204	FORMAT (4H ROW,I3,1X,7E16.8/(8X,7E16.8))
19		DO 205 I=1,N
20	205	X(I)=0.
21		NPM=N+M
22		DO 206 I=NP1,NPM
23		II=I−N
24	206	X(I)=A(II,NP1)
25		PRINT 207
26	207	FORMAT (16H0THE VALUES OF X/)
27		PRINT 208, (I,X(I),I=1,NPM)
28	208	FORMAT (5(5X,I3,E16.8))
29		DO 209 I=1,M
30	209	NIN(I)=N+I
31		DO 210 I=1,N
32	210	INDEX(I)=I
33	501	IF (NSUB−20) 502,502,1
34	502	DO 215 I=1,M
35		IF (A(I,NP1)) 216,215,215
36	215	CONTINUE
37		IF (NSUB−1) 701,217,217
38	217	DO 225 J=1,N
39		IF (A(MP1,J)) 225,711,225
40	225	CONTINUE
41		GO TO 721
42	216	AMIN=1.0E08
43		DO 302 J=1,N
44		IF (A(MP1,J)) 302,306,306
45	306	TEMP1=A(MP1,J)
46		DO 313 I=1,M
47		IF (A(I,J)) 307,313,313
48	307	TEMP2=A(I,NP1)/A(I,J)
49		IF (TEMP2) 313,313,314
50	314	TEMP3=TEMP1*TEMP2
51		IF (TEMP3−AMIN) 315,313,313
52	315	ICOL=J
53		IROW=I
54		AMIN=TEMP3
55	313	CONTINUE

TABLE I.2 (cont.)

Line No.	Stat. No.	Statement
56	302	CONTINUE
57		IF (AMIN−1.0E07) 317,317,731
58	317	NSUB=NSUB+1
59		NTEMP=NIN(IROW)
60		X(NTEMP)=0.
61		NIN(IROW)=INDEX(ICOL)
62		INDEX(ICOL)=NTEMP
63		PIVOT=1./A(IROW,ICOL)
64		A(IROW,ICOL)=1.0
65		DO 322 J=1,NP1
66	322	A(IROW,J)=A(IROW,J)*PIVOT
67		DO 323 I=1,MP1
68		IF (I−IROW) 325,323,325
69	325	TEMP=A(I,ICOL)
70		A(I,ICOL)=0.
71		DO 326 J=1,NP1
72	326	A(I,J)=A(I,J)−A(IROW,J)*TEMP
73	323	CONTINUE
74		DO 331 I=1,M
75		NTEMP=NIN(I)
76	331	X(NTEMP)=A(I,NP1)
77		Z=−A(MP1,NP1)
78		PRINT 401, IROW,ICOL
79	401	FORMAT (9H0PIVOT AT,5X,5HIROW=,I3,5X,5HICOL=,I3/)
80		PRINT 202, NSUB
81		DO 402 I=1,MP1
82	402	PRINT 204, I,(A(I,J),J=1,NP1)
83		PRINT 207
84		PRINT 208, (I,X(I),I=1,NPM)
85		PRINT 403, Z
86	403	FORMAT (20H0VALUE OF FUNCTION =,E16.8/)
87		GO TO 501
88	701	PRINT 702, NSUB
89	702	FORMAT (27H0SOLUTION IS TRIVIAL NSUB=,I3)
90		GO TO 1
91	711	PRINT 712, NSUB
92	712	FORMAT (33H0SOLUTION IS INDETERMINATE NSUB=,I3)
93		GO TO 1
94	721	PRINT 722, NSUB
95	722	FORMAT (30H0SOLUTION IS SUCCESSFUL NSUB=,I3)
96		GO TO 1

TABLE I.2 (cont.)

Line No.	Stat. No.	Statement
97	731	PRINT 732, NSUB
98	732	FORMAT (28H0NO FEASIBLE SOLUTION NSUB=,I3)
99		GO TO 1
100	4	STOP
101		END

TABLE I.3
Minimizing a Linear Function by Simplex Method

Line No.	Stat. No.	Statement
1		DIMENSION A(9,5),X(12),NIN(8),INDEX(4)
2	1	READ 2, NDATA
3	2	FORMAT (I5)
4		IF (NDATA) 4,4,3
5	3	READ 101, N,M
6	101	FORMAT (2I5)
7		MP1=M+1
8		NP1=N+1
9		READ 102, ((A(I,J),J=1,NP1),I=1,MP1)
10	102	FORMAT (5F10.4)
11		PRINT 201
12	201	FORMAT (31H1FIND MINIMUM VALUE OF FUNCTION/)
13		NSUB=0
14		PRINT 202, NSUB
15	202	FORMAT (20H0THE MATRIX A NSUB=,I3/)
16		DO 203 I=1,MP1
17	203	PRINT 204, I,(A(I,J),J=1,NP1)
18	204	FORMAT (4H ROW,I3,1X,7E16.8/(8X,7E16.8))
19		DO 205 I=1,N
20	205	X(I)=0.
21		NPM=N+M
22		DO 206 I=NP1,NPM
23		II=I-N
24	206	X(I)=A(II,NP1)
25		PRINT 207
26	207	FORMAT (16H0THE VALUES OF X/)
27		PRINT 208, (I,X(I),I=1,NPM)
28	208	FORMAT (5(5X,I3,E16.8))

TABLE I.3 (cont.)

Line No.	Stat. No.	Statement
29		DO 209 I=1,M
30	209	NIN(I)=N+I
31		DO 210 I=1,N
32	210	INDEX(I)=I
33	501	IF (NSUB-20) 502,502,1
34	502	DO 215 I=1,M
35		IF (A(I,NP1)) 216,215,215
36	215	CONTINUE
37		IF (NSUB-1) 701,217,217
38	217	DO 225 J=1,N
39		IF (A(MP1,J)) 225,711,225
40	225	CONTINUE
41		GO TO 721
42	216	AMAX=-1.0
43		DO 302 I=1,M
44		DO 302 J=1,N
45		IF (A(I,J)) 303,302,302
46	303	IF (A(I,NP1)) 304,304,302
47	304	TEMP1=A(MP1,)*A(I,NP1)/A(I,J)
48		IF (TEMP1-AMAX) 302,302,305
49	305	DO 306 K=1,N
50		IF (J-K) 307,306,307
51	307	TEMP2=A(MP1,K)-A(MP1,J)*A(I,K)/A(I,J)
52		IF (TEMP2) 302,306,306
53	306	CONTINUE
54		IROW=I
55		ICOL=J
56		AMAX=TEMP1
57	302	CONTINUE
58		IF (AMAX) 731,317,317
59	317	NSUB=NSUB+1
60		NTEMP=NIN(IROW)
61		X(NTEMP)=0.
62		NIN(IROW)=INDEX(ICOL)
63		INDEX(ICOL)=NTEMP
64		PIVOT=1./A(IROW,ICOL)
65		A(IROW,ICOL)=1.0
66		DO 322 J=1,NP1
67	322	A(IROW,J)=A(IROW,J)*PIVOT
68		DO 323 I=1,MP1
69		IF (I-IROW) 325,323,325

TABLE I.3 (cont.)

Line No.	Stat. No.	Statement
70	325	TEMP=A(I,ICOL)
71		A(I,ICOL)=0.
72		DO 326 J=1,NP1
73	326	A(I,J)=A(I,J)-A(IROW,J)*TEMP
74	323	CONTINUE
75		DO 331 I=1,M
76		NTEMP=NIN(I)
77	331	X(NTEMP)=A(I,NP1)
78		Z=-A(MP1,NP1)
79		PRINT 401, IROW,ICOL
80	401	FORMAT (9H0PIVOT AT,5X,5HIROW=,I3,5X,5HICOL=,I3/)
81		PRINT 202, NSUB
82		DO 402 I=1,MP1
83	402	PRINT 204, I,(A(I,J),J=1,NP1)
84		PRINT 207
85		PRINT 208, (I,X(I),I=1,NPM)
86		PRINT 403, Z
87	403	FORMAT (20H0VALUE OF FUNCTION =,E16.8/)
88		GO TO 501
89	701	PRINT 702, NSUB
90	702	FORMAT (27H0SOLUTION IS TRIVIAL NSUB=,I3)
91		GO TO 1
92	711	PRINT 712, NSUB
93	712	FORMAT (33H0SOLUTION IS INDETERMINATE NSUB=,I3)
94		GO TO 1
95	721	PRINT 722, NSUB
96	722	FORMAT (30H0SOLUTION IS SUCCESSFUL NSUB=,I3)
97		GO TO 1
98	731	PRINT 732, NSUB
99	732	FORMAT (28H0NO FEASIBLE SOLUTION NSUB=,I3)
100		GO TO 1
101	4	STOP
102		END

APPENDIX J

■

Coefficients in Minimum Truss Weight Equations

Problem Statement

Let NP be the degree of freedom of a truss; NF be the number of members; and NLC be the number of loading conditions. Given information for each member includes the global degrees of freedom NP1 to NP4 at the initial and terminal points, the coordinates H and V of the terminal point referred to the initial point as origin, the modulus of elasticity E, and the cross-sectional area A. Also given is the external-force matrix P(NPXNLC). Compute (1) the member forces in order of loading conditions, and (2) the approximate changes in the member forces in order of loading conditions due to each successive increase in the magnitude of the member area to twice its original value.

Analysis

The formula for the approximate changes in the member forces due to each successive increase in the magnitude of the member area may be stated as

$$[\Delta F] = [(\Delta S)A^T - SA^T K^{-1} A (\Delta S) A^T][X]$$

Let $\Delta F(i, j, k)$ be the increase in force in the ith bar in the jth loading condition due to a 100 percent increase in the kth bar area. Using the notations

$$SCI, SCK = EA \cos \alpha/L \text{ of the } i\text{th or } k\text{th bar}$$
$$SSI, SSK = EA \sin \alpha/L \text{ of the } i\text{th or } k\text{th bar}$$
$$T1K = EA \cos^2 \alpha/L \text{ of the } k\text{th bar}$$
$$T2K = EA \sin \alpha \cos \alpha/L \text{ of the } k\text{th bar}$$
$$T3K = EA \sin^2 \alpha/L \text{ of the } k\text{th bar}$$
$$i1, i2, i3, i4 = \text{local degrees of freedom of } i\text{th bar}$$
$$k1, k2, k3, k4 = \text{local degrees of freedom of } k\text{th bar}$$
$$\delta(i, j) = \text{element in the } [K^{-1}] \text{ matrix}$$

$\Delta F(i, j, k)$ may be expressed as

$$\Delta F(i, j, k) = \left[\begin{array}{|c|c|c|c|} \hline -SCK & -SSK & +SCK & +SSK \\ \hline \end{array} \right.$$

(only if $i = k$; zero otherwise)

$$-\begin{array}{|c|c|c|c|} \hline -SCI & -SSI & +SCI & +SSI \\ \hline \end{array}$$

$*$

$\delta(i1, k2)$	$\delta(i1, k2)$	$\delta(i1, k3)$	$\delta(i1, k4)$
$\delta(i2, k2)$	$\delta(i2, k2)$	$\delta(i2, k3)$	$\delta(i2, k4)$
$\delta(i3, k1)$	$\delta(i3, k2)$	$\delta(i3, k3)$	$\delta(i3, k4)$
$\delta(i4, k1)$	$\delta(i4, k2)$	$\delta(i4, k3)$	$\delta(i4, k4)$

$*$

$+T1K$	$+T2K$	$-T1K$	$-T2K$
$+T2K$	$+T3K$	$-T2K$	$-T3K$
$-T1K$	$-T2K$	$+T1K$	$+T2K$
$-T2K$	$-T3K$	$+T2K$	$+T3K$

$*$

$X(k1, j)$
$X(k2, j)$
$X(k3, j)$
$X(k4, j)$

$$= \left[\begin{array}{|c|c|c|c|} \hline -SCK & -SSK & +SCK & +SSK \\ \hline \end{array} - \begin{array}{|c|c|c|c|} \hline A1 & B1 & C1 & D1 \\ \hline \end{array} \right.$$

$$
\ast
\begin{bmatrix}
+T1K & +T2K & -T1K & -T2K \\
+T2K & +T3K & -T2K & -T3K \\
-T1K & -T2K & +T1K & +T2K \\
-T2K & -T3K & +T2K & +T3K
\end{bmatrix}
\ast
\begin{bmatrix}
X(k1,j) \\
X(k2,j) \\
X(k3,j) \\
X(k4,j)
\end{bmatrix}
$$

$$
= \begin{bmatrix} -E1 & -F1 & +E1 & +F1 \end{bmatrix}
\ast
\begin{bmatrix}
X(k1,j) \\
X(k2,j) \\
X(k3,j) \\
X(k4,j)
\end{bmatrix}
$$

in which

$$A1 = SCI\,[\delta\,(i3,k1) - \delta\,(i1,k1)] + SSI\,[\delta\,(i4,k1) - \delta\,(i2,k1)]$$
$$B1 = SCI\,[\delta\,(i3,k2) - \delta\,(i1,k2)] + SSI\,[\delta\,(i4,k2) - \delta\,(i2,k2)]$$
$$C1 = SCI\,[\delta\,(i3,k3) - \delta\,(i1,k3)] + SSI\,[\delta\,(i4,k3) - \delta\,(i2,k3)]$$
$$D1 = SCI\,[\delta\,(i3,k4) - \delta\,(i1,k4)] + SSI\,[\delta\,(i4,k4) - \delta\,(i2,k4)]$$
$$E1 = (A1 - C1)\,T1K + (B1 - D1)\,T2K + SCK \;(\text{only if } i = k)$$
$$F1 = (A1 - C1)\,T2K + (B1 - D1)\,T3K + SSK \;(\text{only if } i = k)$$

In the computer program the given truss is first analyzed by the direct element method, yielding the member forces themselves in the order of loading conditions. Then the $[\Delta F]$ matrices in the order of NF by NLC, first due to 100 percent increase in the cross-sectional area of member No. 1, then No. 2, etc., are computed.

FORTRAN Program

Regarding the computer program shown in Table J the following explanatory notes may be made.

1. *Lines 1 and 2.* Dimension statements. NP may be as large as 15; NF, 20; and NLC, 6. Note that the member data is stored in memory.

2. *Lines 3 and 4.* Read the degree of freedom NP, the number of members NF, and the number of loading conditions NLC.

3. *Lines 5 and 6.* Read the modulus of elasticity E.

4. *Lines 7 to 10.* Zero out the entire $[ASA^T]$ matrix. Note the additional $(NP + 1)$th row and column.

5. *Lines 11 to 15.* Print title and heading for member information.

6. *Lines 16 to 46.* Feed the contribution of each member to the global $[ASA^T]$ matrix.

7. *Lines 47 to 71.* Invert the $[ASA^T]$ matrix.

8. *Lines 72 to 76.* Print the $[ASA^T]^{-1}$ matrix.

9. *Lines 77 to 79.* Zero out the $[P]$ matrix.

10. *Lines 80 to 84.* Read the nonzero elements in the $[P]$ matrix.

11. *Lines 85 to 88.* Print the $[P]$ matrix.

12. *Lines 89 to 93.* Compute $[X]$ from $[X] = [ASA^T]^{-1} [P]$.

13. *Lines 94 to 97.* Print the $[X]$ matrix.

14. *Lines 98 and 99.* Print heading for member forces.

15. *Lines 100 and 101.* Zero out the $(NP + 1)$th displacement in all loading conditions.

16. *Lines 102 to 113.* Compute and print member forces.

17. *Lines 114 to 119.* Print heading for changes in member forces.

18. *Lines 120 to 122.* Zero out the $(NP + 1)$th row and the $(NP + 1)$th column of the $[K^{-1}] = [ASA^T]^{-1}$ matrix.

19. *Lines 123 to 159.* The changes in the member forces for all loading conditions are computed and printed, first for 100 percent increase in area of member No. 1, then member No. 2, etc.

20. *Lines 160 and 161.* End of program.

TABLE J
Coefficients in Minimum Truss Weight Equations

Line No.	Stat. No.	Statement
1		DIMENSION ASAT(16,16),P(15,6),X(16,6),F(6),INDEX(15),DELF(6)
2		DIMENSION NP1(20),NP2(20),NP3(20),NP4(20),H(20),V(20),A(20)
3		READ 101, NP,NF,NLC
4	101	FORMAT (3I5)
5		READ 102, E
6	102	FORMAT (F10.4)
7		NPP1=NP+1
8		DO 103 I=1,NPP1
9		DO 103 J=1,NPP1
10	103	ASAT(I,J)=0.
11		PRINT 104

TABLE J (cont.)

Line No.	Stat. No.	Statement
12	104	FORMAT (47H1COEFFICIENTS IN MINIMUM TRUSS WEIGHT EQUATIONS//)
13		PRINT 105
14	105	FORMAT (27H0MEMBER NP1 NP2 NP3 NP4,7X,1HH,11X,1HV,11X, 1HA,
15		111X,1HL,11X,3HCOS,12X,3HSIN/)
16		DO 108 I=1,NF
17		READ 106, I,NP1(I),NP2(I),NP3(I),NP4(I),H(I),V(I),A(I)
18	106	FORMAT (5I5,3F10.4)
19		I1=NP1(I)
20		I2=NP2(I)
21		I3=NP3(I)
22		I4=NP4(I)
23		XL=SQRTF(H(I)*H(I)+V(I)*V(I))
24		CS=H(I)/XL
25		SN=V(I)/XL
26		PRINT 107, I,I1,I2,I3,I4,H(I),V(I),A(I),XL,CS,SN
27	107	FORMAT (1H0,I5,I6,3I5,4F12.4,2F15.8)
28		T1=E*A(I)*CS*CS/XL
29		T2=E*A(I)*CS*SN/XL
30		T3=E*A(I)*SN*SN/XL
31		ASAT(I1,I1)=ASAT(I1,I1)+T1
32		ASAT(I1,I2)=ASAT(I1,I2)+T2
33		ASAT(I1,I3)=ASAT(I1,I3)−T1
34		ASAT(I1,I4)=ASAT(I1,I4)−T2
35		ASAT(I2,I1)=ASAT(I2,I1)+T2
36		ASAT(I2,I2)=ASAT(I2,I2)+T3
37		ASAT(I2,I3)=ASAT(I2,I3)−T2
38		ASAT(I2,I4)=ASAT(I2,I4)−T3
39		ASAT(I3,I1)=ASAT(I3,I1)−T1
40		ASAT(I3,I2)=ASAT(I3,I2)−T2
41		ASAT(I3,I3)=ASAT(I3,I3)+T1
42		ASAT(I3,I4)=ASAT(I3,I4)+T2
43		ASAT(I4,I1)=ASAT(I4,I1)−T2
44		ASAT(I4,I2)=ASAT(I4,I2)−T3
45		ASAT(I4,I3)=ASAT(I4,I3)+T2
46	108	ASAT(I4,I4)=ASAT(I4,I4)+T3
47		DO 110 I=1,NP
48	110	INDEX(I)=0
49	111	AMAX=−1.
50		DO 114 I=1,NP
51		IF (INDEX(I)) 114,112,114
52	112	TEMP=ABSF(ASAT(I,I))
53		IF (TEMP−AMAX) 114,114,113
54	113	ICOL=I

TABLE J (cont.)

Line No.	Stat. No.	Statement
55		AMAX=TEMP
56	114	CONTINUE
57		IF (AMAX) 120,138,115
58	115	INDEX(ICOL)=1
59		PIVOT=ASAT(ICOL,ICOL)
60		ASAT(ICOL,ICOL)=1.0
61		PIVOT=1./PIVOT
62		DO 116 J=1,NP
63	116	ASAT(ICOL,J)=ASAT(ICOL,J)*PIVOT
64		DO 119 I=1,NP
65		IF (I-ICOL) 117,119,117
66	117	TEMP=ASAT(I,ICOL)
67		ASAT(I,ICOL)=0.0
68		DO 118 J=1,NP
69	118	ASAT(I,J)=ASAT(I,J)-ASAT(ICOL,J)*TEMP
70	119	CONTINUE
71		GO TO 111
72	120	PRINT 141
73	141	FORMAT (18H0THE ASAT-1 MATRIX/)
74		DO 142 I=1,NP
75	142	PRINT 128, I,(ASAT(I,J),J=1,NP)
76	128	FORMAT (4H ROW,I3,1X,4E16.7/(8X,4E16.7))
77		DO 121 I=1,NP
78		DO 121 J=1,NLC
79	121	P(I,J)=0.
80	122	READ 123, I,J,PIJ
81	123	FORMAT (2I5,F10.4)
82		IF (I) 125,125,124
83	124	P(I,J)=PIJ
84		GO TO 122
85	125	PRINT 126
86	126	FORMAT (13H0THE MATRIX P)
87		DO 127 I=1,NP
88	127	PRINT 128, I,(P(I,J),J=1,NLC)
89		DO 129 I=1,NP
90		DO 129 J=1,NLC
91		X(I,J)=0.
92		DO 129 K=1,NP
93	129	X(I,J)=X(I,J)+ASAT(I,K)*P(K,J)
94		PRINT 130
95	130	FORMAT (13H0THE MATRIX X)
96		DO 131 I=1,NP
97	131	PRINT 128, I,(X(I,J),J=1,NLC)

TABLE J (cont.)

Line No.	Stat. No.	Statement
98		PRINT 132
99	132	FORMAT (49H0THE MEMBER FORCES IN ORDER OF LOADING CONDITIONS/)
100		DO 133 J=1,NLC
101	133	X(NPP1,J)=0.
102		DO 134 I=1,NF
103		I1=NP1(I)
104		I2=NP2(I)
105		I3=NP3(I)
106		I4=NP4(I)
107		XL=SQRTF(H(I)*H(I)+V(I)*V(I))
108		CS=H(I)/XL
109		SN=V(I)/XL
110		DO 136 J=1,NLC
111	136	F(J)=E*A(I)/XL*(CS*(X(I3,J)−X(I1,J))+SN*(X(I4,J)−X(I2,J)))
112	134	PRINT 137, I,(F(J),J=1,NLC)
113	137	FORMAT (1H ,I5,5F12.4/(6X,5F12.4))
114		PRINT 250
115	250	FORMAT (53H0CHANGES IN BAR FORCES DUE TO SUCCESSIVE AREA CHANGES/)
116		PRINT 251
117	251	FORMAT (15H0 AREA FORCE)
118		PRINT 252
119	252	FORMAT (15H CHANGE CHANGE/)
120		DO 201 I=1,NPP1
121		ASAT(I,NPP1)=0.
122	201	ASAT(NPP1,I)=0.
123		DO 202 K=1,NF
124		K1=NP1(K)
125		K2=NP2(K)
126		K3=NP3(K)
127		K4=NP4(K)
128		XL=SQRTF(H(K)*H(K)+V(K))
129		CSK=H(K)/XL
130		SNK=V(K)/XL
131		SCK=E*A(K)*CSK/XL
132		SSK=E*A(K)*SNK/XL
133		T1K=E*A(K)*CSK*CSK/XL
134		T2K=E*A(K)*CSK*SNK/XL
135		T3K=E*A(K)*SNK*SNK/XL
136		DO 202 I=1,NF
137		I1=NP1(I)
138		I2=NP2(I)

TABLE J (cont.)

Line No.	Stat. No.	Statement
139		I3=NP3(I)
140		I4=NP4(I)
141		XL=SQRTF(H(I)*H(I)+V(I)*V(I))
142		SCI=E*A(I)*H(I)/XL*XL)
143		SSI=E*A(I)*V(I)/(XL*XL)
144		A1=SCI*(ASAT(I3,K1)−ASAT(I1,K1))+SSI*(ASAT(I4,K1)−ASAT(I2,K1))
145		B1=SCI*(ASAT(I3,K2)−ASAT(I1,K2))+SSI*(ASAT(I4,K2)−ASAT(I2,K2))
146		C1=SCI*(ASAT(I3,K3)−ASAT(I1,K3))+SSI*(ASAT(I4,K3)−ASAT(I2,K3))
147		D1=SCI*(ASAT(I3,K4)−ASAT(I1,K4))+SSI*(ASAT(I4,K4)−ASAT(I2,K4))
148		IF (K−I) 241,242,241
149	241	E1=0.
150		F1=0.
151		GO TO 243
152	242	E1=SCK
153		F1=SSK
154	243	E1=E1+(A1−C1)*T1K+(B1−D1)*T2K
155		F1=F1+(A1−C1)*T2K+(B1−D1)*T3K
156		DO 205 J=1,NLC
157	205	DELF(J)=E1*(X(K3,J)−X(K1,J))+F1*(X(K4,J)−X(K2,J))
158	202	PRINT 207, K,I,(DELF(J),J=1,NLC)
159	207	FORMAT (I5,I9,5F12.4/(14X,5F12.4))
160	138	STOP
161		END

Index

A

Amplitude forces, 5, 13
Axial force, primary, 83
Axial rigidity, 1

B

Beam element
  in axial compression, 176
  in free vibration, 182
Bifurcation theory, 81, 117, 120
Buckling load factor, 81, 92, 114
Buckling mode, 81, 98, 114

C

Circular frequency, 5, 8, 183
Compatibility equations, 139, 154
Compatible edge displacement, 210

Compatible edge stress, 210
Constraints, 263, 289

D

D'Alembert's Principle, 1, 66
Damping forces, 66
Deformation matrix, 48, 50, 142, 236
Degrees of freedom, 5, 14, 98, 137, 193
Design variables, 264
Direct element method, 138, 153
Distributed masses, 1, 31
Dynamic stiffness matrix, 39, 62

E

Effective length, 92, 111
Eigenvalues, 8, 18, 114, 187
Eigenvectors, 8, 18
  normalized, 67
  unitized, 8

F

Finite elements, 165, 193
    rectangular, 201
    triangular, 196
Fixed-condition forces, 174, 219, 255
Flexibility coefficients, 143
Flexibility-influence coefficients, 2, 5
Flexibility matrix
    member, 37, 85
    particle, 192, 233
Flexural rigidity, 1
Force function, 71
Forced motion, undamped, 66
Forces
    amplitude, 5
    inertia, 1
Free vibration, 2, 32
Freedom, degrees of, 5
Frequency
    circular, 5, 8, 183
    fundamental, 8, 14
    natural, 8, 18, 34

G

Gauss-Jordan substitution, 270

I

Inertia forces, 1
Influence coefficients
    flexibility, 2, 5
    stiffness, 2, 5
Initial design, 282

L

Lumped masses, 1

M

Mass matrix, 13
Masses
    distributed, 1, 31
    lumped, 1
Matrix condensation, 7, 117
Member-flexibility matrix, 37, 85
Member-stiffness matrix, 38, 85, 142
Merit function, 264

Mode shape, 8, 18, 34
    fundamental, 8, 14
Mode vectors
    normalized, 67
    unitized, 8

N

Natural frequency, 8, 34
    matrix, 69
Nodes, 193

O

Optimization, 293
Orthogonality, 13

P

Particle-flexibility matrix, 191, 233
Particle-stiffness matrix, 191, 233
Plane strain analysis, 189
Plane stress analysis, 189
Primary axial force, 83
Principal stress modes, 211, 247

R

Reciprocal energy theorem, 166
Rectangular finite element, 201
Rigidity
    axial, 1
    flexural, 1

S

Second-order moments, 83, 101
Second-order stiffness matrix, 103, 118
Sidesway flexibility matrix, 118
Sidesway inertia-force matrix, 49, 50
Sidesway mass matrix, 50
Simplex method, 272
Slack variables, 268
Stability angle, 92
    critical, 92, 111
Stability stiffness matrix, 85
    first-order, 86
    second-order, 86, 95, 103, 118
Statics matrix, 46, 94, 142
Stiffness coefficients, 143
Stiffness-influence coefficients, 2, 5

Stiffness matrix
   dynamic, 39, 62
   member, 38, 85
   particle, 192, 233
   stability, 85
Stiffness matrix
   of a finite element, 194
   of beam element in axial compression,
      176
   of beam element in free vibration, 182
   of ordinary beam element, 169
   of rectangular element in bending, 240

Superposition, principle of, 166

T

Transformation matrix, 68
Triangular finite element, 196

V

Vibration, free, 2, 32